MAKING
SENSE
OF
DATA

Donald J. Wheeler

SPC Press

Knoxville, Tennessee

SPC Press

5908 Toole Drive, Suite C
Knoxville, Tennessee 37919
(865) 584–5005
Fax (865) 588–9440
www.spcpress.com

ISBN 0–945320–61–2

xii + 396 pages
233 figures
62 data tables
6 reference tables

3 4 5 6 7 8 9 0

Contents

About the Author

Donald J. Wheeler is a consulting statistician and author of some of the most popular books on industrial and business applications of statistics, including:

Understanding Variation, the Key to Managing Chaos

Understanding Statistical Process Control

Evaluating the Measurement Process

Advanced Topics in Statistical Process Control

SPC at the Esquire Club

Short Run SPC

Normality and the Process Behavior Chart

Beyond Capability Confusion

Understanding Industrial Experimentation

Dr. Wheeler's consultations have taken him all over the world and have allowed him to work with companies in such diverse fields as Banking, Healthcare, Chemicals, Electronics, Automotive Manufacturing, Aerospace, Paper, Textiles, Steel, Aluminum, and Medical Products.

Dr. Wheeler graduated from the University of Texas, Austin, with a Bachelor's degree in Physics and Mathematics, and holds Master's and Ph.D. degrees in Statistics from Southern Methodist University. From 1970 to 1982 he taught in the Statistics Department at the University of Tennessee, Knoxville, where he was Associate Professor. During this time he had the good fortune to work with Dr. W. Edwards Deming and Prof. David S. Chambers. Between 1981 and 1993 he periodically assisted Dr. Deming with his four-day seminars. He is author or co-author of 24 books and over 130 articles, and is a Fellow of the American Statistical Association.

Introduction

"I'm not in manufacturing. How can I use data?"

While this question has been asked by many, only a few have attempted to provide an answer. One immediate barrier that exists for those outside manufacturing is the very terminology of data analysis. For example, Statistical Process Control (SPC) just doesn't sound like something that is needed in a service sector environment. Even the less technical "Continual Improvement" sounds like something that applies to widgets rather than transactions. This book shows how techniques for working with data may be used in service-sector environments to improve operations for the future. As a label for this blend of concepts and techniques, I find the phrase Continual Improvement to be the most descriptive of those in common usage.

Since Continual Improvement requires a blend of concepts and techniques, this book must also be a blend. While the actual techniques are quite simple, the concepts of Continual Improvement are new to most people. This is why it takes time to create an environment in which these techniques can be fully utilized. However, when this environment is created and when the concepts and techniques of Continual Improvement are actively used throughout an organization, the results can be spectacular.

The foundation for the techniques of Continual Improvement was laid by Dr. Walter Shewhart, a physicist who worked with Western Electric and Bell Laboratories. His pioneering work in the 1920s was focused on quality in manufacturing. However, his approach is universally applicable, valid with all kinds of data, and useful in all types of organizations.

Dr. W. Edwards Deming extended Shewhart's work by developing and explaining its applications, first in the U.S., then in Japan after World War II, and finally throughout the world in the 80s and 90s.

I will make reference to the work of both of these pioneers throughout this book. However, this book is merely an introduction. It is not intended as an explanation of the work of these two men. When you embark on your own journey of Continual Improvement you will want to know more about the origins and development of this remarkable philosophy, and to that end, I recommend the books listed in the bibliography.

Chapter One

Why Continual Improvement?

Every organization has to generate revenues in order to continue to exist. These revenues must cover the expenses of the organization and also provide working capital for future operations. When an organization is "for profit" these revenues must also provide the profits expected by the shareholders. Because of this economic fact of life, all managers have to focus on the bottom line of the cash flow statement. From an executive's point of view the world consists of three things: income, expenses, and profits. The objective is clear: increase income and lower expenses in order to maximize profit. So how can you and your organization achieve this objective?

Managers commonly seek to meet this objective by setting sales goals, establishing quotas, having contests, launching advertising campaigns, creating new products or repackaging old products in different ways, or charging whatever the market will bear. At the same time, in order to lower expenses, managers cut back on inventory levels, lower the levels of service, decrease staffing, and slash all indirect expenses. As a result, we live in an age with decreasing levels of service; with a growing sense that everyone is increasingly harried as they are left to do more work with fewer resources. Every department, and often every person, is in competition for scarce internal resources, and cooperation is rare. As everyone scrambles to take care of his or her own turf, the organization suffers, and so new waves of cost reductions are put in place, continuing the downward cycle.

This downward cycle is seen in many different companies. It is the inevitable consequence of "management by results." When the corporate numbers are not good, the divisions are given goals and targets. When the divisional numbers are not good, the departments get goals and targets. And when the department numbers are not good, the manager is reprimanded and individuals are given "stretch goals." This endless game of "making your numbers" leads to a "cover your anatomy" mentality in which the need to survive the internal competition becomes dominant, taking precedence over the needs of the company and the needs of the customer. The company becomes a financial football—a collection of assets to be reorganized, stripped, sold, and resold.

While the objectives of increased revenues, reduced expenses, and increased profits are legitimate, the real question is how this goal will be met. By far the simplest way to meet goals and targets is to massage the data—"Isn't there some way to show a five percent increase in productivity by the end of the year?" Of course, when the data are massaged they become distorted. While this distortion of the data requires the least effort, it has the disadvantage of coming back to haunt you later, requiring further distortions and resulting in unrealistic expectations.

The second way you can meet your goals and targets is to "work the system." This can take many forms ranging from simply shifting the blame to another person (or another department or another division), to changing the way the numbers are collected, to changing the actual processes to hide the problems. "Put the incomplete units in boxes and ship them—we'll let the service department finish assembling them in the field." Business becomes a game of tag where the objective is to avoid being "it" at the end of the month.

These "distort the data" and "distort the system" approaches are so common that many people have come to think that the major purpose for collecting data is to hide the problems. "We collect data to show how good things are, whether or not they are." This use of data to lie to the numerically illiterate has been a common practice for so long that "statistics" has come to be a synonym for obfuscation, distortion, and confusion.

There is a better way...

There is a way to simultaneously increase quality, boost productivity, and ensure an advantageous competitive position.

This better way does not consist of management by results.

Instead of focusing on outcomes, such as expenses and profits, this better way focuses on the processes and systems that generate the outcomes. Rather than trying to directly manipulate the results, it works to improve the system that causes the results. Rather than distorting the system or distorting the data, it seeks to use the data to understand the system as a basis for improving the system. This better way is known as Continual Improvement.

How is Continual Improvement different from "doing the same old thing" under a new banner? How can Continual Improvement have an impact upon the bottom line? Take, for example, the problem of reducing costs. Continual Improvement looks at costs as outcomes. In the traditional way of working we would focus directly upon reducing costs, and as a result we might well undermine the future to make the current numbers look better. Continual Improvement focuses on the causes of those costs—the processes that generate them. When this is done, it is common to find that a substantial portion of the costs are due to rework, things not done right, correcting errors and mistakes, and the complexity that these introduce. By working to eliminate these causes of poor quality, and thereby to reduce the complexity of our processes, we can reduce costs while improving our operations.

The traditional focus upon income and expenses will tend to place different departments in competition, destroying cooperation, and undermining the delivery of products or services that the customers want. The objective has been to make your numbers by whatever means possible. By shifting the focus to those process and systems that generate both the income and the expenses, the techniques of Continual Improvement provide a basis for cooperation between departments. By encouraging internal *cooperation* instead of internal *competition* Continual Improvement releases the creative energy within your organization that was formerly devoted to survival. It encourages communication instead of secrecy, which builds trust rather than distrust, and thereby creates an organization that can respond to changes in the business environment. The alternative is to "continue the beatings" until your company goes out of business.

Of course, Continual Improvement requires a methodology for studying processes and systems and a way of differentiating between the different types of variation present in processes and systems. There are techniques to be learned. But there is also a way of thinking to be practiced, and that is where it gets hard. However, those who have traveled down this road universally proclaim the new way of thinking to be worth the effort, and the results do show up on the bottom line.

This book is intended to serve as an introduction to both the techniques and the way of thinking that comprise the approach known as Continual Improvement. To that end, I shall begin with a definition of quality.

1.1 What Is Quality?

Karen, a sales representative of a printing company, was talking with one of her customers when the issue of quality came up. The customer was concerned about the quality of work turned out by the printing company. Karen's response was, "We don't have a problem with quality. We just have a problem with variation."

David, a consulting statistician in the United Kingdom, told a group from the postal service that their main problem was one of variation. "Oh, no," they responded. "We have no variation—our procedures are rigid!" "Okay," said David. "Perhaps you don't have any variation, but I wager that you have some chaos." "Oh yes," they said. "We have lots of chaos."

No matter what name it goes under, everyone struggles with quality. We want quality. We often fail to get it. Hence, a major question of the day is: "How can we get quality?" Of course, as soon as you ask this question you have to begin by defining quality.

- One definition of quality has been "fitness for use." This definition is clearly centered on an object rather than a service. Moreover, it implies a trade-off between that which is desirable and that which is merely acceptable.

- Another definition of quality has been "zero defects." While the factory origins of this definition are clear, it is possible to apply this definition to services—a defect would be an error or mistake on the part of the provider. However, since it should be self-evident that quality must be more than the absence of defects, this definition must be defective.

- Some would say that quality is a state of mind—if everyone simply does his or her best, then we will get quality. The naive simplicity of this definition is revealed by simply asking, "Would those who have not been doing their best please raise their hand?"

- Others say quality is a matter of reinforcement. Simply tell everyone how well they are doing, and do this often enough, and the result will be quality. While this may work with puppies, it sounds like wishful thinking here.

- Dreamers think of quality in terms of a goal. We need to have an impossible dream, and then fail, and then try again before we can achieve quality. "We have to have something to shoot for."

- And then there is the approach that is as old as Pharaoh and as common as dirt: "The beatings will continue until morale (and quality) improves."

What do these approaches have in common? While they may contain valid elements, in the end they depend upon wishes and hopes (or occasional threats) for achieving quality. Quality is reduced to a simple formula—"do this and you will get that."

W. Edwards Deming went beyond the simplistic level of wishes and hopes and defined quality in terms of a never-ending cycle of Continual Improvement—a process by which people could start where they are and work to improve, gradually over a period of time, their products, their processes, and their organization.

This is why Continual Improvement is different from all other approaches to quality. It provides a method for assessing the present and working to improve the future. While it can contain some of the elements mentioned above, it is more than goal setting, it is more than positive reinforcement, it is more than an appeal to an archetype, and it is much more than "everyone doing their best." Continual Improvement is not a magic formula that you can invoke. It is not a quick fix—"do this and you will get that." It is, instead, a way of thinking, a way of acting, and a way of understanding the data generated by your processes, that will collectively result in improved quality, increased productivity, and an advantageous competitive position.

1.2 The Three Questions

Continual Improvement requires a framework. We all need some way to align our efforts and focus on a specific objective. To this end I have found the following questions to be especially helpful.

What do you want to accomplish?

Until you have a clearly stated objective, you risk everyone running off in different directions, working on their own pet projects, and not cooperating for the common good. Whether it is a specific project with a limited scope, or the general day-to-day operations of your organization, a clearly stated purpose or objective is important to help focus the thoughts and efforts of everyone involved.

Any situation in which this question remains unanswered will rapidly deteriorate into chaos. However, merely specifying your objective will not be enough.

By what method will you accomplish your objective?

While it may be necessary to have a goal, merely having a goal is, by itself, not sufficient. Remember the old saying, "If wishes were horses then beggars would ride." Until you have a plan for achieving your objective, it will be nothing more than wishful thinking. All of our targets, all of our goals, and all of our plans are merely wishes and hopes until we have some specific method for making them come true.

This book contains specific techniques for using data to learn about your current process and to predict what to expect in the future. Since these two activities are fundamental to making constructive changes they are the basic elements of any methodology for improvement.

How will you know when you have accomplished your objective?

If you are going to have a goal, and if you hope to move toward that goal, then you will also need some way to measure how far you have come and how far you have yet to go in reaching that goal. Moreover, you will need a way to evaluate that measure to determine if a change has occurred.

Any measure you might use will, in the normal course of events, vary. Some months it will go up, and other months it will go down. If you do not know how to determine when a change has occurred, you will have difficulty in separating these meaningless changes from a signal that you have made progress toward your goal.

Thus there are Three Questions that need to be answered before real improvements can be made: What do you want to accomplish? By what method? How will you know?

We are very good at telling others what we want them to accomplish. Managers do this all the time. But we are much less accomplished at answering the last two questions. But until these last two questions are answered, we are just "wishing for horses." While we may need a goal, we also need a method and a way of measuring our progress.

The three questions above are quite similar to the three questions listed in the preface of *The Improvement Guide* by Gerald Langley et. al., and used by the Associates in Quality Improvement. This similarity is to be expected given that both sets of questions were derived from the same source—the life and work of W. Edwards Deming. In particular, this author heard Dr. Deming use the second and third questions repeatedly as responses to inquiries about what he thought about some organization's latest quality initiative. For further information about how to put these three questions to work in your organization, *The Improvement Guide* is listed in the bibliography and is recommended reading.

1.3 Summary

So what is Continual Improvement? It is more than wishes and hopes. It is more than graphs and data. It is more than using the right bit of arithmetic. And it is more than a technique.

- It is the ability to understand the messages contained in your data.
- It is the ability to differentiate between routine variation and exceptional variation.
- It is the difference between reacting to noise and understanding signals.
- It is ultimately an incredibly powerful way of thinking
    that will enable you to conduct your business more effectively.

How does Continual Improvement differ from traditional improvement programs? Rather than attempting to improve a process by throwing resources at the problems, Continual Improvement allows you to utilize your current resources to the fullest extent. Once you use Continual Improvement throughout the organization as the way of doing business you will discover that it allows you to get the most improvement from the least effort and with the least expense.

Chapter Two

Visualize Your Process

Any attempt at improvement should begin with a careful and thoughtful analysis of the current system. To this end it is helpful to visualize your process, and the tools for doing this are flowcharts and cause-and-effect diagrams. While both of these techniques are simple, they are also profoundly useful.

These graphic techniques are profound in the way they clarify relationships between individuals, between departments, between causes and effects, and between suppliers and customers. But the chief value of flowcharts and cause-and-effect diagrams is the way they highlight those places in which the system or process breaks down. If a branch of the chart cannot be connected back to the main flow, then the process has not been completely defined. If some simple cause is the source of problematic effects, then the process has not been completely de-bugged.

The tools that are taught in this chapter are best used by groups or teams of people who feel secure in openly discussing their work. The people working in the process are the most qualified people to diagram or document the process. They are the only people who really know what's going on. Diagrams constructed by supervisors or managers are more likely to depict wishes and hopes than to be true pictures of the process.

2.1 Brainstorming

To construct a flowchart, it is necessary for employees to discuss how they do their jobs. In many work situations, people are afraid to talk about their work in front of others—particularly if supervisors are in the group. Without a free flow of information, however, it will not be possible to construct an accurate flowchart or cause-and-effect diagram. Important steps or components may be hidden. One way of getting this free flow of information is to train people in the use of brainstorming.

Brainstorming is an effective way of getting people to speak freely. It may be helpful to practice this technique with an innocuous topic before using it to construct flowcharts of work processes or cause-and-effect diagrams. The rules should be explained to everyone (and enforced throughout the activity). They are:

1. A recorder is selected to write the ideas on a chalk board or flip chart. It is important for everyone to have a clear view of this record.
2. The group leader will clarify the topic (and enforce the rules as needed). It is very important that the topic be clearly defined in such a way that everyone in the group understands it.
3. All members of the group should be encouraged to participate.
4. It will be helpful to encourage people to use five words or less to express their ideas.
5. All ideas should be recorded verbatim without interpretation by others.
6. All group members must understand that every suggestion, however unusual or unexpected, has possible value. No one should be ridiculed in any way.
7. Statements should not be evaluated, organized, or criticized in any way.

In the beginning some may not feel comfortable with the brainstorming process. One way to minimize this discomfort is to take a few minutes at the start to have the group members privately write down their ideas before anyone begins to share them. Then the group leader can ask each person in turn to share items from their list. After a couple of circuits it is usually much easier to get participation in the free flow of ideas that is the essence of the brainstorming technique.

After the brainstorming session is completed group members can work to organize the ideas, evaluate their accuracy or usefulness, construct a chart, or use the input in other useful ways.

Brainstorming not only helps to visualize your process, but it can be a powerful way to generate new ideas and suggestions for improvement, while facilitating the improved communication that is needed to make any organization work effectively.

2.2 Flowcharts

Flowcharting emerged in the 1950s with the increasing need to write computer programs. Since the details involved in writing thousands of lines of code were so great, some way to obtain a view of the overall process was needed, and the flowchart was invented. Because of the simplicity and power of this technique the use of flowcharts has spread far beyond the writing of software.

Flowcharts allow you to visualize the process by which the work is actually done. They allow you to characterize your current processes, assess weaknesses in your current system, spot breakdowns that were formerly invisible, streamline existing processes, and design new processes. Flowcharts help to identify internal suppliers and internal customers, and they allow you to eliminate duplication of effort.

Since flowcharts give you a graphical representation of your process, they help you share this process with others, making training easier and creating greater consistency in your operations.

Conventions have been developed to symbolically show different parts of the flowchart. While these conventions are helpful, the real power of a flowchart resides in the overall picture itself. A few of the more common symbols are below. These conventions may work for you, or you may develop your own symbols for flowcharting.

Flowchart Conventions

Boxes with rounded corners are commonly used to denote starting points, input points, and ending points.

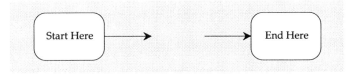

Regular boxes are used for ordinary steps and transactions.

Diamonds are commonly used to denote decision points. Decision points are points where the flowchart will branch. The branch you take will depend upon the answer to the question posed in the diamond.

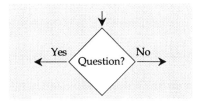

Circles are used to denote connections to remote portions of the flowchart. They allow a large flowchart to be shown as a sequence of smaller flowcharts. They also minimize the spaghetti effect of a large flowchart.

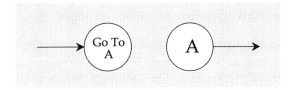

And, of course, arrows are used to show the direction of the flow.

The simplest type of flowchart is a block diagram. Figure 2.1 shows a block diagram for taking a turn in the game of Monopoly. This block diagram is expanded into a full blown flowchart in Figure 2.2. The flowchart in Figure 2.2. contains thirteen decision diamonds—this simple game has a fair degree of complexity.

Figure 2.1: Block Diagram for a Turn in Monopoly

Your turn begins when you receive the dice.

If you are in jail, you may pay your fine, you may play a "Get Out Of Jail" card, or you may try to roll a double. If you have not rolled a double after three turns you must pay your fine and move your piece.

When you move your piece you will either land on a property or on one of the eight "special" spaces. If your piece lands on a property which you own, you may choose to improve it. If your piece lands on a property which someone else owns, you are liable for paying rent. If your piece lands on a property which no one owns, you may buy it from the bank.

If your piece does not land on a property, then you may be required to take some action. If you pass "Go," you get to collect $200. If you rolled a double, you get a repeat turn. However, if you used the double to get out of jail, you do not get this repeat turn. If you happen to roll three doubles in succession, you will have to go to jail. Your turn ends when you pass the dice to the next player.

The flowchart in Figure 2.2 outlines 122 possible ways for a turn to be played, and it does this using only 27 steps. By concentrating on the sequence of decisions and actions, and allowing the reader to progress one step at a time, the flowchart makes complexity comprehensible.

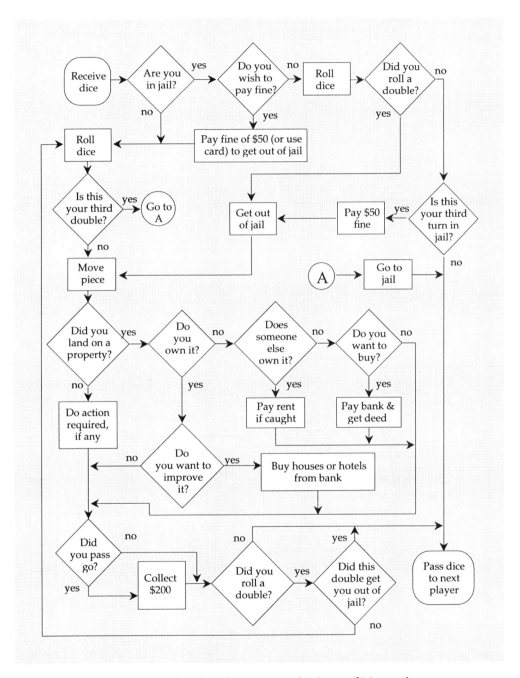

Figure 2.2: Flowchart for a Turn in the Game of Monopoly

2.3 Constructing Flowcharts

A block diagram which shows the process on a large scale (with few details) may be helpful as a starting point for the construction of a flowchart. A small mail order company created the block diagram in Figure 2.3 for their order process.

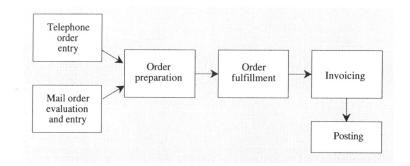

Figure 2.3: Block Diagram for Order Process

A block diagram allows you to break the overall process down into subprocesses and thereby simplifies the job of creating the flowchart. Furthermore, the block diagram for your process can be a useful way to organize your data about problems when you do a Pareto chart in Chapter Four. Notice that the six blocks in Figure 2.3 define the major portions of the overall order process. Given the complexity of this process, they began by constructing a flowchart for each portion of the process shown in the block diagram.

When you move beyond the level of the block diagram, the key task is to correctly identify the decision points. The decision points define the branches on the flowchart. If you miss a decision point, you will be leaving out a portion of the process. In between the decision diamonds, you may place more or less detail as appropriate. However, be sure to consider each branch carefully in order to spot any embedded decision points that might lead to sub-branches.

Avoid ambiguity. All arrows are one-way streets.

Since the sequence of the steps is the focal point of the flowchart, the actual form of the chart is secondary. As long as the overall picture is not too crowded, or too hard to follow, the chart will be satisfactory.

The flowchart for the "Mail Order Evaluation and Entry" portion of the block diagram of Figure 2.3 is shown in Figure 2.4. This flowchart is the second page of a five page flowchart. It was constructed as a first step in improving the order process. This company was preparing to change from a manual order entry system to a computerized system. Before they implemented a new system, the managers wanted to fully understand the current system,

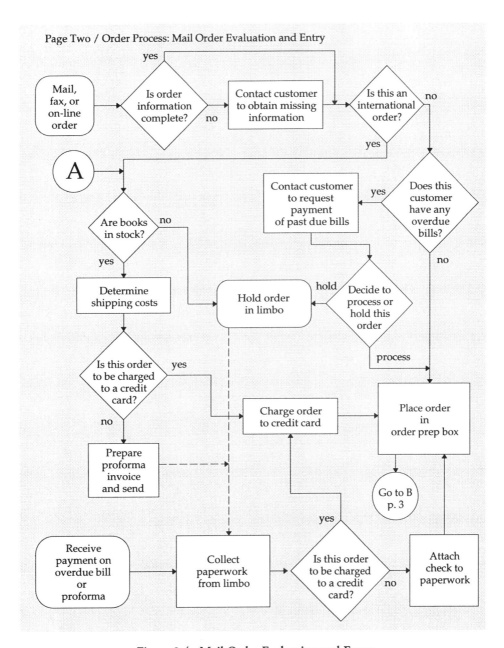

Figure 2.4: Mail Order Evaluation and Entry

with all of its accumulated problems, so that they could be sure that the new system would be better than the old one.

While many employees will have some knowledge of the process, few individuals will have the global perspective provided by a flowchart. This is why you always want to create a flowchart by talking with the people who actually perform the work. Flowcharts drawn by those who do not do the work have no contact with reality. They commonly depict nothing more than wishes and hopes. "Make-believe" flowcharts do not provide the foundation needed for Continual Improvement. The objective is not to create a "glamour shot" of your process, but rather to spot the problems and inconsistencies which exist. Therefore, if your current process actually contains "limbo boxes," be sure to include them. The objective is to understand the *actual* process. Honesty is a prerequisite for *useful* flowcharts.

It is helpful to use sticky notes as the different steps in the flowchart are discussed. Their use makes it easy to move steps around as new branches are added. The final flowchart will be a revision of many rough diagrams, and may even take more than one session to complete. (The Monopoly flowchart went through four revisions before it was finished.)

To construct the flowchart in Figure 2.4 the managers of the mail order company sat down with those who did the work in each part of the process shown in the block diagram of Figure 2.3. They created a five-part flowchart, one page of which is shown in Figure 2.4. Not only did this help the managers, it also gave the workers a global view of the process in which they worked. It gave the managers a chance to discuss and design the new system with the workers and allowed the workers to "buy into" the changeover.

Following the creation of the flowchart, the managers proceeded to look for opportunities for improvement—places where the flowchart could be streamlined or where the process could be automated. This knowledge was then used as the basis for purchasing and organizing a computerized order entry and accounting system that would fit the needs of their business.

Next a dummy set of records were created on the new system, and workers were given practice exercises to perform each day using the new system. As they did these exercises they found problems with their own understanding, and occasionally, problems with the system. Based on this experience the new system was tweaked, and after two months of practice, the company was ready to change over. The supplier of the new computerized accounting system was amazed at how few troubles this company had with the transition.

The original five-page flowchart had 50 steps and 25 decision diamonds. The new flowchart, shown in Figure 2.5 and made after the new process was fully operational, contained 49 steps and 20 decision diamonds. The gray boxes in Figure 2.5 show the steps that were automated: of the 49 steps, 12 were automated; of the 20 decisions, 10 were automated. So the new process contained 37 manual steps and 10 manual decision diamonds. While this may not sound like a major reduction in work, the benefits were spectacular.

It previously took about one-half man-hour to process a single order from receipt to posting, and because of the interface between the different phases of this process, this 30 minutes was spread out over a 15-day period. With the new system, the time was reduced to under 10 minutes, including order picking and packing. In most cases the new system allowed orders to be completely processed on the same day they were received.

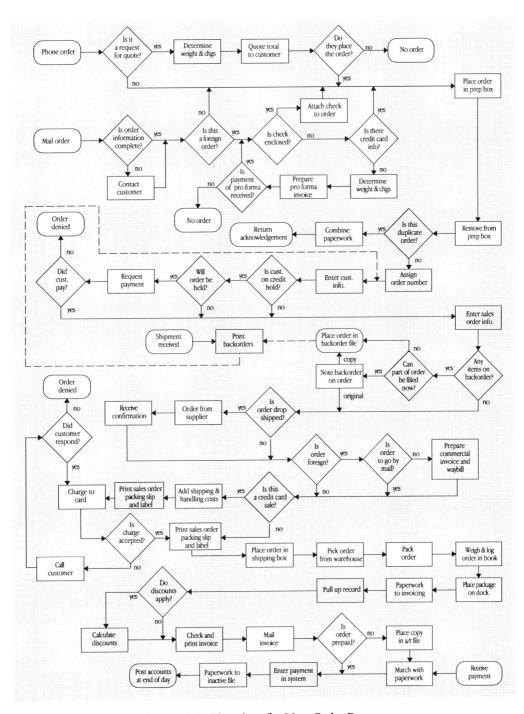

Figure 2.5: Flowchart for New Order Process

Previously, invoicing had a two- to three-day backlog. Now invoices go out on the same day as the shipment. The posting of accounts receivable had previously been running 10 days behind. With the new system the journal entries are automatically made at the end of each day.

Since the company was understaffed at the start of this improvement project, some things were simply not getting done. Now, with the increased productivity of the new system, the personnel have more time to spend on these formerly neglected areas.

The automated system provides much more effective inventory control, better accounting information, and more timely sales information than was formerly available. The personnel love the new system. When asked, no one wanted to go back to the old system. The customers get their orders faster, with fewer errors. The workers can respond to customer's questions more quickly, more completely, and with greater consistency. Finally, the new system allows the workers to respond to the special requests of the customers more easily.

Those who have used flowcharts have found that there is a lot of "low hanging fruit" out there. These items that are easy to fix are made visible by the flowchart. After using flowcharts successfully, some practitioners have even taken a vow that they will no longer start a project without first creating a flowchart. It seems extraordinarily simple, but it works.

Flowchart Summary

The process of creating a flowchart is a process of discovery...

"You mean we do that?"

"What happens after this?"

"How does an order ever get out of Limbo?"

"What kind of follow-up is needed here?"

The advantages of flowcharting should be self-evident. Flowcharts provide a structure to use in understanding complex processes. They communicate the options and branches more effectively than words on a page will do. They provide a bird's-eye view that makes it easy to spot inconsistencies.

So why don't more people use flowcharts? Perhaps it is because they work in an environment where the truth is hard to accept, where complexity is thought to be profound, or where communication is strictly forbidden. It may be dangerous to point out that the Emperor is wearing no clothes.

2.4 Deployment Flowcharts

Deployment flowcharts break the overall process up into pieces: Each piece is performed by one department, one area, or one person. The pieces for each department are then shown side by side, and the arrows from one zone to another depict the hand-offs between departments or people, and in some instances, the transactions back and forth between them.

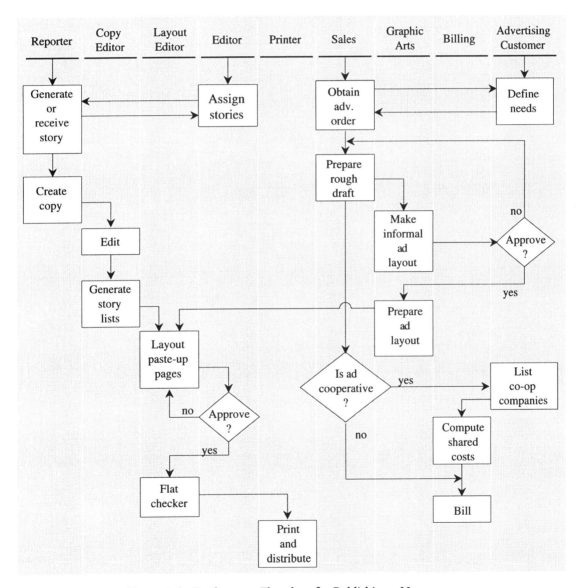

Figure 2.6: Deployment Flowchart for Publishing a Newspaper

The example in Figure 2.6 is based on a deployment flowchart created by Myron Tribus and shown in his book, *Quality First*. It shows the process for producing a newspaper. Across the top are nine categories—the people dimension. From top to bottom we have the work sequence. Horizontal relationships show customers and suppliers. Vertical lines entering a box indicate who has responsibility for that activity. Horizontal lines indicate a shift in responsibility. The lack of horizontal lines between the editorial side of the process and the advertising side show the relative independence of these two different parts of the operation.

Of course the various activities shown on a deployment flowchart may need to have their own detailed flowcharts. Yet there is a distinct advantage to having a deployment flowchart for your process—it shows the overall process and makes visible some very important relationships that are not obvious on block diagrams. At the same time, the excessive detail of a more extensive flowchart can obscure those interrelationships that are made visible by the deployment flowchart. It is this visualization of these interrelationships between departments that is one of the chief advantages of the deployment flowchart—barriers cannot be removed until they are perceived.

2.5 PERT Diagrams

PERT networks or diagrams are flowcharts of the work in a project. PERT stands for Process Evaluation and Review Technique. The heart of a PERT diagram is a flowchart which shows the steps in a project. The emphasis of a PERT diagram is on showing which steps can be done concurrently and which steps depend on others. Figure 2.7 shows the PERT diagram from a project carried out by waitresses at the Esquire Club, a nightclub in Osaka, Japan.

Figure 2.7: PERT Diagram for "Let's Reduce Losses on Beer and Sake Sales"

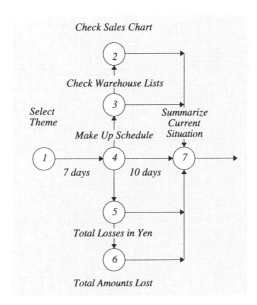

Figure 2.8: The Planning Phase of "Let's Reduce Losses on Beer and Sake Sales"

In this project the waitresses and their supervisor followed the Plan, Do, Study, Act Cycle. In the "Plan" phase we might place Steps 1 through 7, as shown in Figure 2.8.

The selection of a theme was followed by the collection of the relevant information. Source documents were checked, losses were quantified, and this information was gathered into a summary of the current situation. From other parts of the story, it appears that this planning phase was primarily carried out by the supervisor of the waitresses and the managers of the club. This portion of the project was scheduled to last a little over two weeks.

The "Do" phase of this project consists of Steps 8 through 16 shown in Figure 2.9. In a two-week period the team of seven waitresses, along with their supervisor and the club managers, went to work to identify reasons for the losses, to set up a check list, to identify areas where improvement was feasible, and to look at ways of making these improvements. Finally they came up with a plan and put it into effect.

The "Study" phase of this project consists of Steps 16, 17, and 18, shown in Figure 2.10. This phase was planned to last 50 days, during which they would collect data to use in before-and-after comparisons. Notice that Step 18 is "Make Up Graphs." This is where they summarize their accomplishments and improvements.

The "Act" phase of this project is contained in Steps 19, 20 and 21. Here they plan to make certain changes permanent, and assign responsibility for follow-up in the future.

The rest of this story will be given later. For now it is sufficient to ask, "When was the last time you were part of an improvement project that was this carefully planned?"

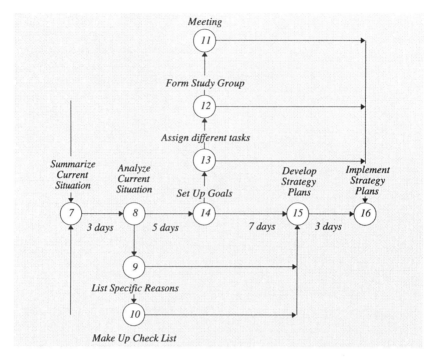

Figure 2.9: The Doing Phase of "Let's Reduce Losses on Beer and Sake Sales"

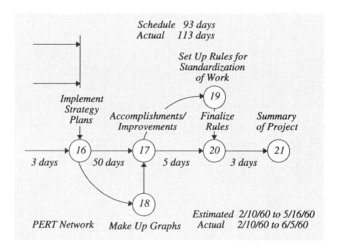

Figure 2.10: The Study and Act Phases of "Let's Reduce Losses on Beer and Sake Sales"

2.6 Do People Really Do This Stuff?

One large automotive supplier, having discovered the power of flowcharts, began to use them with all sorts of administrative processes. One flowchart which they constructed was for the budget process. They already knew that they were spending an average of 190 working days on the preparation of each budget, and they knew that the uncertainty created by this long lead-time was not good. However, over the years, the process seemed to have gotten longer rather than shorter.

After they constructed a flowchart for the budget-planning process, they went through each step of the process and asked the all-important question: "What value is added by this step?" By cutting out those steps that did not add value they streamlined the process, and the time required to complete it, down to 109 working days. With this shorter lead-time, the budget process was not only easier, it was also better—a savings of both time and money.

REQUESTS FOR QUOTATIONS

Another manufacturing company, upon discovering the advantages of flowcharting, decided to apply the technique to their service functions. One of the flowcharts they constructed covered the process for responding to a "request for quotation" (RFQ). This process involved the Sales, Engineering, Purchasing, and Manufacturing departments. Each department created its own flowchart for their part of the RFQ process. In spite of this organized approach, and in spite of well-defined processes within each department, they were still having a problem in responding to RFQs. So they used a deployment flowchart to look at their overall process across departmental boundaries. That is when they discovered that while everyone knew how to do their own job, they did not know who their customer was—they did not know where the paperwork should go next. There was, in essence, a box marked "No Longer My Responsibility" between each department. The RFQs were being dropped at the hand-off between departments. By dovetailing the different departmental flowcharts, they could eliminate these areas of uncertainty. When they did so, they reduced the average time to respond to an RFQ from 3 months to 2 weeks.

Based upon this company's success, one of their customers decided to examine its own RFQ process. The block diagram for this (larger) company had 17 steps. However, when they began to fill in the details and outline the many different branches, they found that their RFQ process contained over 400 steps, and that fully 70% of these steps did not add value. Immediately, there were 280 steps that were candidates for removal! It was not hard to make dramatic improvements in their processing of RFQs.

ORDERING TOOLS

The maintenance department at a chemical plant created the flowchart in Figure 2.11 to show the steps required to obtain a tool from the Central Tool Room.

Figure 2.11: Flowchart for "Ordering Tools From Central Tool Room"

While this flowchart is not legible at this scale, it contains 66 steps, including 19 decision diamonds. After they created this flowchart it became obvious that they were treating every tool as if it were a major piece of equipment. As a result of this insight they created two categories of tools, depending upon their value, and then created a simplified process for the cheaper tools.

Improvements do not have to be complex in order to be profound. In many cases it is just a matter of identifying the opportunity and then doing what you know you need to do. Remember the three questions: What do you want to accomplish? By what method? and How will you know?

2.7 Processes and Systems

Everything we do can be described in terms of processes and systems. Taking an order, making an appointment, scheduling a delivery, selling an item—and virtually every transaction we are involved in—are all processes and are parts of systems. We may not give much thought to these processes, at least not until they go wrong, but they do exist.

While it may help to think of "systems" as a collection of "processes" it is not our intent to be overly precise here. Systems and processes have to be defined according to your own needs. However, fuzzy thinking here can get you in trouble, so you should begin by characterizing your process or system graphically by using a block diagram.

Figure 2.12 shows a generic block diagram for a production process. This is the diagram used in Dr. Deming's lectures in Japan in 1950, and is Figure 1 in his book, *Out of the Crisis.* Figure 2.12 may be adapted to fit many different environments. To suggest how this might be done, Figure 2.13 shows a block diagram for the delivery of a service.

Figure 2.12: Production Viewed as a System

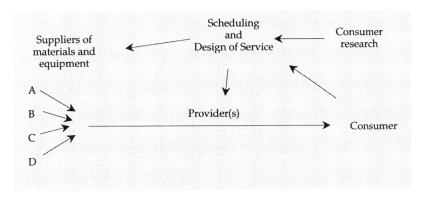

Figure 2.13: A System for the Delivery of a Service

These block diagrams show the flow of work that keeps the organization in business. They help everyone to think in terms of their customers, instead of the hierarchy within the organization. While the delivery of a service, or the delivery of a product, may not be quite as complex as a manufacturing operation, each has its own sources of complexity. Each involves several different streams of information, and each has multiple points at which this flow of information can break down. When the organization is viewed as a system the complex web of relationships becomes visible, facilitating understanding and efforts at improvement.

2.8 Cause-and-Effect Diagrams

Quite often, a large number of factors will be involved in a problem. When this happens an organized approach is necessary in order to reduce the effect of the problem. One of the simplest tools for this organization is the cause-and-effect diagram.

The cause-and-effect diagram was first applied in conjunction with Continual Improvement efforts in Japan. Dr. Kaoru Ishikawa found that most plant personnel were overwhelmed by the number of factors that could influence a particular product or process. Thus, in the early 1950s he began using a "fault tree" as a tool for organizing the attack on a particular problem. This practice proved to be so effective that it spread rapidly throughout Japan. The versatility of a cause-and-effect diagram makes it a useful tool for organizing problem-solving efforts in every area of the manufacturing and service industries.

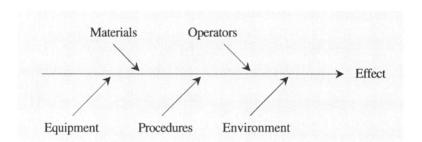

Figure 2.14: A Typical Framework for a Cause-and-Effect Diagram

The versatility comes from the way in which a cause-and-effect diagram is created. Its power comes from the graphic representation of the relationship between problems and their sources. The general procedure for making a cause-and-effect diagram follows.

1. Choose the effect to be studied, and write it at the end of a horizontal arrow.
2. List all the causes that influence the effect under consideration.
3. Arrange and stratify these causes. Choose the principal causes and show these as the major branches off the horizontal arrow.

4. Draw the sub-branches for the various subsidiary causes. This process of subdividing is continued until all causes are included on the diagram.

5. Check the diagram to make sure that all known causes of variation are included on the chart.

A common guideline for creating cause-and-effect diagrams is to use five major branches: Materials, Equipment, Operators, Procedures, and Environment. This approach is shown in Figure 2.14. Other ways of organizing cause-and-effect diagrams are possible. The key is to make the cause-and-effect diagram fit the problem.

A simple cause-and-effect diagram for delays in delivery is shown in Figure 2.15. In this case the two major branches were taken to be the responsibilities of the two partners in the sale.

Since the intent is to use the diagram to conceptualize the process, it is best if the diagram reflects the perspective of the many different individuals who are closely connected with the process. Diagrams drawn by only one or two individuals are usually rather poor because they lack this broad base of observation of the process. For this reason, cause-and-effect diagrams are often drawn during brainstorming sessions that include the workers.

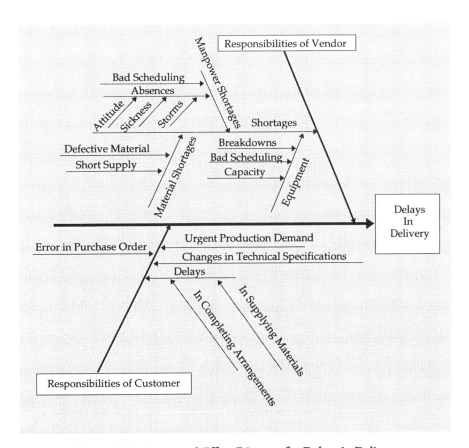

Figure 2.15: Cause-and-Effect Diagram for Delays in Delivery

After a cause-and-effect diagram has been generated, it may need to be modified and realigned to show the causes in their proper relationships. There should be many sub-branches and even some sub-sub-branches. Even though this kind of chart has been called a fishbone diagram, the finished chart should not look like the skeleton of a fish. Such a cause-and-effect diagram would not effectively show the relationships between the various causes and sub-causes because every factor would appear to be a primary factor, making it difficult to decide where to start.

After the cause-and-effect diagram has been drawn, and rearranged if necessary, the group which generated the diagram should analyze each of the causes to see if there are any obvious things that need to be done, if there are any data that could be collected, and if not, if there is any indirect way of characterizing whether or not this cause is changing. If these things are noted directly on the cause-and-effect diagram it will help to highlight those areas needing immediate action. Following the initial changes resulting from the use of a cause-and-effect diagram, plans should be made for using it on a continuing basis.

The cause-and-effect diagram provides a framework for collective efforts. In Chapter Seven you will learn how to make a distinction between processes that are predictable and those that are not predictable. When a process is predictable, the cause-and-effect diagram will help organize efforts to make the process better. When a process is unpredictable, the diagram will suggest areas for investigation.

A second way to use a cause-and-effect diagram is to review what has already been accomplished. The diagram often prevents personnel from overlooking various aspects of the problem. Vast improvement for one principal cause may have only a slight impact on the quality characteristic, while modest improvements on several principal causes may result in dramatic improvements in product quality.

The third way that the cause-and-effect diagram can be used on a continuing basis is to orient new personnel to the problems in a given area. Then they can be smoothly integrated into the work force, without repeating the mistakes of their predecessors.

A fourth way to use the cause-and-effect diagram is in the integration of operations in different areas or different departments. This can be especially important in administrative applications, since the delivery of a service is often quite hard to visualize and coordinate.

CRACKS

At one steel mill the appropriate operators and supervisors were called into the plant manager's office during their lunch hour and asked to produce a cause-and-effect diagram on the problem of "Cracks." (A crack would result when a surface imperfection on the steel billet was rolled into the finished steel bar. Pieces with cracks were defective.) Cracks had been the number one problem in this mill for the past six months, and nothing they had done had really reduced on this problem. Everyone had their own unique ideas about what caused Cracks, and the cause-and-effect diagram combined all of these perspectives into one global picture. When everyone could see the big picture, and could put the potential causes down in an organized manner, it was much easier to work together to reduce the occurrence of

Cracks. Out of these efforts the incidence of Cracks was cut in half each month for the next four months. This represented a sixteen-fold reduction in their major problem—after months with no progress.

The cause-and-effect diagram is effective in the various areas and ways listed above because the process of producing the chart is a thought-provoking and informative process. It helps all involved personnel systematize their thoughts. Yet it is so easy that virtually anyone can understand and participate in its construction.

2.9 Exercises

EXERCISE 2.1:

Read through the flowchart in Figure 2.4. It is a picture of a portion of a real process as it existed at that time and place. Since it is a real process it has the problems that are common to real processes. Can you spot some of the flaws or shortcomings in this process?

What do these flaws mean for the customer? What do they cost this company?

EXERCISE 2.2:

From the perspective of the bank, the steps in providing service at an Automatic Teller Machine consist of Verification, Selection, Delivery, and Completion of Service. For the Verification phase the steps are:

1. Card is presented by customer.
2. Is card presented a valid card? If not, eject card and end transaction.
3. Ask for PIN.
4. Is PIN correct? If not, go to 5. Otherwise go to 6.
5. Is this the customer's third try at entering a valid PIN?
    If yes, keep card and end transaction. If no, Go to 3.
6. Present Menu for Selection phase of service.

Draw a flowchart for the Verification Step of an ATM transaction.

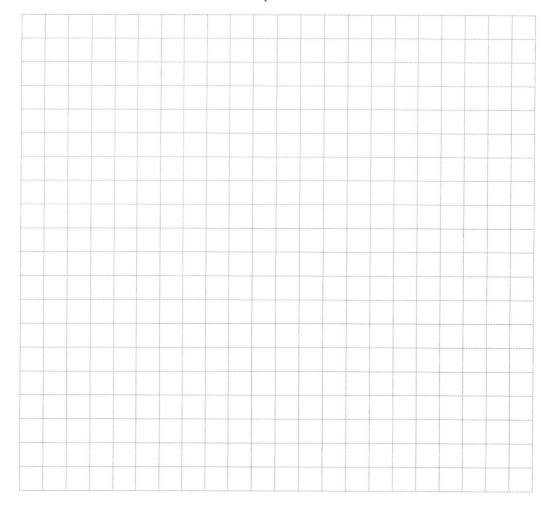

EXERCISE 2.3:

For the Withdrawal Portion of the Selection and Delivery phase of an ATM transaction the steps are:

1. Is this a payment? If yes, go to A.
2. Is this a deposit? If yes, go to B.
3. Transaction is a withdrawal.
4. Present menu for customer to select account for withdrawal.
5. Ask for amount of withdrawal.
6. Does account have sufficient funds to cover the withdrawal?
   If not send message and return to Step 4. If yes go to 7.
7. Does ATM have sufficient funds to cover withdrawal?
   If not send message and go to 5. If yes go to 8.
8. Debit account and dispense funds.

Draw a flowchart for this Withdrawal Portion of an ATM transaction.

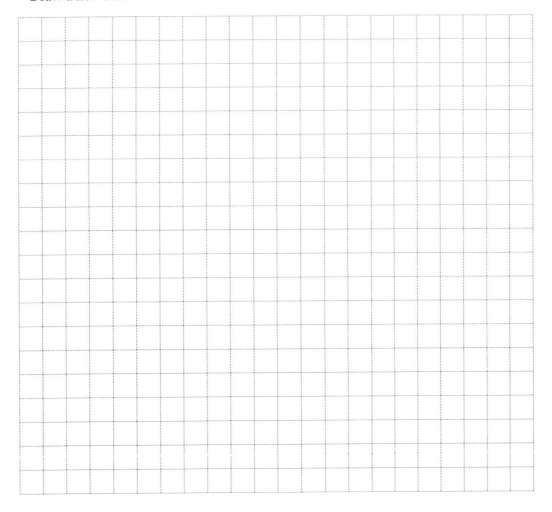

EXERCISE 2.4: There are many different reasons why an ATM transaction might not be successfully completed. Among these are the following:

Wrong card used	Wrong PIN entered
Mag strip on card unreadable	Invalid amount requested
Lack of funds in account	ATM out of cash
Warped card jammed in ATM	ATM malfunctions
Wrong key strokes	

Create a Cause and Effect diagram for Incomplete ATM Transactions using two branches: Responsibilities of the Customer, and Responsibilities of the Bank.

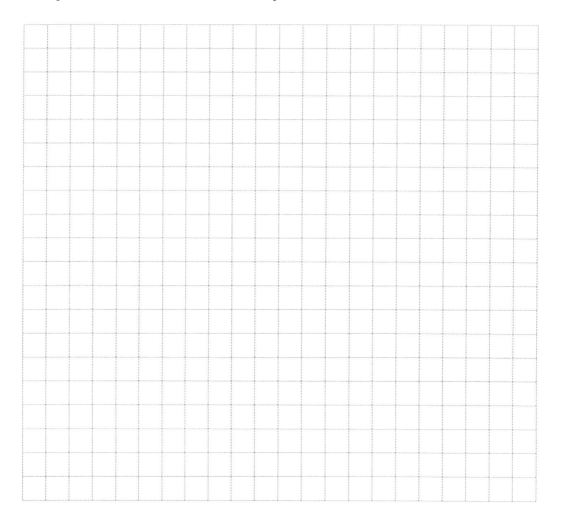

Chapter Three

Collecting Good Data

After you visualize your process you may need to collect some data in order to quantify some aspect of that process. This chapter will address some of the issues concerning the collection of data, and some of the problems, pitfalls, and just plain nonsense that you will encounter along the way.

3.1 What Are You Trying To Do?

The following comes from *Real People, Real Work* by Lee Cheaney and Maury Cotter.

> One day, I noticed that Sara was really grinding away at putting numbers on spreadsheet paper in a black binder. Sara was a hard worker. She prided herself in her excellent productivity and her impeccable accuracy. All that day she worked on the binder. She worked from large piles of computer printouts that were stacked around her. Her fingers were a blur as they flew over her adding machine.

> I didn't get a chance to chat with Sara the first day I noticed her working on the binder. I only noticed because it wasn't a task I had seen her perform before. On the second day she was still busy, head bent over the black binder. I went over to her area. "Hi Sara," I said. "What are you working on?"

> "These are my stats," said Sara. I asked if she pulled this data together for the monthly production schedules that ultimately came to me.

> "No, these numbers don't go in those schedules," she replied.

> "Oh," said I, "you must be pulling these numbers together to serve as a quick reference in answering the dozens of calls you get each day."

> "No," Sara explained, "I don't need the binder for them."

> "Oh, you must run these tabulations for Roy, and then he uses them in his unit."

> "No, these aren't used over there."

> "Sara, who uses this binder?"

> "I don't know."

"Do you keep this binder here in your area?"

"Yes."

"Does anyone ever come here and look in this binder?"

"No."

"Sara, do you ever use the information in this binder?"

"Nope," said Sara.

In the next few moments, I learned about a complexity existing in one of the systems within my jurisdiction. Complexity is work or tasks that people do which do not add any value to the product or service the organization provides. *Complexity is not real work.* Sara told me proudly that she had gotten the length of time necessary to do these monthly tabulations down to two days. She told me she had been doing these tabulations and recording the results in the black binder for almost ten years. That's two days a month, twelve months a year, for almost ten years.

When I asked her why she did this, she told me about a dead guy—a guy I had never met, but had heard of. Well, the guy had asked Sara, back when she worked for him, to pull together a certain kind of data in a black binder because he had a hunch that another party might call and ask for the numbers and he wanted to be prepared—just in case. Then he died. He never told her to stop. Neither did anyone else.

Sara was doing things right. She was accomplishing the task perfectly. There never was a doubt about Sara's accuracy, speed, dependability. But she wasn't doing the right work.

So for the data which your organization routinely collects you should begin by asking, "Who uses these numbers?" Then you should ask, "How do they use them?" The answer to these two questions will help to focus your data collection efforts. If no one is using a measure, and you are not required to keep and report this measure, then it should be dropped. For those measures that are being used, or are required, how are they used?

The data you collect should serve as a basis for insight into your process, so that you can take action to make the process better in the future. Specific methodologies for doing this will be given in this book, but the whole process begins with the data, which brings us to the first of two rules for collecting data:

> *Unless all the values in a set of values*
> *are collected in a consistent manner,*
> *the values will not be comparable.*

This means, among other things, that the pedigree of your data will need to be known before you can make much use of them. In order to be useful, data need to satisfy three conditions:

1. the data must be the right data,

2. the data must be analyzed and presented in an understandable manner, and

3. the results must be interpreted in the context of the original data.

What is your purpose in collecting data? Who is going to use the data? How are they going to use it? How are the values obtained? What assumptions were made in obtaining the values?

Collecting good and focused data is a prerequisite for making sense of those data. The issues of discovery, investigation, communication, and persuasion are all promoted by effective and useful data analysis, but the analysis cannot be any better than the original data.

3.2 Operational Definitions

Operational definitions are needed everywhere you have decisions to make. Say that you are asked to count how many people are in your building. Sounds simple doesn't it? But what do you mean by "in your building?" Do you count anyone that enters the building throughout the day? Or do you count the people who are in the building at a specific time? And when would that be, 8:30 p.m.? Let's say you are told, "Just count those who are routinely in the building." Do you count the mail man? The delivery men? The customers? The consultants?

Whenever you are asked to collect some data the problems of what to measure, how to measure, and when to measure all raise their heads. An operational definition puts written and documented meaning into a concept so that it can be communicated and understood by everyone involved. It is an agreed upon way of making decisions so that consistent results can be obtained by different people at different times.

Many years ago, W. Edwards Deming wrote that an operational definition consists of three parts:

1. a criterion to be applied,

2. a test of compliance to be applied, and

3. a decision rule for interpreting the test results.

You may specify anything you like—weight, color, performance—but a specification, a goal, or a target is not enough for an operational definition. An operational definition must also contain a method of determining when you have satisfied the criterion.

Returning to the problem of counting the people in your building, until you have a criterion on whom to count you cannot even get started.

Once you have a criterion, then you have to have a *method* of counting. How would you count everyone in your building? How long will it take you to simply walk around the building? Different methods of obtaining the count could result in different values.

Finally, a way to decide whom to count and whom to exclude from the count will be needed to avoid confusion.

Now, what if your sister division is given the same job of counting how many people are in their building. Without an operational definition of how to perform the count, is it likely that they will count their people the same way you counted yours?

While you may think this example is silly, it is the problem faced by the Census Bureau every decade. How many people live in Atlanta? While this question is easy to ask, *there is no exact answer to this question.* Which is why it is nonsense to claim that "this census was the most accurate ever." The census uses a given method to obtain a count. Change the method and you will change the count. A particular method may do a better job, or a poorer job, of counting people in a given segment of the population than will an alternative method. Nevertheless, there is no way to claim that one method is more accurate than another method. The number you get will be the result of the method you use.

This is why you need to know how the data are going to be used in order to define how the data will be collected. If all you want to know is the population of Atlanta to the nearest million, then call the Atlanta Chamber of Commerce. The objective will affect the way the data need to be collected. Which brings us to the second rule for collecting good data:

> **It is rarely satisfactory to use data**
> **which have been collected for one purpose**
> **for a different purpose.**

One plant manager was frustrated to be told that his productivity figures were the lowest in the company. According to his calculations he was doing better than several other plants. Yet, every month in the company report, his plant was listed last in productivity. After a particularly bad month he went to the Comptroller and found that the productivity figures were obtained by dividing the revenues for a plant by the headcount for that site. Since this manager's plant also housed the engineering division, his numbers were always deflated by the calculation. The headcount number used was not collected for purposes of computing the productivity.

A healthy appreciation of operational definitions is fundamental to being able to do business. Much of the confusion and mistrust about nonconforming materials and not meeting standards comes from a failure to use, in advance, operational definitions of conformance or performance.

An operational definition puts communicable meaning into an adjective. Adjectives like good, reliable, uniform, prompt, on-time, safe, unsafe, finished, consistent, and unemployed have no communicable meaning until they are expressed in operational terms of criterion, test, and decision rule. Whatever they mean to one person cannot be known to another until both agree on a communicable definition. A communicable definition is operational, because it involves doing something, carrying out a test, recording the result, and interpreting the result according to the agreed upon decision rule. This means that there can be different operational definitions for the same thing. It is not a matter of being right or wrong, but rather a matter of agreement between the parties involved. The result of an operational definition is consistency. The result of not having an operational definition is a lack of consistency.

The link between the three parts of an operational definition and the three questions of Chapter One is no accident. "What do you want to accomplish?" is the criterion. "By what method?" is the test procedure. And "How will you know?" is the decision rule. These three questions provide an operational definition of how to go about the job of improving your life, your job, your organization. Anything less will be incomplete, and will usually be ineffective as well.

3.3 Counts, Categories, and Types of Data

When you get into the counting game there is always the problem of counting events which have different degrees of severity. Many times this problem has been addressed by creating categories for the different degrees of severity and then awarding different numbers of "demerits" for the different categories. While it may be helpful to create such categories, you should resist the temptation of adding up the demerits. An example of the absurdities that can result from adding demerits comes from the University of Texas, where, in the 1960s, the campus police could issue tickets to students. The tickets came in three flavors; minor, major and flagrant. Four minor violations would get you expelled. The list of minor violations included such things as jaywalking and littering. Major violations consisted of more serious infractions, such as parking in a faculty space, or hitting a pedestrian with your car. Two major violations would get you expelled. And then there was the flagrant category. One flagrant citation and the Eyes of Texas would no longer shine upon you. The only infraction listed for a flagrant citation was moving a campus police barricade. So, if you had to make a choice between running into a barricade or hitting a jaywalking pedestrian, you should chose the pedestrian every time—after all, it takes two pedestrians to equal one barricade.

Of course the problem illustrated here is that of using numbers to denote severity even though there is no logical, or proper, definition of *distance* for the numbers. When working with counts, four is twice as many as two. But when working with demerits, is flagrant (four demerits) twice as bad as major (two demerits)? Simply assigning numbers does not create what mathematicians call a "metric." And without a well-defined concept of distance you will always end up with absurdities like the one in the previous paragraph.

Ordinal Data

While numbers may be used to denote an ordering among categories, such numbers do not possess the property of distance. The term for numbers used in this way is ordinal data. This type of data is often seen when the responses to a survey question are spread out on a five-point scale. While it is true that there is a natural ordering to the five responses strongly agree, agree, neutral, disagree, and strongly disagree, there is no guarantee that the distance between "strongly agree" (5) and "agree" (4) is the same as the distance from "agree" (4) to "neutral" (3), yet on the number line the distance from 3 to 4 is the same as from 4 to 5.

About all that you can do to "analyze" such ordinal data is to compute the proportion of positive (or negative) responses (on that one question), or compute a pseudo-average. An example of a pseudo-average computed using ordinal scale data would be a student's grade-point-average. While pseudo-averages are technically questionable, they have enough practical utility and interpretability to justify their use.

For an example of survey data I shall use a question from one company's annual internal employee survey shown in Figure 3.1.

	strongly disagree	disagree	neutral	agree	strongly agree
This company is a good place to work.	1	2	3	4	5

Figure 3.1: Typical Internal Survey Question

Out of 7262 employees who answered this question, 496 strongly disagreed, 232 disagreed, 992 were neutral, 3024 agreed and 2518 strongly agreed. Thus a total of 5542 out of 7262 gave a positive response, which is 76.3 percent. The pseudo-average response is:

$$\frac{496\,(\,1\,) \,+\, 232\,(\,2\,) \,+\, 992\,(\,3\,) \,+\, 3024\,(\,4\,) \,+\, 2518\,(\,5\,)}{7262} = 3.94$$

Both the 76.3 percent and the 3.94 could be used to track the responses to this question from year to year. If these values go up, things are likely to be improving. If they drop, it is likely to be a signal of lower morale. If they simply meander around then things are not likely to be changing.

Another issue for interpreting the results of questions like the one in Figure 3.1 is the tendency for people who are really neutral to be biased toward the positive answers. For example, many of the readers of Consumer Reports use a four-point scale to rate movies. The four possible ratings are (1) poor, (2) fair, (3) good, and (4) excellent. If we combined the responses for thousands of evaluations of hundreds of films we might well expect everything to average out, with each rating getting about 25% of the total. However, in this case we end up with 10% poor, 25% fair, 40% good, and 25% excellent. This is 65% positive, with a pseudo-average of 2.80. So either all the films were above average, or else the average response is skewed toward the positive end. In other words, returning to the question in Figure 3.1, the 76% positive and the pseudo-average of 3.94 are not as strongly positive as they sound.

Another example of survey data comes from an evaluation form used at a conference. The attendees at each presentation were asked to fill out forms, which were summarized in the manner shown in Figure 3.2.

The summary in Figure 3.2 would be better if it reported the number of responses for each category, rather than using percentages. There were a total of 33 evaluations filled out, and so a single response would correspond to 3%. While this is not a serious instance of over-reporting, what would the percentages mean if there were only 10 evaluations filled out? By using percentages the reader is automatically shifted to think in parts per hundred, even when that might not be supported by the data. When the actual counts are used, this shift does not occur and the data are presented with greater integrity.

	excellent	very good	average	below average	poor
1. Usefulness of subject.	67%	33%	0%	0%	0%
2. Organization and clarity of presentation	76%	21%	3%	0%	0%
3. Speaker's knowledge of subject	91%	9%	0%	0%	0%
4. Use of audio-visual aids	52%	33%	15%	0%	0%
5. Overall evaluation of presentation	67%	30%	3%	0%	0%
TOTAL AVERAGE	70%	25%	4%	0%	0%

Figure 3.2: Summary of Responses to Questions on the Evaluation Form

Another issue that is obscured by the use of percentages in Figure 3.2 is the fact that not every person will fill out every item in a survey. Some questions might have only 30 responses rather than 33. Once again, reporting the counts rather than the percentages would correct this problem.

Finally, what are we to make of the "Total Average" line in Figure 3.2? Item five has already asked the respondents for an overall summary evaluation. While we can certainly total the counts for each category across the different questions, what do these totals mean? And while we can convert these totals into percentages, what sense can we make of this fruit salad? The Total Average line in Figure 3.2 is essentially a triumph of computation over common sense. It should be deleted from the summary. (I know that I just did the same sort of thing with the movie evaluations on the previous page, but that was a summary for statistical purposes, to display the overall psychology of using such scales, rather than to summarize and interpret a set of responses for a specific set of questions.)

If we assigned values of 0 to poor, 1 to below average, 2 to average, 3 to very good, and 4 to excellent, we would have the familiar grade-point scale. The 33 evaluations could be summarized by a single number for each item. For example, this speaker received an average rating of 3.67 for usefulness of subject; an average rating of 3.72 for organization and clarity of presentation; an average rating of 3.91 for knowledge of subject; an average rating of 3.36 on use of audio-visual aids; and an average rating of 3.64 for the overall evaluation of the presentation. Of course, given numbers like these, who can resist averaging them into a single number of 3.66? While such a global pseudo-average could be used to provide a one-number summary for each presenter at the conference, the meaning of such global pseudo-averages is slippery at best.

Of course every pseudo-average is dependent upon the numbers assigned to each category. For the previous example, are you really sure that the distance from poor to below-average should be the same as the distance from below-average to average? Shouldn't there be a category of good between average and very good? If so, shouldn't it be twice as far from average to very good as it is from very good to excellent?

Pseudo averages are very convenient, but they are essentially an arbitrary scoring system which is used with ordinal data. They have limited meaning, and should not be over interpreted.

Another practice to be avoided is the computation of a measure of dispersion for the responses to a single item. The arbitrary distance created by the scale will make all measures of dispersion merely arbitrary and meaningless.

Nominal Data

In the scheme of things, the next step below ordinal data would be "numbers used as labels." Telephone numbers are examples of this use of numbers. Numbers as labels do not possess either the property of *order* or *distance*. About the only type of analysis that is appropriate for such "numbers" is a tally of occurrences for each label. This is illustrated in Figure 4.6, where the operator numbers are used as labels for a bar graph. "Numbers as labels" have been called nominal data, but they are not data at all. If letters would work as well, then you are merely using numbers as symbols.

In the hierarchy of data types there are two more categories, known respectively as Interval Scale Data and Ratio Scale Data. These will be discussed in Chapter Six.

Because we use numbers for different things and in different ways you will always need to know the context for a set of numbers before you can have any idea how to use them, how to interpret them, or how to analyze them.

Chapter Four

Visualize Your Data

The human brain does not easily absorb large sets of numbers. That is why a page full of tabular data is so hard to assimilate.

If you want to impress your audience
    show them page after page of numbers in tables—
        you will either intimidate them or alienate them.

But if you want to *really communicate* with your audience,
    use *good graphs* which reveal the information contained in the numbers
        in a clear and concise manner.

You have about thirty seconds to communicate the content of your data to your audience. After that, their eyes glaze over. The only way that you can consistently beat this thirty-second deadline is to use effective graphs.

This chapter will introduce some of the basic graphs you can use to make sense of data. You will learn how to effectively construct and use running records, bar charts, Pareto charts, histograms, and stem-and-leaf plots.

4.1 Running Records

Data tend to be associated with time: When was this value obtained? What time period does that value represent? As a result of this association with time, the time-order sequence of the values will contain information about your process. To recover this information you will need to look at your data in a time-ordered plot, which is commonly called a running record or a time-series graph.

A running record is a simple graph where one scale represents time and the other scale represents values of the measure of interest. Traditionally the time scale is horizontal and the value scale is vertical. The running record in Figure 4.1 shows the Quarterly Sales for Region D over the past five years.

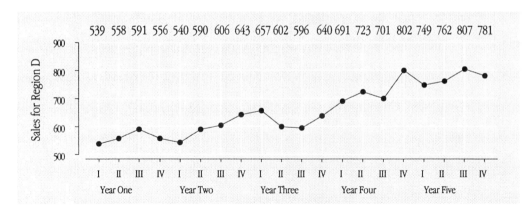

Figure 4.1: Running Record for the Quarterly Sales for Region D

The running record in Figure 4.1:
1. conveys the overall level of sales by the vertical scale,
2. shows the amount by which the sales vary from quarter to quarter,
3. shows the overall trend in sales over the past five years, and
4. places the current value in context;

which is a lot to accomplish with such a simple graph!

The lines on a running record draw our eyes and help us to instantly comprehend the message contained in the values. The points without the lines do not create as powerful a graph. However, there are situations where the graph can be improved by the judicious deletion of certain line segments. In Figure 4.2, gaps are left between the years. These gaps give our eyes visual anchors and allow us to know which quarter is which without even consulting the horizontal scale.

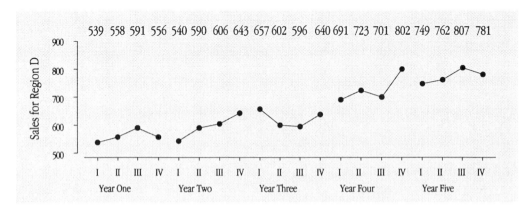

Figure 4.2: Running Record for the Quarterly Sales for Region D

By including the values in the margin of the running record you make the graph even easier for your readers to use. If they want to know a particular value, they do not have to hunt it up on some table on another piece of paper, but can simply look it up in the margin of the plot.

In constructing a running record the value scale only needs to represent those values which are present in the data. A glance at the values in Figure 4.1 shows values ranging from the 500s up to the 800s, so a scale from 500 to 900 should be sufficient. By using a vertical scale that ranges from just below the minimum value to just above the maximum value, you will end up with a running record that uses the vertical space on the graph effectively.

An example of what a poor choice for the vertical scale can do is seen in Figure 4.3, where all of the values are crowded into the upper 20% of the graph and most of the graph is empty.

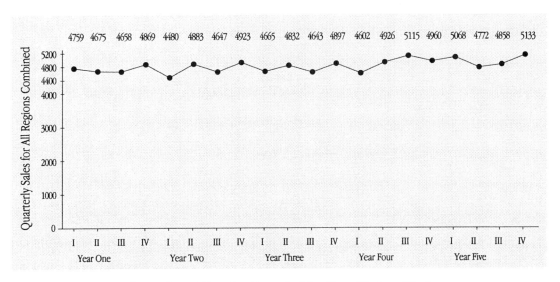

Figure 4.3: A Running Record with a Poor Choice of Scale

Occasionally you may combine two or more running records on a single graph. One executive routinely plotted the inventory level, accounts receivable, and the cash reserves for his company. Since these were all measured in the same units (dollars), he used the same graph for all three records with a different colored ink for each time series. As long as you can easily distinguish between the different running records, this practice is acceptable.

Figure 4.4 shows two of these three running records over a seven year period. The heavy line represents the cash reserves, while the light line shows the inventory levels. Both curves use the same vertical scale, which, in this case, starts with zero. The breaks in the lines show the ends of each year, and the arrows at the bottom show new product release dates.

This pair of running records tells a dramatic story. At the end of Year Three this company launched two new products. At that time their inventory levels began to climb while their cash position began to erode. Since these graphs made the change in status so obvious, actions could be taken in a timely manner to avoid a crisis. Steps were taken to hold the line on inventory. New manufacturing and stocking policies were adopted, allowing

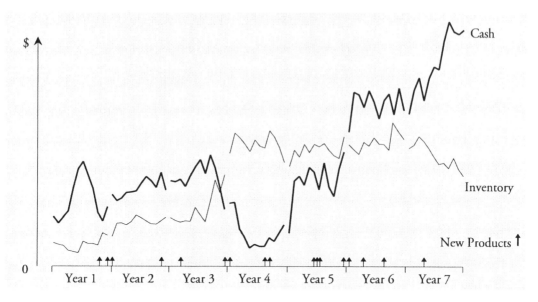

Figure 4.4: **Monthly Cash on Hand and Monthly Inventory Levels for Seven Years**

tighter inventory control. At the same time, steps were taken to conserve cash and to reduce or defer expenses.

With these corrective actions in place they still had to endure a cash crunch during Year Four, but it was not so severe as to prevent them from launching two new products during that time. Since one of these products proved to be very popular, its introduction was the beginning of the turn-around. During Years Four, Five, Six, and Seven the inventory levels remained fairly steady in spite of the fact that the company introduced ten new products during this period. At the same time the cash position of the company has steadily grown. After a two-year sojourn in the land of the inventory-rich-but-cash-strapped, this company returned to the land of the cash-rich and inventory-lean.

Much of the interesting information available in your data is tied up in the time-order sequence of the values. The running record unlocks this interesting information. Of all the different types of graphs that exist, this simple plot of the values in their time-order sequence is one of the most useful, one of the most powerful, and one of the most easily interpreted of them all.

The beauty of a running record is that
the lines draw your eye
in the direction
that your mind wants to go.

4.2 Bar Charts

The purpose of a bar chart is to compare values or amounts across different categories.

One Monday morning in the restaurant of a large hotel, I offered to pay for breakfast with a twenty-dollar bill. Since the amount of the check was under ten dollars the cashier asked if I had a smaller bill.

"I'll bet you get a lot of twenty-dollar bills on Mondays." I said.

"Oh yes. I never have enough change on Mondays and Fridays."

"Have you ever asked your boss for more change on those days?"

"Oh yes, but he won't ever give me any more. I always have the same amount of change each day."

"Here's an idea. Keep a tally of the number of twenty-dollar bills offered each day. That way you will have some data to back up your request for more change."

"Oh wow! What a great idea!"

If the cashier did keep a tally, her data might have looked something like the following:

Sunday																				18
Monday	||||| ||||| ||||| ||||| ||||| ||||| ||||| ||||| ||||| ||||| ||||| ||||| ||||| ||||| ||	77
Tuesday																																		32
Wednesday																																			33
Thursday																						20
Friday	||||| ||||| ||||| ||||| ||||| ||||| ||||| ||||| ||||| ||||| ||||| ||||| ||||| ||||	69
Saturday															13

Figure 4.5: Number of Twenty-Dollar Bills Presented

While tally sheets such as this may be converted into other graphs, they are already a powerful and graphic representation of the data. The magnitude of the problem is thus presented in a form that everyone—including the manager—can immediately grasp: The cashier needs more change for big bills on Mondays and Fridays.

Simple tally sheets like Figure 4.5 are a primitive form of a bar chart. A bar chart is a two-dimensional plot where one dimension consists of a list of categories and the other dimension consists of frequencies or amounts for some measure. A bar is constructed for each category where the length of the bar represents the value of the measure for that category. If we were to construct a bar chart for Figure 4.5, the days of the weeks would be the categories, the other scale would list the possible numbers of twenty-dollar bills presented, and the length of each bar would be the number of twenty-dollar bills presented each day.

The data in Table 4.1 are from a telephone service center. These data came from a report which was generated by a computerized monitoring system. The Call Lengths are the times in minutes for calls that came during one hour and which lasted longer than 15 seconds.

Table 4.1: Hourly Call Summary for Service Center Five

Operator I.D.	10:00 to 11:00 am on February 12 Call Lengths (in minutes)									No. of Calls	Total Time	Average Call Length
1	10.0	10.7	11.4	10.7	9.8					5	52.6	10.5
2	9.1	7.4	6.6	5.8	2.8	16.9				6	48.6	8.1
3	13.2	12.3	10.8	10.1						4	46.4	11.6
4	10.9	12.2	10.6	12.4						4	46.1	11.5
5	14.2	22.0	13.9							3	50.1	16.7
6	11.7	10.4	9.7	8.0	6.8	6.1				6	52.7	8.8
7	5.4	3.1	16.8	3.2	3.1	5.8	6.3	6.0		8	49.7	6.2
8	6.9	7.6	9.0	13.4	15.3					5	52.2	10.4
9	6.1	10.3	10.4	7.0	11.2					5	45.0	9.0
10	7.5	11.5	12.0	8.1	12.7					5	51.8	10.4
11	13.1	9.3	15.0	6.1						4	43.4	10.9
12	10.0	19.7	6.6							3	36.3	12.1
13	11.0	1.1	2.0	12.5	9.1	5.7	15.3			7	56.7	8.1
14	10.0	6.2	6.6	7.3	1.4	2.1	3.2	5.4	5.7	9	47.9	5.3
15	15.8	18.3	6.1							3	40.2	13.4
16	24.7	11.3	7.6	3.2						4	46.8	11.7
17	5.6	9.3	10.3	7.0	8.0					5	40.2	8.0
18	9.2	6.1	6.7	8.5	10.5					5	41.0	8.2
19	17.8	7.7	9.7							3	35.2	11.7
20	16.0	9.2	3.2	7.4	9.3					5	45.1	9.0
21	11.3	12.8	11.4							3	35.5	11.8
22	10.2	9.6	8.7	1.9	6.4	7.2				6	44.0	7.3

Table 4.1 is already a pseudo bar chart: Each row shows the number of calls taken by each of the 22 operators during this time period. While some operators logged only three calls, others logged seven, eight, or nine calls. However, these simple counts do not take into account the duration of the calls. We could construct a bar chart to show the Total Connect Time for each of the 22 operators for this hour. This bar chart is shown in Figure 4.6. The Operator IDs are the categories along the bottom and the Total Connect Time is the measure along the vertical scale.

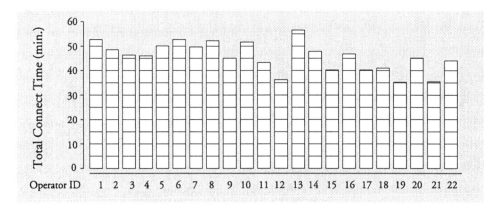

Figure 4.6: Bar Chart for Total Connect Time

The purpose of a bar chart is to compare amounts across categories. The emphasis is upon the length of the bars in the graph, and this is the essential mechanism for the comparisons. The categories may be people, regions, countries, companies, departments, or any classification that makes sense for a given collection of data. Since the purpose is to compare the lengths of the bars, it is customary to begin the scale of possible values with a value of zero. If this scale started with some value other than zero, or if some the intermediate values were suppressed, then the lengths would be distorted and the comparisons would be skewed. The integrity of the comparisons depends upon the lengths of the bars representing the values of the measure of interest.

In 1786, William Playfair produced the first known bar chart. It showed the exports and imports for Scotland for the 12-month period from Christmas 1780 to Christmas 1781. A facsimile of this chart is shown in Figure 4.7.

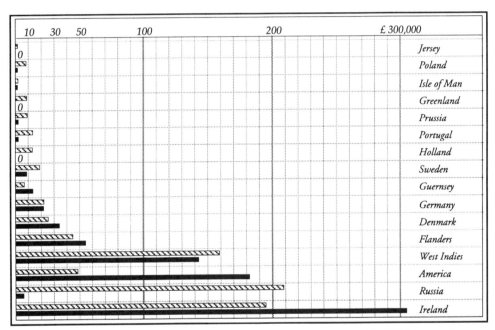

The upright divisions are Ten Thousand Pounds each.   *The Black Lines are Exports.*   *The Ribbed Lines are Imports.*

Figure 4.7: The First Known Bar Chart

The categories in Playfair's bar chart consist of those counties, countries, and colonies who were Scotland's trading partners.* He arranged them, in a general way, in order of increasing levels of trade. In this he anticipated a particular form of the bar chart which is in use today—the Pareto chart.

---

* This bar chart was in Playfair's book *The Commercial and Political Atlas*, London, 1786. Several of the interesting graphics in this landmark book were resurrected by Professor Edward R. Tufte in his lovely book *The Visual Display of Quantitative Information*, Graphics Press, Cheshire, Connecticut, 1983.

4.3 Pareto Charts

The Pareto chart is named after an Italian economist, Vilfredo Pareto, who observed in 1897 that 80% of the wealth of a country was held by 20% of the population. Over time it was observed that many different sets of data display this same type of behavior. Most of the problems, most of the defects, most of the costs are due to a minority of the categories. This idea came to be known as the Pareto principle. Therefore, if we can identify the few categories that contribute the greatest amount toward the total number of problems, defects, or costs, then we will know where to concentrate our efforts for improvement.

Traditionally, costs are the preferred scale to use with the Pareto chart.

The Pareto chart is a bar chart in which the categories have been arranged according to their values. The chart begins with the category having the greatest amount, and then proceeds in the order of progressively smaller amounts. If we rearrange the export data from Playfair's bar chart (Figure 4.7) we get Figure 4.8. This chart shows at a glance that the bulk of Scotland's exports are purchased by three trading partners: Ireland, America, and the West Indies. But does the Pareto principle apply?

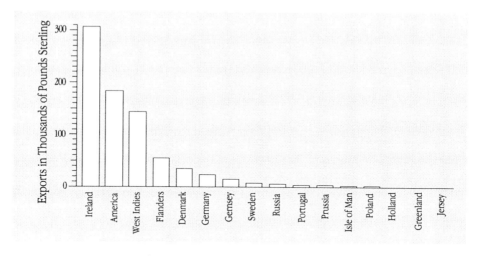

Figure 4.8: Bar Chart for Scotland's Exports, 1781

While some consider Figure 4.8 to already be a Pareto chart, it is easier to interpret the plot if we add a few elements. We begin by extending the vertical scale upward to cover the total amount of all bars combined. In this case, the total amount of Scotland's exports in 1781 was, approximately, £783,000. This value will be represented as 100%. In many cases a second scale marked in percentages will be placed on the right-hand side of the Pareto chart. These scales are shown in Figure 4.9.

Next, a cumulative percentage curve is added to the plot. To obtain these cumulative

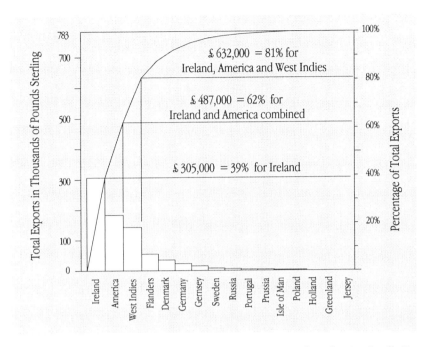

Figure 4.9: Plotting Cumulative Percentages on the Pareto Chart for Scotland's Exports

percentages you proceed in the following manner. Beginning with the category on the left, the percentage of the total represented by this one category is computed. For Playfair's data, Ireland bought £ 305,000 out of the £ 783,000 of exports, which is about 39% of the total. This percentage defines the first point (after zero) on the cumulative percentage curve (see Figure 4.9).

Next, the combined amounts for Ireland and America are used. These two countries bought £ 487,000 worth of goods, about 62% of the total. This amount defines a second point on the cumulative percentage curve, which is plotted directly above the right edge of the second bar in Figure 4.9.

Ireland, America, and the West Indies bought £ 632,000 worth of goods, about 81% of the total. This defines the third point on the cumulative percentage curve, and is plotted directly above the right edge of the third bar on the graph.

The points on the cumulative percentage curve are then connected with lines to get the full Pareto chart shown in Figure 4.9.

In Figure 4.9 we see the Pareto principle at work, even though Playfair's bar chart predated Pareto's observation by 116 years. Ireland, America, and the West Indies were three of Scotland's 16 trading partners in 1781. Three out of 16 is about 19 percent, and they accounted for 81 percent of Scotland's exports.

The extra scales and curves added to the bar chart are intended to facilitate the determination of whether or not the Pareto principle applies. While we may be content with Figure 4.8, Figure 4.9 is the preferred form for a Pareto chart.

Figure 4.10: Pareto Chart for Losses at the Esquire Club

Figure 4.10 is a Pareto chart prepared by the members of a QC (quality control) Circle whose members were seven waitresses and their supervisor. This chart is an analysis of the sources of monetary losses at the Esquire Club, a nightclub in Osaka, Japan.

The six categories on this Pareto chart are, respectively from left to right: sake, beer, side orders, latecomers, bottle losses, and others. The scale on the left shows the cumulative percentage of total losses. The scale on the right shows the total amount of losses in thousands of Yen. These losses were accumulated over the period from October 24 to the end of February and totaled ¥270,228.

They clearly broke the categories into three groups. Group A contains the losses on beer and sake sales. These two categories accounted for over 70% of the losses. Group B included side orders and losses on service charges due to latecomers. Finally, Group C consisted of the last two categories, which accounted for less than 5% of all losses.

Based on this analysis, the QC Circle began a project to find ways to cut down on the losses on beer and sake sales. They created a flowchart for the various steps in their project, planned the work for a 93-day period, and were able to complete the work in 113 days, including a 50-day evaluation period. They cut the losses on beer and sake sales by almost 90 percent, and could document these gains.

The Pareto principle, that a minority of categories will account for the vast majority of the problems, is another facet of what has been called the law of diminishing returns. It is a phenomenon that occurs in all types of endeavors, and is therefore seen in all kinds of data. The major use of a Pareto chart is to make that law visible. To deal effectively with problems, we must know where most of the problems occur. When looking for opportunities for improvement, what areas have the greatest (negative) impact upon the operation? Which problems cause the majority of the complaints? Which steps in the process create the majority of errors?

It does not matter whether you are dealing with problems in manufacturing or service processes. Both types of work involve a series of transactions. Each transaction may or may not have a problem. If a transaction has a problem, then the type of problem it has must be determined. Keeping track of the types of problems that you encounter, and the number of times that each problem occurs, will provide the raw data for a Pareto chart.

Flat Pareto Charts

If 20% to 30% of the categories do not account for 70% to 80% of problems, then you have what is known as a flat Pareto chart.

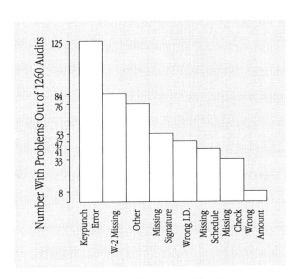

Figure 4.11: Problems with Tax Returns

This problem was encountered by a tax collection agency that was attempting to determine which of their problems should be tackled first. They put the problems that they found in a weekly audit of 1260 tax returns on a bar chart and created Figure 4.11.

In Figure 4.11 the third largest count corresponds to the category labeled "Other." If you decide that this category is one of the "critical few," what are you going to do about it?

Because of this problem, catch-all categories are, by convention, placed at the extreme right hand side of the category scale on a Pareto chart. When this is done, and the cumulative percentage curve is added, we see a *flat* Pareto chart in Figure 4.12.

In Figure 4.12 six of the eight categories account for 80% of the problems. This is hardly the Pareto principle at work! The *flat* Pareto chart is usually telling you that *all* the categories are problems. You cannot identify a critical few because they are all alike. This was made apparent the next week. When the data for the next weekly audit were used to construct a Pareto chart, the two leading problems were "Wrong Amount" and "Wrong I.D." And just where were these two categories in Figure 4.12?

This month-to-month rotation of the categories is itself a signal that all of the categories are problematic. When the leading problems one month fade away the next, and former cellar dwellers take over the lead, then all the categories are in need of attention.

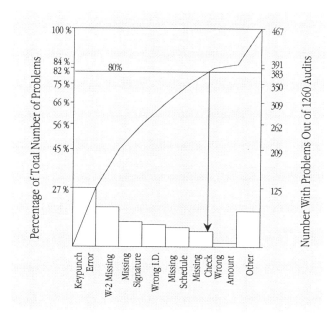

Figure 4.12: Flat Pareto Chart for Problems with Tax Returns

WARRANTY CLAIMS

One day the Quality Director of a company told the author about the Pareto analysis they performed on their warranty claims each year. He complained that the Pareto chart was always flat. Nothing stood out. To which I replied, "Of course the Pareto is flat, Joe. Your processes are unpredictable, and over the course of a year every problem has its fifteen minutes of fame! By the end of the year they all average out, giving you a flat Pareto chart."

The rotation of categories from month to month and flat Pareto charts are ways that your process can tell you that it could be a mistake to concentrate on a critical few of the categories. When the same categories persist in the lead position on a Pareto chart month after month, and when the Pareto principle seems to be at work, then you can benefit by concentrating on the critical few.

A patient survey at one hospital included a space for write-in comments. A tabulation of these comments from 73 surveys was used to produce the Pareto chart in Figure 4.13.

Here it takes 50% of the categories to account for 80% of the complaints. This is hardly the same phenomenon that Vilfredo Pareto described!

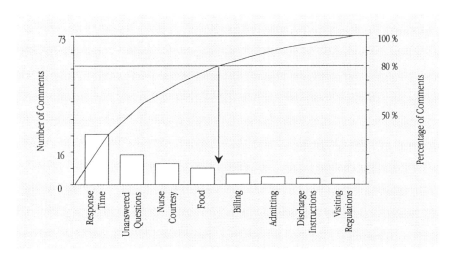

Figure 4.13: Pareto Chart for Patient Complaints

The 73 surveys in Figure 4.13 were all surveys on which someone took the effort to write in a complaint. If this is 73 out of one or two hundred surveys, then perhaps these issues need to be addressed. If this is 73 out of one or two thousand surveys, then there may be little merit in this ranking of problems. (Some people will manufacture complaints just because they think they are supposed to fill in the blank space on the survey form; others are just plain troublemakers.) When dealing with count data it is critical to know the "area of opportunity" for the count in order to interpret the count correctly. See Chapter Thirteen for more about this important concept.

In general, if the vast majority of the problems (say 70% or more) are not attributable to a minority of the categories (say 30% or less), or if the categories take turns "leading the parade," then it will be a mistake to tackle the critical few categories. You will only be chasing the wind. When there are only a few dominant categories, the Pareto chart will help to make them known. When no categories dominate the others, it becomes obvious that all the parts of the process need work.

The power of graphic communication is demonstrated in the Pareto chart. It is especially useful in developing a consensus about which categories to tackle in a problem-solving mode. However, Continual Improvement requires more than merely working on isolated problems. Many problems are built into the system and can only be addressed by changing the system. While it may help to remove the "things gone wrong," it will take more than that to *delight* the customer.

4.4 Histograms and Stem-and-Leaf Plots

Histograms and stem-and-leaf plots are simple ways of organizing large amounts of data to convey a sense of how a collection of values vary. For example, I shall again use the data from the Hourly Call Summary shown in Table 4.1.

Table 4.1: Hourly Call Summary for Service Center Five

Operator I.D.	10:00 to 11:00 am on February 12 Call Lengths (in minutes)									No. of Calls	Total Time	Average Call Length
1	10.0	10.7	11.4	10.7	9.8					5	52.6	10.5
2	9.1	7.4	6.6	5.8	2.8	16.9				6	48.6	8.1
3	13.2	12.3	10.8	10.1						4	46.4	11.6
4	10.9	12.2	10.6	12.4						4	46.1	11.5
5	14.2	22.0	13.9							3	50.1	16.7
6	11.7	10.4	9.7	8.0	6.8	6.1				6	52.7	8.8
7	5.4	3.1	16.8	3.2	3.1	5.8	6.3	6.0		8	49.7	6.2
8	6.9	7.6	9.0	13.4	15.3					5	52.2	10.4
9	6.1	10.3	10.4	7.0	11.2					5	45.0	9.0
10	7.5	11.5	12.0	8.1	12.7					5	51.8	10.4
11	13.1	9.3	15.0	6.1						4	43.4	10.9
12	10.0	19.7	6.6							3	36.3	12.1
13	11.0	1.1	2.0	12.5	9.1	5.7	15.3			7	56.7	8.1
14	10.0	6.2	6.6	7.3	1.4	2.1	3.2	5.4	5.7	9	47.9	5.3
15	15.8	18.3	6.1							3	40.2	13.4
16	24.7	11.3	7.6	3.2						4	46.8	11.7
17	5.6	9.3	10.3	7.0	8.0					5	40.2	8.0
18	9.2	6.1	6.7	8.5	10.5					5	41.0	8.2
19	17.8	7.7	9.7							3	35.2	11.7
20	16.0	9.2	3.2	7.4	9.3					5	45.1	9.0
21	11.3	12.8	11.4							3	35.5	11.8
22	10.2	9.6	8.7	1.9	6.4	7.2				6	44.0	7.3

The values shown in Table 4.1 are Call Lengths in minutes for 108 calls received during a period of one hour. In order to learn something about the behavior of the Call Length data we could quickly place these 108 values in a "stem-and-leaf plot." To begin this plot we need to obtain a rough idea of what range of values is present in these data. The left-hand portion of the numbers will be used to make up the "stem" of our plot. A quick glance at the data, plus knowledge that these values are minutes, suggests that we can begin our stem with 0 and extend it out to 20 or so. (If we grouped the data in ten-minute intervals we would basically end up with two groups, 0 to 9 and 10 to 19. This would obscure too much detail, so we use one-minute intervals instead.) Thus the stem for our plot would start out as a line:

| 0 | 1 | 2 | 3 | 4 | 5 | 6 | 7 | 8 | 9 | 10 | 11 | 12 | 13 | 14 | 15 | 16 | 17 | 18 | 19 | 20 |

Since it is generally easier to create stem-and-leaf plots in a vertical format, it is common to rotate the stem as shown in panel (a) of Figure 4.14. Next we read the data and place the right hand portion of each value as the "leaves" on the stem. The first value is 10.0, so we place a "0" leaf beside the 10 position on the stem to mark this value. Moving down the first column of Table 4.1 the second value is 9.1, so a "1" leaf is placed beside the 9 position on the stem to mark this value. These first two values are shown in Panel (a) of Figure 4.14.

The next two values in the first column are 13.2 and 10.9. The placement of these two values is shown in Panel (b) of Figure 4.14.

Continuing in this manner the next 104 values are added to get the stem-and-leaf plot shown in Panel (c) of Figure 4.14:

(a) (b) (c) (d)

Figure 4.14: Stem-and-Leaf Plot for Call Lengths

PRACTICE: The next two values in the first column of Table 4.1 are 14.2 and 11.7. Place the appropriate leaves in Panel (b) of Figure 4.14 for these two values.

Finally, by numerically sorting the values on each row of Panel (c) of Figure 4.14, we can completely order the data into the form shown in Panel (d) of Figure 4.14. This last graphic is an elegant combination of table and graph. Each value is preserved, the data have been ranked, and the shape of the histogram is revealed all at the same time. A glance at Panel (d) reveals that the gap around 4 minutes is actually over two minutes long (from 3.2 minutes to 5.4 minutes). The interpretation of this gap would be that any call that lasts much beyond three minutes is complex enough for it to take over five minutes to complete.

For the calls that last more than 5 minutes there are two mounds, one centered around 6 minutes and another centered around 10 minutes. While there is no distinct gap at 8 minutes, there is a distinct valley. There may even be another dip at around 14 minutes, but we would need this dip to persist before it would be worth interpreting. Thus, these data have three or four distinct clusters within the histogram, and all of this is revealed by one of the simplest of graphs.

If the data in Figure 4.14 were reproduced as a histogram, Figure 4.15 would result. Histograms are like the stem-and-leaf plot, but bars replace each stack of "leaves." Thus the main difference between the stem-and-leaf plot of Figure 4.14 and the histogram of Figure 4.15 is that the stem-and-leaf plot preserves the values, while the histogram is a form of a bar chart.

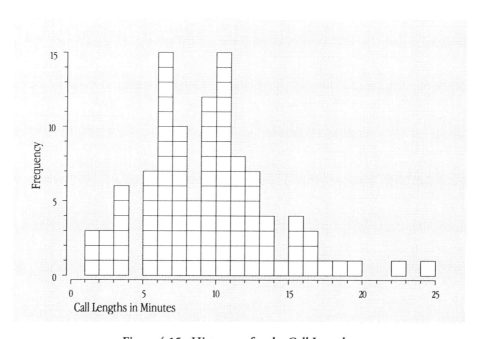

Figure 4.15: Histogram for the Call Lengths

But a different grouping of data could be used. For example, we could use intervals centered on whole numbers. Or we could change the width of the intervals. As the "groupings" for the data become larger, the histogram will become less detailed. For example, if the Call Lengths were grouped in five minute intervals (e.g. 0 to 4.9, 5.0 to 9.9, etc.) then the rather disappointing histogram in Figure 4.16 would be the result. The wider intervals obscure the interesting details in these data.

Figure 4.16: A Disappointing Histogram for Call Lengths

The art of creating a histogram lies in selecting intervals that are:

1. easy for the reader to interpret,
2. narrow enough to reveal the interesting details, and
3. wide enough to show how the data "pile up."

Thus, the art of creating a useful histogram involves finding the right balance between the simplification of the overall picture and the loss of detail that is necessarily part of that simplification. This balance point will differ with different data sets. It will depend upon the structure present in the data, the amount of data, and the purpose of the histogram. Constructing a stem-and-leaf plot is one of the best ways to get this feeling for the data, and so the stem-and-leaf plot can be considered to be a preliminary step in preparing a useful histogram.

If the data consist of fewer than 20 or 30 values, the stem-and-leaf plot will generally suffice. When the data consist of hundreds of values, some grouping will generally improve the picture. One common guideline is that there should be about 20 categories, or fewer, in the region where the bulk of the data occur. In the past, elaborate formulas were given as guidelines for establishing the intervals for the horizontal axis of the histogram, but today it is usually simpler to try different sized intervals and let a computer do the work.

Decorated Histograms Are Dangerous and Misleading

Computer programs for histograms bring their own problems—they tend to give you more than you can use. First, they overwhelm you with numerical summaries. Then, they tend to superimpose extra curves on the histogram. To see the impact of these extra curves consider what they do to the histogram of the Call Length Data. The top panel of Figure 4.17 shows the simple, undecorated histogram for these data; the middle panel shows the most common situation where a bell-shaped curve is superimposed on the histogram; and the bottom panel shows a more complex curve fitted to the "shape" of this histogram.

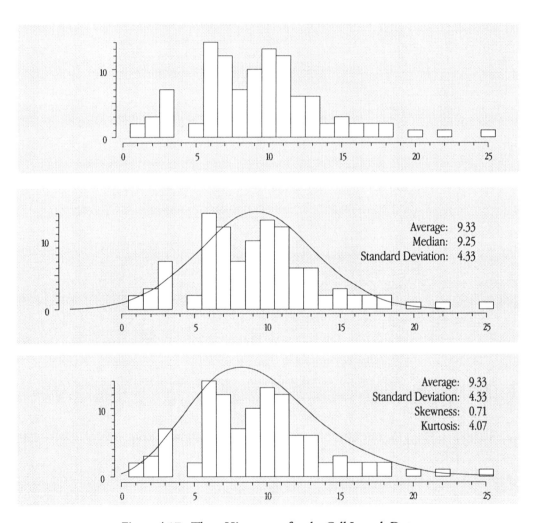

Figure 4.17: Three Histograms for the Call Length Data

The first problem with these superimposed curves is that they are not real—they are purely imaginary. At best, they are a mathematical approximation of reality. They should never be confused with reality itself. At the worst, these curves can be totally misleading.

The second problem with these superimposed curves has to do with the way we see things—notice how your eyes tend to follow the smooth curves. In each case the curves draw your attention away from the gaps at 4 minutes and 8 minutes, while in the top panel your eye tends to follow the tops of the bars. Thus, superimposed curves actually distract, interrupt, and distort the message of the graph.

Finally, which of these superimposed curves is right? You can always come up with many different curves to fit any one histogram. When you have a few hundred observed values, or less, you simply do not have enough information to make an informed choice between the different mathematical approximations. This means that the particular curve which your computer program may display on a histogram is more of a reflection of the assumptions of the computer programmer than a revelation of the characteristics of the data. Edward R. Tufte coined a technical term for these superimposed curves—he called them "chartjunk." And that is exactly what they are—a waste of ink. So if you use a software package to create histograms, turn off the chartjunk options!

In addition, the computer-generated histograms shown in Figure 4.17 contain another triumph of computation over common sense—who on earth knows (or even cares) about the "skewness" and "kurtosis" for these data? So be careful. It is easier to get much more than you want or can use from computer-generated histograms.

By creating a histogram of the Call Lengths from Table 4.1 we have gained some insight into the system. With an average call length of 9.3 minutes it is unreasonable to expect operators to average more than about 6.5 calls per hour. Therefore, 22 operators will be able to handle an average of 130 to 140 calls per hour. Higher volumes will require more operators. Of course, such generalizations depend upon the degree to which this one hour's worth of data is representative of the way the system performs at other times, with other operators, and with other supervisors.

You should consider using a histogram whenever you want to see how the values for some measure vary. Variation is present in every measure. In subsequent chapters you will learn more about characterizing variation as a way to improve a process. In that context histograms are one of the basic tools for visualizing routine variation.

4.5 Summary of Bar Charts and Running Records

Histograms and Pareto charts are special types of bar charts, while time-series plots are fundamentally different from bar charts

Bar Charts: The distinguishing characteristics of bar charts are:
- One scale is a list of categories.
- The other scale shows the possible values for some measure.
- Each bar displays the value of the measure for a particular category.
- The lengths of the bars make the comparisons between categories.

Pareto Charts: Pareto charts begin life as bar charts:
- Categories are organized according to the height of the bars,
    except that a miscellaneous category is placed last.
- Costs, rather than counts, are the preferred measure for use in a Pareto chart.
- A cumulative percentage curve adds perspective to the chart
    and allows you to check to see if the Pareto principle is present.
- The stair-step of the bars and the cumulative percentage curve
    make the comparisons.

Histograms: The distinguishing characteristics of a histogram are:
- One scale consists of possible values for the observed measure.
    (Traditionally this scale is on the horizontal axis.)
- The other scale consists of frequency values.
- Each bar on the histogram shows the frequency with which
    the observed measure falls into the relevant interval.
- The bars show the mounding of the data
    and the taper-off toward each extreme.

Running Records: The distinguishing characteristics of a running record are:
- One scale consists of possible values for the observed measure.
- The other scale consists of time periods.
- The values of this one measure are plotted in their time-order sequence.
- The variation of this measure over time is displayed, and the comparison
    is a comparison of a single measure *with itself* at different time periods.

Bar charts, by their very nature, use the bars to make comparisons. For this reason the value scale of any bar chart should always begin at zero. Baselines other than zero will distort the comparisons. Additionally, the value scale should have no breaks—all the possible values between zero and the observed values should be represented on the value scale. Finally, the value scales should be linear—that is, one unit at the top of the value scale should represent the same range of values as one unit at the bottom of the scale.

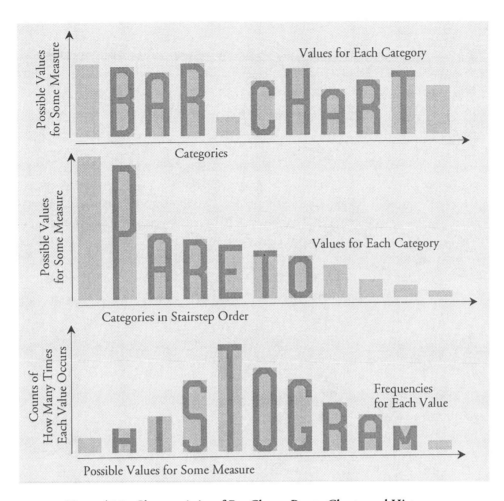

Figure 4.18: **Characteristics of Bar Charts, Pareto Charts, and Histograms**

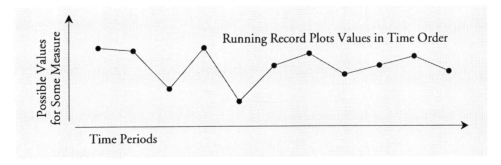

4.19: **How a Running Record Differs from Bar Charts, Pareto Charts, and Histograms**

Bar charts and running records do different jobs. Bar charts are useful for comparing different categories, at a single point in time, using a single measure. Histograms compare the frequency with which the different values of a single measure occur without respect to their time order. A running record uses a single measure, for a single category, and compares this measure with itself at different points in time.

It is important that you recognize the different roles for these different graphs. Otherwise you cannot use them effectively.

The bar chart in Figure 4.20 uses a common measure, quarterly sales, to compare six regions. It is a snapshot taken at one point in time. While a common measure is apparently being used, there are no guarantees that the measure is computed in the same manner from region to region. Neither is there anything that says that the regions should be comparable. This graph merely shows the relative contributions of the different regions to the total sales of the corporation. The emphasis in Figure 4.20 is upon the height of each bar. It is the amounts that are being compared, not the trends over time. The time element in Figure 4.20 is static. While the comparisons of Figure 4.20 may allow us to rank the six regions, they do not provide any insight into what is happening to the sales in each region.

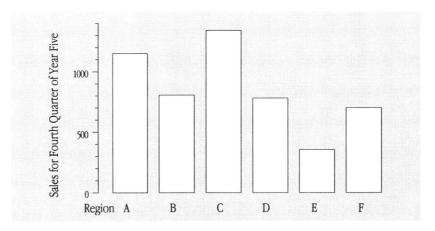

Figure 4.20: Sales by Region for Fourth Quarter of Year Five.

Unlike the bar graph above, which compares regions, the running record in Figure 4.21 shows how the sales in Region D have varied over the past 20 quarters.

When the emphasis is upon the amounts for different categories, bars make the interesting characteristics apparent and easy to grasp. But when the emphasis is upon the variation over time, the use of bars is distracting and inappropriate. Consider what happens when the time-series of Figure 4.21 masquerades as a bar chart in Figure 4.22.

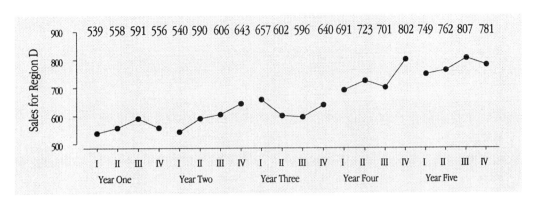

Figure 4.21: Running Record Quarterly Sales for Region D

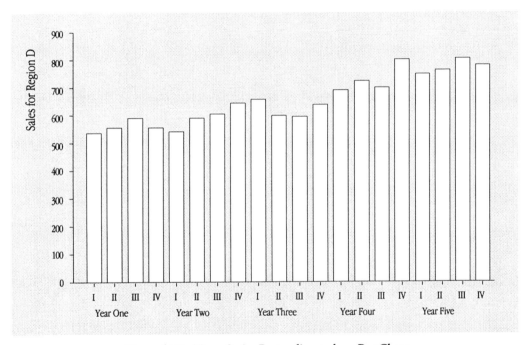

Figure 4.22: Time-Series Pretending to be a Bar Chart

Figure 4.22 contains the same information as Figure 4.21—it presents the time-order sequence of the quarterly sales values, but it does so in an awkward and inefficient manner. Over half of the vertical scale is wasted. All of the variation is crowded into the upper portion of the vertical scale. So while the overall trend is visible, the details are obscured by the use of bars rather than connected points. Our eyes get lost in the "clutter" of the skyline and the vertical emphasis of the graph itself. While you may get away with the graphs like Figure 4.22, the use of a bar graph to represent a time-series is not good practice. It is not exactly incorrect, but it is a sign of naiveté.

4.6 Pie Charts

Pie charts perform a job that is similar to that of a bar chart. They compare the amounts for various categories at a fixed point in time. However, rather than dealing with the actual amounts, they convert these amounts into percentages of the total amount, and then show these percentages as pieces of pie.

Pie charts are not easy to construct by hand, but today's software makes them available at the click of a button. They show the relative proportion due to each of several categories. For example the data in Table 4.2 consist of a breakdown of the operating expenses, in thousands of dollars, for two months. The pie charts for September and October are shown in Figure 4.23. There you can see which categories amounted to the biggest proportion of the total expenses for each month.

Table 4.2: Operating Expenses

	September		October	
Compensation	127.6	36.6%	125.2	36.5%
Benefits	17.0	4.9%	17.0	5.0%
Depreciation	36.0	10.3%	18.8	5.5%
Advertising	64.4	18.5%	121.2	35.3%
Travel	67.5	19.4%	19.3	5.6%
Operations	36.2	10.3%	41.5	12.1%
Total	348.7	100 %	343.0	100 %

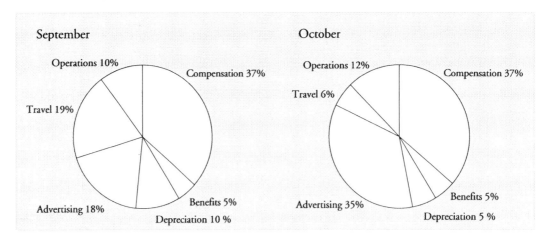

Figure 4.23: Pie Charts for Operating Expenses

While the advertising expenses went up in October, the travel expenses declined. While pie charts provide a visual breakdown for the data, they do not provide a comparison between the totals for each month. Can you tell from Figure 4.23 which month had the greater total expenses? No—you will need to look in Table 4.2 to answer this question. This is why pie charts should always be presented with a table of values—so they do not obscure more than they reveal.

Pie charts provide interesting and useful descriptions of the data. And if all you are trying to convey is a general impression of the relative contributions of different categories to a total, the pie chart will suffice. But if you are trying to compare amounts, or make careful distinctions between similar values, the pie chart will be unsatisfactory. This is because people have more difficulty in distinguishing differences in angles than in distinguishing different heights of bars. And this problem becomes more severe when the circles are distorted into ellipses, as is commonly done with pie charts.

Therefore, while you may use pie charts for simple descriptions, you will need to go beyond pie charts to really understand your processes.

4.7 Exercises

The monthly report on the ATM transactions of a particular bank contained a summary regarding incomplete transactions. The labels in the table on the next page are explained below:

UIS = number of units in service
NT = number of transactions initiated
IT = number of incomplete transactions
R1 = number of incomplete transactions due to Wrong Card Used
R2 = number of incomplete transactions due to Invalid Amount Requested
R3 = number of incomplete transactions due to Lack of Funds in Account
R4 = number of incomplete transactions due to Warped Card Jammed
R5 = number of incomplete transactions due to ATM Malfunctions
R6 = number of incomplete transactions due to Wrong PIN entered
R7 = number of incomplete transactions due to Mag Strip Unreadable
R8 = number of incomplete transactions due to Wrong Key Strokes
R9 = number of incomplete transactions due to ATM Out of Cash

Date	UIS	NT	IT	R1	R2	R3	R4	R5	R6	R7	R8	R9
Wed 1-Jan	50	7552	49	18	3	1	1	1	22	1	1	1
Thu 2-Jan	50	7513	38	14	1	0	0	0	23	0	0	0
Fri 3-Jan	50	7630	71	18	7	4	3	3	27	3	3	3
Sat 4-Jan	49	7643	78	28	5	3	1	0	37	1	2	1
Sun 5-Jan	**50**	**7757**	**59**	**19**	**9**	**3**	**0**	**0**	**26**	**0**	**2**	**0**
Mon 6-Jan	50	7292	81	23	6	4	3	3	32	3	4	3
Tue 7-Jan	50	7435	64	19	7	4	1	1	26	1	4	1
Wed 8-Jan	50	7620	59	19	8	3	1	1	22	1	3	1
Thu 9-Jan	50	7577	91	22	11	6	4	4	32	4	4	4
Fri10-Jan	50	7514	85	26	7	5	3	2	33	3	3	3
Sat 11-Jan	50	7720	79	24	8	4	2	1	32	2	4	2
Sun 12-Jan	**50**	**7900**	**69**	**22**	**9**	**3**	**1**	**0**	**31**	**1**	**1**	**1**
Mon 13-Jan	50	7167	63	20	5	2	1	0	31	1	2	1
Tue 14-Jan	50	7290	81	23	7	4	3	2	33	3	3	3
Wed 15-Jan	50	7464	62	21	6	2	2	1	24	2	2	2
Thu 16-Jan	49	7496	76	21	8	7	2	2	25	2	7	2
Fri 17-Jan	49	7568	101	28	10	6	4	3	36	4	6	4
Sat 18-Jan	50	8025	86	23	10	4	3	3	34	3	3	3
Sun 19-Jan	**50**	**7864**	**90**	**26**	**9**	**5**	**4**	**2**	**32**	**4**	**4**	**4**
Mon 20-Jan	50	7365	101	26	9	7	5	4	33	5	7	5
Tue 21-Jan	49	7350	70	18	10	5	2	2	26	2	3	2
Wed 22-Jan	50	7625	68	19	6	3	2	2	29	2	3	2
Thu 23-Jan	50	7544	55	19	7	1	0	0	27	0	1	0
Fri 24-Jan	50	7552	83	20	9	5	4	3	30	4	4	4
Sat 25-Jan	49	8131	66	19	7	4	2	2	25	2	3	2
Sun 26-Jan	**48**	**7745**	**57**	**15**	**5**	**3**	**2**	**2**	**23**	**2**	**3**	**2**
Mon 27-Jan	50	7051	107	28	12	7	5	4	35	5	6	5
Tue 28-Jan	50	7347	57	18	7	2	1	1	25	1	1	1
Wed 29-Jan	50	7467	114	36	13	4	3	2	46	3	4	3
Thu 30-Jan	50	7586	70	20	8	3	2	2	28	2	3	2
Fri 31-Jan	50	7608	71	21	8	4	1	0	31	1	4	1
Totals		234398	2301	673	237	118	68	53	916	68	100	68

EXERCISE 4.1:

Create a Stem and Leaf Plot for the daily number of transactions (NT) above.

```
70 |
71 |
72 |
73 |
74 |
75 |
76 |
77 |
78 |
79 |
80 |
81 |
```

Without performing any calculations, use the Stem-and-Leaf plot to give a ballpark value for the average number of transactions each day.

EXERCISE 4.2:

Create a running record for the daily number of transactions (NT) shown on the previous page. (Hint, for an easier job of plotting, round off each value to the nearest multiple of 10 before plotting a point.)

When connecting the dots, leave a gap after each Saturday's value.

Does the running record reveal any aspect of these data that the Stem-and-Leaf plot does not also reveal?

EXERCISE 4.3:

Create a Pareto chart of the reasons for incomplete transactions on page 64.

Begin by listing the reasons for an incomplete transaction in order of descending frequencies of occurrence in the table below. Compute the percentages for each reason and then find the cumulative percentages.

Reason Code R1-R9	Total for this Reason	Reason for Incomplete Transaction	As a percentage of all incomplete transactions	Cumulative Percentages
___	___	_____	___	___
___	___	_____	___	___
___	___	_____	___	___
___	___	_____	___	___
___	___	_____	___	___
___	___	_____	___	___
___	___	_____	___	___
___	___	_____	___	___
___	___	_____	___	___

To make this Pareto chart intelligible to your audience you should label each category on the horizontal axis with the reason for the incomplete transactions (rather than using the numerical code).

EXERCISE 4.4:

Of the reasons for an incomplete transaction shown above, which ones were identified as the responsibility of the bank on the Cause-and-effect Diagram in Exercise 2.3?

Are there any actions that the bank can take that will significantly reduce the number of incomplete transactions?

EXERCISE 4.5:

Create a running record for the daily number of incomplete transactions (IT).
When connecting the dots, leave a gap after each Saturday's value.

Does this running record show the same pattern as the one in Exercise 4.2?

Chapter Five

Graphical Purgatory

Unlike William Playfair, who drew his graphs by hand using India ink, today we have the ability to generate many different graphs almost instantaneously using any of the popular spreadsheet programs. But not all change is progress. Along with the proliferation of graphing options has come an abundance of chartjunk, decoration, and inappropriate graphics. This chapter is intended to help you create good graphs by taking you on a guided tour of "graphical purgatory"—a territory in which many of you live and work.

The data of Table 5.1 will be used to create the various graphics throughout this chapter. The values shown are the quarterly sales figures for each of six regions. Each column pertains to a single region, and within each column the first four values are the average quarterly sales for each year, while the last four values shown are the actual quarterly sales for Year Five.

Table 5.1: Average Quarterly Sales and Last Year's Quarterly Sales

		Region A	Region B	Region C	Region D	Region E	Region F
Year One	Averages	1007	1251	1076	561	402	443
Year Two	Averages	929	1130	1145	595	422	511
Year Three	Averages	1076	1030	1200	624	425	405
Year Four	Averages	941	902	1342	729	431	556
Year Five	Quarter I	1,041	939	1,330	749	420	588
	Quarter II	1,020	834	1,003	762	454	699
	Quarter III	976	688	1,197	807	447	743
	Quarter IV	1,148	806	1,337	781	359	702

5.1 Computer-Generated Bar Charts

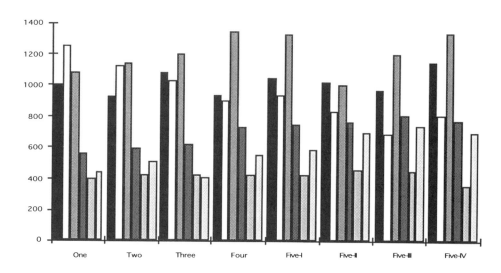

Figure 5.1: A Simple Bar Graph

The default option for many programs is a bar chart. When the values of Table 5.1 are plotted using this option the result might look like Figure 5.1.

The bar chart in Figure 5.1 can hardly be said to be an improvement on the table. In the table we at least had rows and columns to differentiate the region-to-region variation from the year-to-year variation—reading across each row showed the variation between regions, while reading down a column showed the variation over time for a single region. Figure 5.1 shows both the year-to-year information and the region-to-region information along a single (horizontal) axis—which makes this graph harder to use than the table!

But wait. Did not Playfair (Figure 4.7) show imports and exports for each region on his bar chart? Yes, but while a bar chart with two values for each of 16 categories may be complex, it is still comprehensible. A bar chart such as Figure 5.1 which has six values for each of eight categories is merely confusing.

Another problem with Figure 5.1 is the horrible (automatic) shading. The solid black bars catch your eye. The white bars disappear, and the gray bars simply vibrate. This vibration is essentially an op-art effect that is the result of high contrast, narrow bars, and the heavy black lines outlining each bar. All in all, Figure 5.1 is a failure to communicate combined with bad art.

Good graphics should amplify and clarify a table of values, not compete with it.

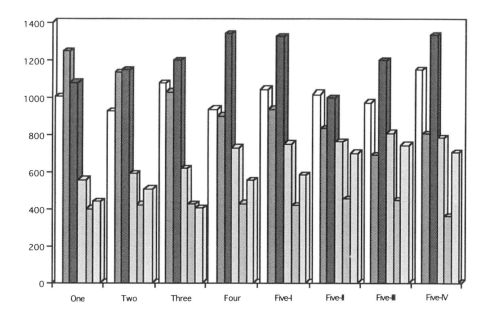

Figure 5.2: A Three-Dimensional Bar Chart

But things can get worse. Figure 5.2 is a decorated version of Figure 5.1.

While this bar chart still has two dimensions (regions and years) compressed onto a single horizontal axis, it adds a third dimension for the sake of decoration. Making the bars of Figure 5.1 into three-dimensional sticks does not improve things any.

Both Figures 5.1 and 5.2 use different shades for the different bars. With six regions for each time period, six different shades are used. While you may get away with using two shades or colors, three or more shades tend to create so much visual confusion that they hurt the overall graph. In general, if you have to use different shades for the bars of a bar chart you are probably trying to present too much information in a single graph.

The problem with Figure 5.1 is confusion about what is being represented. The problem with Figure 5.2 is that it is decorated confusion.

The objective of using graphs
to communicate numerical information
is to make it easy for your readers
to understand the information.

If the graph is not easier to understand
than the table of numbers,
then the graph is a failure.

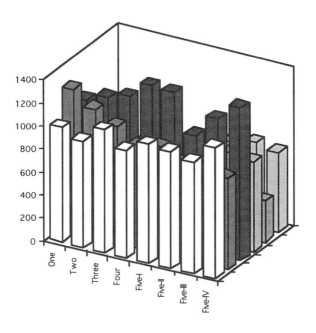

Figure 5.3: Another Three-Dimensional Bar Graph

Figure 5.3 might be considered to be an improvement over Figure 5.2 because it does at least use the third dimension to represent the different regions.

While this graph is very pretty, only 25 of the 48 values in the table are visible. If we make a distinction between ink used for decoration and ink used to represent the data, the problem of Figure 5.3 is that some of the data-ink is hidden behind the bars. For this reason this plot is also less useful than the table of values.

This graph calls more attention to itself than it does to the data it is supposedly trying to present. When ornamentation overwhelms the message, the result is pure chartjunk.

5.2 Computer-Generated Running Records

Figure 5.4 displays the same shortcoming that was seen in Figure 5.3—most of the values are hidden.

Figure 5.5 removes the solid volumes under each time series in Figure 5.4, which does clarify the situation some. However, the limitations of projecting three dimensions into two dimensions results in some confusion as to which ribbon belongs to which region. Is it obvious that the black ribbon is Region C? To which region does the lowest ribbon belong? In fact, which is the lowest ribbon?

Figure 5.4: A Three-Dimensional Running Record

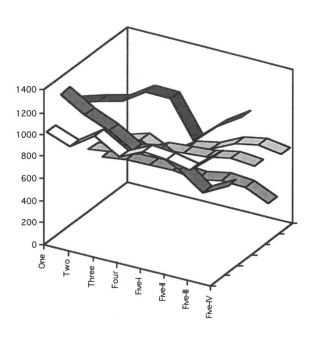

Figure 5.5: A Three-Dimensional Ribbon Chart

Perhaps we should abandon efforts at decorating our graph. Let's try a simple graph with six running records.

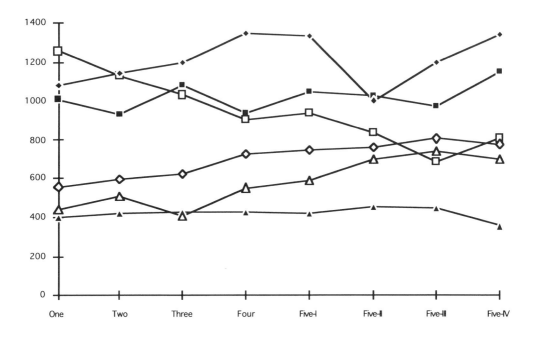

Figure 5.6: Running Records for Six Regions

While Figure 5.6 may not be as colorful or as decorated as the preceding figures, it is intelligible, it is useful, and it communicates clearly, without distortion.

The different sizes for the "dots," and the heavy black lines combine to make this graph look very amateurish, but it is still a vast improvement over the five preceding graphs. In fact, out of the six different graphs considered so far, only this graph is an improvement upon Table 5.1. With the addition of a legend, Figure 5.6 could essentially replace the table of values.

No matter how decorated, no matter how colorful, no matter how traditional, a graph that does not clearly and honestly present the data is worse than useless. When the graphs are simple enough, some decoration may be acceptable, but it is very easy for the decoration to overwhelm the data...

Decoration is not analysis.

5.3 Stacked Bars and Linear Pie Charts

Another way that the data of Table 5.1 might be plotted is as a set of segmented bars.

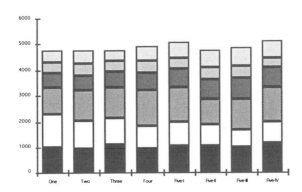

Figure 5.7: A Stacked Bar Chart

Figure 5.7 does overcome the basic problem of Figure 5.1. Seven time series (six regions plus the total) are shown stacked up on top of each other, while the regions are compared within each bar. However, bars are still a poor way to show time series data.

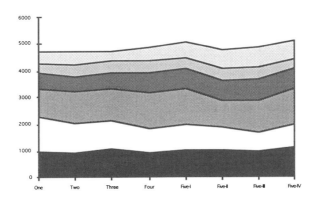

Figure 5.8: A Linear Pie Chart

Figure 5.8 is a linear pie chart. It is a definite improvement over Figure 5.7.

Of the eight different ways of plotting the data of Table 5.1 which have been considered, only Figures 5.6 and 5.8 are friendly to the reader. Only these two, which are the least decorated, least busy, and least splashy of the lot communicate the information of Table 5.1 to the reader.

5.4 Radar Plots

Finally, there are graphics which are so far from being useful that they are positive snares—graphics that are guaranteed to entrap, confuse, and alienate the reader.

Radar plots belong in this category. The radar plot presents the same information as a traditional graph, but it uses polar coordinates to do so. For example compare Figure 5.6 with the radar plot in Figure 5.9. The six points for Year One are plotted on the 12 o'clock axis of the radar plot; the six points for Year Two are plotted on the 1:30 axis; the six points for Year Three are plotted on the 3 o'clock axis, etc. So the six time series in Figure 5.6 become "circles" in Figure 5.9. Which of these two plots is easier to interpret correctly?

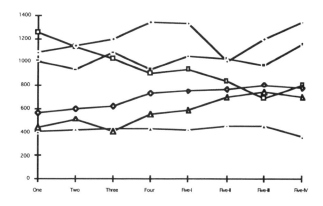

Figure 5.6: The Regional Sales for Six Regions (repeated)

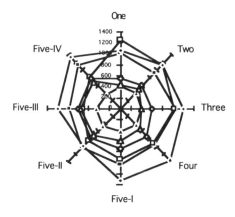

Figure 5.9: The Regional Sales for Six Regions as a Radar Plot

If we change the perspective, and let each axis on the radar plot represent a region we get Figure 5.10.

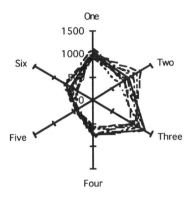

Figure 5.10: Radar Plot for Regional Sales

This plot attempts to compare the six regions. (As if they should be the same!) (In case you have difficulty interpreting the radar plot in Figure 5.10, the same information is shown in an unwrapped form in Figure 5.11.) These figures might be interpreted as follows: Region One (A) is consistently near 1000; Region Two (B) is highly variable; Region Three (C) is also variable, but at a higher level; Regions Four (D) and Five (E) are consistent at a low level, and Region Six (F) is variable at a low level. While this may seem like interesting information about the six regions, you can learn more about each of these regions by using Figure 5.6. Figure 5.10 does not produce any insight that cannot be obtained more easily some other way, and it can be misleading.

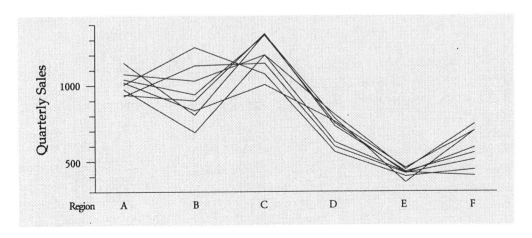

Figure 5.11: The Radar Plot of Figure 5.10 Replotted

Figures 5.10 and 5.11 connect the points from region to region, rather than showing the variation over time. They connect things which are known to be different (and therefore are not comparable), while they fail to reveal the time ordered sequence that exists in these data. This is why Figures 5.10 and 5.11 are meager and unsatisfactory plots.

Radar plots also distort the data they present. Consider what happens to the pair of parallel lines shown on the bottom of Figure 5.12. On a radar plot they become a pair of spirals which, segment by segment, are definitely not parallel.

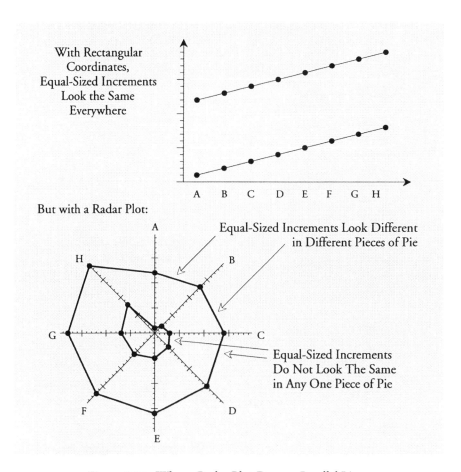

Figure 5.12: What a Radar Plot Does to Parallel Lines

Thus, by replacing the customary rectangular coordinates with polar coordinates, the radar plot substitutes angles for parallel lines, distorts the relationships between levels, and in general, plots simple data in a complex manner which is virtually guaranteed to confuse the reader.

Radar plots are pure obfuscation, and should not be used under any circumstances.

5.5 Improving the Two Best Computer Graphs of Table 5.1

Figures 5.6 and 5.8 are the two best computer-generated representations of the data in Table 5.1. These two graphs are reformatted in Figures 5.13 and 5.14.

Figure 5.8 was already much better than most of the other computer generated graphs, but it could still be improved. The first improvement is to lose the shading. The different intensities of the different shades distracts the eye. Next the heavy lines are replaced with lighter lines. The result is Figure 5.13, which shows the total sales for the eight time periods, and shows the relative contribution of each region to these totals.

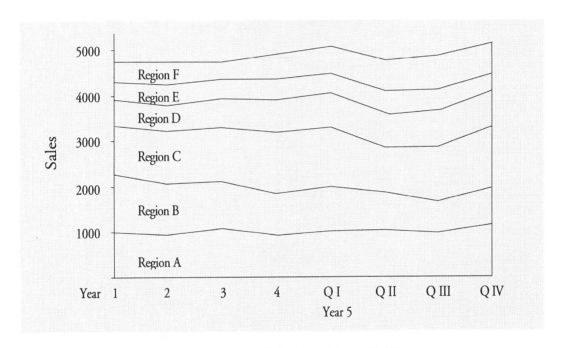

Figure 5.13: Improved Version of Linear Pie Chart

In Figure 5.13 the stacked bands show the total sales, but the stack makes it more difficult to interpret the information about any one region. For example, is it clear from Figure 5.13 that Region D's sales are growing? Is it clear from Figure 5.13 that Region C's sales are essentially unchanged?

While Figure 5.13 attempts to provide information about seven time series, six of these series are represented by the width of a band, rather than a simple curve. On the other hand, Figure 5.14 shows the six time series as six curves.

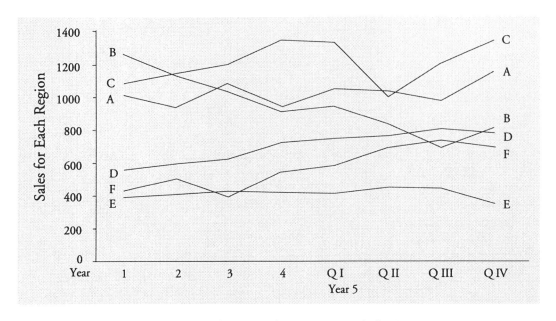

Figure 5.14: Improved Version of Running Records for Six Regions

Figure 5.14 is a modified form of Figure 5.6. One way to improve Figure 5.6 is to replace the heavy lines with lighter lines. It is the continuity of the line that attracts our eye, and with a time series the lines are merely connectors to lead our eyes to the points, therefore light lines are more friendly than heavy lines. Another way to improve Figure 5.6 is to lose the awkward points on the curve. In this case we can leave the points out. This is possible because the six "curves" are sufficiently easy to follow (they do not overlap too much). Also, because of the low amount of overlap we can label each curve to enhance the interpretation of the graph. Finally, the graph is improved by moving the vertical scale over to the left so that it does not compete with the data.

So while Figure 5.13 provides a usable representation of these data, Figure 5.14 reveals more real information.

5.6 Summary

Less is more.

Chapter Six

Some Arithmetic

In the previous chapters we looked at graphical summaries of data. Before we continue we need to discuss several computations and concepts that will be used in the remainder of this book.

First we will look at the common numerical summaries used with collections of data. Then we will make some observations on the relationships between ratios, percentages, and proportions. Next is a discussion about the number of digits to use. Finally the problem of using the right tools in the wrong way will be discussed.

6.1 Measures of Location

The first class of numerical summaries consists of measures of location. These statistics characterize the "location" of the "mid-point" of the data in different ways. We shall be concerned with only two measures of location: averages and medians.

Averages

The simplest measure of location for a set of values is the arithmetic average. This is the first statistic taught in school, and is widely used. It is found by adding up the values and dividing the sum by the number of values.

For the data { 3, 5, 2, 6, 2, 1, 9, 1, 7 } the arithmetic average is:

$$\frac{3+5+2+6+2+1+9+1+7}{9} = \frac{36}{9} = 4.0$$

If we use the symbol X to denote our values, then we denote the average of a set of X values by placing a bar over the X to create the symbol:

$$\bar{X} = \text{average of the } X \text{ values}$$

The arithmetic average is the balance point for the data. If we constructed a simple histogram for our data, the average would be the balance point for the histogram. The nine

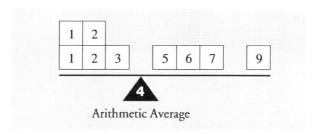

Arithmetic Average

Figure 6.1: The Average as Balance Point

values $\{3, 5, 2, 6, 2, 1, 9, 1, 7\}$ are shown in this way in Figure 6.1.

While other types of averages exist, whenever the word average is used in this book it will be referring to the arithmetic average.

Medians

A second measure of location is the median. A median divides a set of values into two halves, thus a median defines the 50th percentile for the data.

If we use the symbol X to denote our values, it is customary to denote the median for these values by using a tilde (~) above the X, creating the symbol:

$$\tilde{X} = \text{median of the } X \text{ values}$$

Whenever there is an odd number of values (n is odd)
the median will be the middle value
from the ordered listing of the set of values.

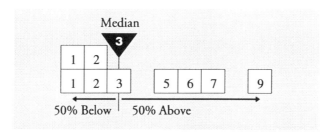

50% Below | 50% Above

Figure 6.2: The Median as Fiftieth Percentile

To find the median for the nine numbers

$$\{3, 5, 2, 6, 2, 1, 9, 1, 7\}$$

we begin by arranging them in ascending order:

$$\{1, 1, 2, 2, 3, 5, 6, 7, 9\}$$

Since this data set contains $n = 9$ values, the median will be the middle value in this ordered listing:

$$\tilde{X} = 3$$

Because of the possibility of several values being equal to the median, we have to interpret a median in the following way:

- Fifty percent, or more, of the data will be greater than, or equal to, the median;

- and fifty percent, or more, of the data will be less than, or equal to, the median.

In Figure 6.2, five out of the nine values are less than or equal to 3, while five out of the nine values are greater than or equal to 3.

Whenever there is an even number of values (n is even)
the median will be the average of the two middle values
from the ordered listing of the set of values.

To find the median for the six values in the data set

$$\{ 12, 15, 18, 19, 14, 16 \}$$

we again arrange the values in ascending order:

$$\{ 12, 14, 15, 16, 18, 19 \}$$

Since this data set has $n = 6$ values the median will be the average of the two middle values from this ordered listing:

$$\tilde{X} = \frac{15 + 16}{2} = 15.5$$

6.2 Measures of Dispersion

Once we have summarized the location of the data by characterizing the balance point (by using an average) or the fiftieth percentile (by using a median), our next question concerns how the data are spread out around this location.

Ranges

The first, and simplest, measure of dispersion is the range. It is defined to be the difference between the *maximum* value and the *minimum* value. It characterizes the total spread of the data, and is commonly denoted by the capital letter R:

$$R = \text{Maximum} - \text{Minimum}$$

For the data set $\{ 3, 5, 2, 6, 2, 1, 9, 1, 7 \}$ the maximum value is 9, the minimum value is 1, so the range is $R = 9 - 1 = 8$ units.

Figure 6.3: The Range is the Spread for the Data

If all the values are identical, the maximum value will be the same as the minimum value and the range will be zero.

The range is intuitive and natural to use. Therefore we shall use it throughout this book. Along with the range you should also report how many values were used to compute the range. To see why this is the case consider what would happen if we were to add more data to the histogram in Figure 6.3. Some values would fall in between the values of 1 and 9, and these values would not change the range. But some values might fall above 9, while some values might fall below 1, and these values would affect the range. Therefore, as the number of data points in the histogram increases, we expect to see larger values for the range. This is why we will always need to know just how many values are spanned by the range. In Figure 6.3, the range spans $n = 9$ data. This value for n is needed to properly interpret any range value.

There are several other measures of dispersion in use today. For small data sets they offer little advantage over the range. However, with the computational power now available, you are likely to encounter some of these other measures of dispersion. Therefore, even though we will not explicitly use them, it is necessary to describe the most common alternatives to the range: the root mean square deviation and the standard deviation statistic.

Root Mean Square Deviations

The root mean square deviation is denoted by many different symbols. I shall use the symbol s_n to represent this measure of dispersion. When taken in reverse order the four words "root mean square deviation" define the four steps required for the computation of this measure of dispersion. They are:

1. Find the DEVIATIONS: measure the amount by which each point deviates from the arithmetic average.

2. SQUARE the deviations from Step 1.

3. Find the MEAN of the squared deviations: i.e., find the *average* of the squared deviations.

4. Find the square ROOT of the average of the squared deviations.

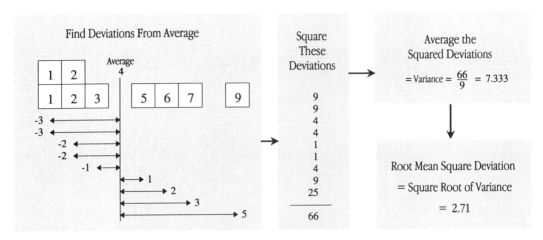

Figure 6.4: The Root Mean Square Deviation as a Measure of Dispersion

These four steps are illustrated in Figure 6.4. For the data set { 3, 5, 2, 6, 2, 1, 9, 1, 7 } the root mean square deviation is $s_n = \sqrt{7.333} = 2.71$ units.

There is no simple interpretation for the root mean square deviation. (A physicist would tell you that it is technically the square root of the rotational inertia, but this interpretation is too esoteric to be of any practical use.)

Standard Deviation Statistics

A measure of dispersion more commonly used today is the standard deviation statistic, s. This measure of dispersion is quite similar to the root mean square deviation, except that in Step 3 you divide by $(n-1)$ rather than n. This makes a slight difference in the value obtained, but it still contains the same basic information about dispersion.

For the data set { 3, 5, 2, 6, 2, 1, 9, 1, 7 } the standard deviation statistic would be:

$$s = \sqrt{\frac{66}{8}} = \sqrt{8.25} = 2.87 \text{ units}$$

While the notation used here is the mainstream notation for these statistics, the advent of computers and calculators has seriously undermined this notation. The only way to be sure just which number you may be getting is to check out the divisor in the formula. This inconsistency of notation, along with the fact that some calculators allow you to compute both the standard deviation statistic and the root mean square deviation, are two more good reasons for using the range.

—◆—

Thus, there are two common measures of location and three commonly used measures of dispersion. Since most are already familiar with the average, and because the range is so simple, it is best to start out with these two measures. For reasonable cause you might later wish to shift to one of the other measures, but they are not recommended for beginners.

6.3 Numerical Summaries and Data Types

Numerical summaries are simply the result of some arithmetic—do *this* with your data and you will get *that* summary value. Since arithmetic cannot create meaning, the interpretation of any numerical summary will depend upon the original data used in the computation. This means that you must think about the nature of your data and make sure that the numerical summary you are computing makes sense for the data you are using. For example, a spreadsheet program does not have any inhibitions about computing the average for a set of telephone numbers—but hopefully you know better than to do this.

As was mentioned in Chapter Three, telephone numbers are examples of *Nominal Scale Data*—numbers used as labels. They contain no information about location or distance, and so measures of location and distance have no meaning with applied to such "numbers."

Ordinal Scale Data are data that contain information about order but which do not describe the distance between the ordered points. Answers to survey questions often fall into this category. As was described in Chapter Three, pseudo-averages may be computed for such data, but measures of dispersion should not be computed from Ordinal Scale Data.

In contrast to Nominal and Ordinal Scale Data we have measurements of time, temperature, distance, weight and height, as well as counts of events, items, and transactions. Such counts and measurements are said to be *Interval Scale Data* or *Ratio Scale Data*. They all characterize the amount of something, and as such, the notion of distance is meaningful. Here it is appropriate to compute both measures of location and measures of dispersion from the original data. Throughout this book Interval and Ratio Scale Data will be referred to by the generic term "measures." The analysis techniques given in this book will not commonly require for you to make a distinction between Ratio Scale Data and Interval Scale Data.

		Counts and Measurements	
Nominal Scale Data	Ordinal Scale Data	Interval Scale Data	Ratio Scale Data
Numbers as labels	Numbers represent order of items or categories	No fixed zero point: Compare using differences	Fixed zero point: Compare using ratios or differences

Figure 6.5 The Four Types of Data

However, as a point of clarification for those who are interested, Ratio Scale Data are data for which the value of zero actually represents a quantity of zero. Interval Scale Data are data for which the value of zero represents a convenient reference point but which is not a true zero point. An example of Interval Scale Data would be temperatures expressed in Fahrenheit or Centigrade. With Interval Scale Data we can make comparisons using differences but we cannot make comparisons using ratios. (For example, 60°F is ten degrees hotter than 50°F, but it is not 60/50 = 1.2 times as hot as 50°F.) With Ratio Scale Data we can make comparisons using either differences or ratios.

Since all of the analysis techniques given in this book are appropriate for *both* Interval Scale Data and Ratio Scale Data, it is not necessary for the reader to belabor the distinction, which was included here primarily for the sake of completeness.

The concept that the meaning of any numerical summary depends on the context for the original values is increasingly important because of the computational power available to us today. In order to avoid a "triumph of computation over common sense" it is important for you to think about the nature of your data. Not all data are suitable for the computation of averages and ranges. Numbers which are used as labels should not be summarized numerically. Numbers which quantify some process characteristic may be suitable for a numerical summary. The presence of numbers does not automatically mean that numerical summaries need to be computed.

6.4 Ratios, Percentages, and Proportions

Many of the measures used in business are ratios. Some of these ratios are percentages, and some of these percentages are proportions. In the interest of clear thinking it is helpful to distinguish between these different types of ratios.

Ratios

If you want to know your gas mileage you have to record more than the number of miles between fill-ups; you also need to know how many gallons were used. To characterize fuel consumption, we divide the number of miles driven between fill-ups by the number of gallons needed to fill the tank.

$$\frac{\text{number of miles driven}}{\text{number of gallons consumed}} = \text{miles per gallon}$$

This is an example of a measure that is a ratio. Many management numbers are ratios—frequently the value for one measure is adjusted by dividing by the value for another measure. Ratios such as these will be described by the units attached. In the example above, the label "miles per gallon" describes the ratio—miles go in the numerator, while gallons go in the denominator. This label also helps to prevent an accidental inversion of this ratio; you are not likely to confuse "miles per gallon" with "gallons per mile." Another example of this type of ratio would be the number of dollars spent by a school system divided by the average daily attendance (dollars per student).

Many aspects of operations require the use of ratios. For example, consider a bank with branch offices throughout a city. A small branch office in a residential area is not likely to have the same number of transactions, or the same dollar volume, as a larger branch office located in a commercial district. So how can you compare the two offices? How can you decide on the appropriate level of staffing? If you divide the number of transactions in a week at a branch by the number of teller-hours worked that week you obtain the ratio of transactions per teller-hour. The adjustment of some direct measure of activity by a measure of opportunity is common in all types of businesses. In order to understand fully such ratios it is necessary to understand each measure and the assumptions used in the calculation of each measure.

The ratios described above have the following characteristic in common. The units of measurement for the numerator are different from the units of measurement for the denominator. When this is the case the ratio may be conveniently described by the units as [numerator units] per [denominator units]. But what happens when the numerator and the denominator are measured in the same units? It would be strange to talk about "miles per mile," or "dollars per dollar." So in this case, we express the ratio as a percentage.

Percentages

Percentages are a type of ratio. A ratio is commonly expressed as a percentage when the numerator and the denominator have the same measurement units. A percentage is therefore a ratio where the two measures have the same measurement units, and which has had the decimal place shifted over two spaces to the right. This shift of the decimal is similar to the conversion from dollars to cents, and is merely a matter of convenience. Which is easier to say: "Auto imports constituted 21 percent of the trade deficit last month." or, "The ratio of the auto imports to the total trade deficit last month was 0.21." More importantly, which is easier to understand? If you want to communicate the ratio of two measures which have the same measurement unit, use percentages.

Figure 6.6: Percentages Are a Subset of the Class of All Ratios

In Chapter Seven an example will use data for accounts receivable. Rather than looking at the accounts receivable values in their raw form, these values will be adjusted—they will be divided by the total sales over the past three months. Since both numerator and denominator are measured in dollars, we will express this ratio as a percentage.

Proportions

All percentages are ratios. But only some percentages are proportions.

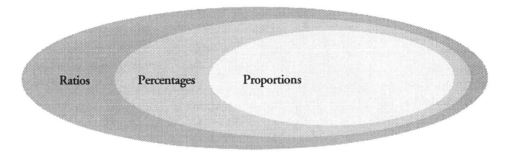

Figure 6.7: Proportions Are a Subset of the Class of All Percentages

A percentage becomes a proportion when the denominator limits or restricts the numerator in some way. For example, for a given time period, the ratio of

$$\frac{\text{the sales for one region}}{\text{the total sales for the whole organization}}$$

would be a proportion because the sales for one region cannot be any greater than the sales for the whole organization. The denominator places a limit on the value of the numerator. This is why proportions must always fall between 0.00 and 1.00 (0% to 100%).[*]

Another example of a proportion would be the ratio of

$$\frac{\text{number of transactions at the drive-in window}}{\text{total number of transactions}}$$

for a given time period at a single bank office. Once again, the numerator is restricted by the denominator. However, the ratio of

$$\frac{\text{accounts receivable in dollars}}{\text{three month sales in dollars}}$$

would not be a proportion. If a company had some large invoices go uncollected for more than 90 days, their accounts receivable could exceed the total sales for the past three months. Thus, the denominator does not limit the numerator, and this ratio is not a proportion.

---

[*] At this time we are not making a distinction between the alternate expressions of a proportion as a dimensionless ratio or as a percentage. In Chapter Fourteen some calculations require the use of proportions as dimensionless ratios.

There are several ways of expressing this special relationship between numerator and denominator that is the hallmark of a proportion. One way is to say that the denominator represents the "total area of opportunity" for the numerator. Another way is to say that with a proportion "numerator plus something equals denominator." Both of these expressions characterize the limitation that is the essential characteristic of all proportions.

While this distinction between ratios, percentages, and proportions will not be critical with regard to the methods of analysis given in this book, it will help you to avoid the embarrassment of confusing one type of ratio with another. Moreover, clear thinking about the nature of various ratios will help you to construct ratios that will be useful in your work.

6.5 How Many Digits Do You Need?

How many digits should you use with your percentages? The sentence "Auto imports constituted 21.1 percent of the trade deficit last month" works, but "Auto imports constituted 21.0526 percent of the trade deficit last month" is more than our minds want or need to absorb. The extra digits are visual clutter, providing unwanted information. Because of our familiarity with decimal monetary systems it will usually suffice to report percentages to the nearest whole number (21 percent). Occasionally one decimal place will be acceptable (21.2 percent). More than one decimal place will be excessive in most situations.

When it comes to making sense of numbers it is generally sufficient to use three-digit or four-digit values. Consider a measure that we all come in contact with—our own weight. Weights may be recorded in various units. In England, for example, one stone is equal to 14 pounds, so a 200 pound man would be listed as being "a little over 14 stone." In this system of measurement a one-unit increment would amount to one part in 14, or about 7 parts per hundred (also known as 7 percent). While your weight in stones may be sufficiently precise for a general description, think about how absurd it would be to say: "I've starved myself for two months and still haven't lost a stone." (Which is presumably why the English also use pounds to measure their weights.)

By recording our weight in pounds we get values that commonly use three digits. For a 200 pound man a one-pound increment is one part in 200, or about one-half of one percent of the total. The use of pounds gives us a "parts-per-hundred" precision in the value reported.

But newborns are not weighed in pounds! They are weighed in pounds and ounces. Why do we do this? Because, for a typical newborn baby, an increment of one pound is one part in six or seven and this is not sufficiently precise. By using pounds and ounces we change the precision. There are 16 ounces per pound, so six pounds is equal to 96 ounces, and by recording the weights of newborns to pounds and ounces we once again have characterized weight to the nearest parts-per-hundred level of precision. But with adults, the use of ounces would be excessive. A 200 pound man would be 3,200 ounces, and so a one-ounce increment would consist of one part per 3200, or about 3 parts-per-ten-thousand.

Finally, if you were to record your weight in grams, of which there are about 28 per ounce, a person weighing approximately 14 stone would be about 90,000 grams. A one-gram increment would therefore be about one part-per-hundred-thousand. Excessive precision indeed! However, since 90,000 grams is 90 kilograms, recording weights to the nearest kilogram is again sufficient to give approximate parts-per-hundred precision.

What about heights? Do we measure how tall we are to the nearest foot or the nearest meter? No, we use inches or centimeters. For most individuals the use of inches gives a precision of one part in 60, while the use of centimeters gives a precision of one part in 150.

These common approaches to measuring weights and heights give us a clue to the way we use and interpret data. In most cases we are content with knowing a value to the nearest parts-per-hundred or parts-per-thousand level. Rarely do we need greater precision than this. When our measurement unit is so large that it does not allow for approximate parts-per-hundred precision, we tend to shift to smaller increments. When our measurement unit is sufficient to allow better than parts-per-hundred precision we begin to round off the values in the interest of simplicity.

To achieve this level of precision in our measures we will generally need to record values to at least three or four digits. Since arithmetic operations can introduce round-off errors, it is always better to err on the side of slightly more digits than fewer. Therefore, four or five digits will suffice for most routine business computations. While there is nothing wrong with letting your computer or calculator work with eight-digit numbers, you will commonly find it helpful to round such numbers off to three or four digits when communicating with others.

6.6 Comparing Apples and Oranges

You can pick the best graphic format, and compute the best numerical summaries, and still end up with nonsense because you are comparing apples to oranges.

In Chapter Five every graphic was created using the data of Table 5.1. The first four rows of Table 5.1 consist of averages. The last four rows of Table 5.1 consist of quarterly values. And while it might be nice to compare the current value with some historical average value (so you can be happy about half the time), there is a problem in placing averages and individual values side by side. Averages can never vary as much as the individual values will vary.

This difference between the variation of individual values and the variation of averages is the result of the arithmetic of computing an average. It will happen in spite of extraneous issues such as seasonal effects and yearly trends. To illustrate this effect Table 6.1 contains 192 counts obtained from a bead box. Each of these counts is the number of yellow beads in a sample of 50 beads drawn from the bead box.

If we think of each count as a "monthly value," we could average each group of 12 counts to obtain an average for each "year." The histograms for the 192 counts and the 16 "annual averages" are shown in Figure 6.8.

Table 6.1: Monthly Counts and Annual Average Counts

Monthly Counts												Annual
J	F	M	A	M	J	J	A	S	O	N	D	Average
11	4	6	4	5	7	5	4	7	12	4	2	5.92
4	5	6	4	2	2	5	9	5	6	5	9	5.17
8	6	5	7	3	2	5	8	6	7	6	5	5.67
5	4	2	7	11	5	6	4	5	7	6	2	5.33
8	3	6	5	5	5	4	8	5	7	7	8	5.92
6	6	3	5	7	4	6	6	4	6	3	6	5.17
9	4	4	3	4	6	7	5	10	5	7	3	5.58
5	4	5	10	4	8	5	4	3	2	4	4	4.83
4	7	6	6	4	5	4	8	4	8	3	8	5.58
6	4	6	4	6	3	9	4	5	2	3	7	4.92
7	2	8	4	7	7	6	5	6	5	9	3	5.75
8	3	9	4	4	7	4	5	6	6	3	6	5.42
3	4	4	6	4	6	5	6	6	10	1	7	5.17
8	4	4	4	8	7	5	4	3	8	6	4	5.42
4	6	4	10	5	5	1	6	7	6	8	9	5.92
6	5	7	3	4	6	9	2	8	7	6	4	5.58

Figure 6.8: Histograms of Monthly Counts and Average Monthly Counts

The histogram of averages does not vary as much as the histogram of the individual counts. It never has, and it never will. Moreover, the averages can take on values which are impossible for the individual values. These two properties of averages create a problem when people compare averages with individual values. The most common way in which this happens is seen in Figure 6.9 where the average monthly counts for the first 15 years are fol-

Figure 6.9: A Bar Chart Used to Compare Averages and Monthly Values

lowed by the monthly counts for the current year.

The error of using a bar chart to represent a time series was discussed in Chapter Four. Figure 6.10 corrects this misuse of a bar chart seen in Figure 6.9, but it cannot correct the mistake of comparing apples to oranges.

Figure 6.10: Averages Compared to Monthly Values

The problem with Figure 6.10 is a subtle one. It occurs when you try to understand a current value in the light of the previous averages. The average values show the general level for these counts, but they also create an expectation about the amount of variation. This mental impression of the routine variation is shown by a horizontal band in Figure 6.11.

When you attempt to make sense of the current values you will naturally carry this horizontal band along. Since the current values will *always* display more variation than the averages, some of the current values will routinely fall outside the band, creating the impression that some months are great, and other months are terrible.

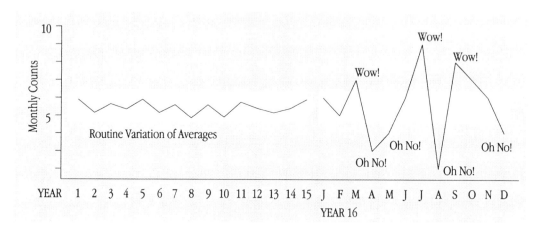

Figure 6.11: Routine Variation of Averages Used to Interpret Monthly Values

In other words, the common practice of comparing current values with the averages from the preceding years actually sets you up to make mistakes in your interpretation of the data. It inevitably leads to alternating euphoria and depression, and can result in increased sales of Prozac. In the next chapter you will learn how to separate routine variation from exceptional variation, but this only makes sense when comparing apples to apples. So, before we go on to consider one of the most powerful techniques for understanding data, you need to know better than to compare averages to individual values.

PRACTICE: Averages, medians and ranges will be used throughout the remainder of this book. For those who need the practice, the following exercises are recommended.

- Verify that the average of the data set { 3, 10, 16, 1, 5, 14, 11, 6 } is 8.25.

- Verify that the median of the data set { 3, 10, 16, 1, 5, 14, 11, 6 } is 8.0.

- Verify that the range of the data set { 3, 10, 16, 1, 5, 14, 11, 6 } is 15.

- Find the average of the data set { 10, 25, 12, 32, 26 }.

- Find the median of the data set { 10, 25, 12, 32, 26 }.

- Find the range of the data set { 10, 25, 12, 32, 26 }.

Chapter Seven

Visualize Your Process Behavior

Flowcharts and cause-and-effect diagrams help you to visualize your process—to see it as a whole and to gain the perspective that is needed to improve your processes and systems. Bar charts allow you to make descriptive comparisons across categories. Running records allow you to see how a measure is changing over time—to spot trends and sudden changes that can be crucial to know about.

What do all of these techniques have in common? They are all graphical representations. The flowchart and cause-and-effect diagram are graphical representations of relationships. Bar charts and running records provide pictures of your data. In each case you obtain a picture that displays relationships or data in their context. In many cases these contextual displays will be sufficient (in connection with your own insight into the relationships, processes and systems represented) to suggest improvements that can be made immediately. And that is why context is the beginning of improvement.

But what happens when context is not enough? What comes next? The next step is to characterize your process behavior so you can choose an appropriate improvement strategy. And to this end you will need a way of visualizing your process behavior. You will need a way of interpreting the graphs, and you will need a guide as to how to go about making improvements. This is where the *process behavior chart* comes in.

7.1 Two Types of Variation

No matter what your process, no matter what your data, all data display variation. Any measure you can think of that will be of interest to your business will vary from time period to time period. The reasons for this variation are many. There are all sorts of causes that have an impact on your process. Remember the cause-and-effect diagram? Even for the simple diagram in Figure 2.15 there were 20 causes listed for delays in delivery. Thus it is not unrealistic to think that your processes and systems will be subject to dozens, or even hundreds, of cause-and-effect relationships. And this multiplicity of causes has two consequences: It makes it easy for you to pick out an explanation for why the current value is so high, or so low; and it makes it very hard for you to know if your explanation is even close to being right.

So in your heart, you know that there is considerable uncertainty in your interpretation of the current value of any measure. But what are you going to do about this? How can you interpret the current value when the previous values are so variable? The key to understanding any time series is to make a distinction between two types of variation.

The first type of variation is routine variation. It is always present. It is unavoidable. It is inherent in the process. Because this type of variation is routine, it is also predictable. The second type of variation is exceptional variation. It is not always present. It is not routine. It comes and it goes. Because this type of variation is exceptional, it will be unpredictable.

The first benefit of this distinction is that it provides a way to know what to expect in the future, which is the essence of management.

> *While every process displays variation,*
> *some processes display predictable variation,*
> *while others display unpredictable variation.*

- A process that displays predictable variation is consistent over time. Because of this consistency we may use the past as a guide to the future.

- A process that displays unpredictable variation is changing over time. Because of these changes we cannot depend upon the past to be a reliable guide to the future.

Having made this *conceptual* distinction between predictable processes and unpredictable processes, we now need a way to do the same in *practice*. We begin by observing that while a predictable process will be the result of routine variation, an unpredictable process will possess both routine variation and exceptional variation. Thus, if we can devise a way to detect the presence of exceptional variation, we will be able to characterize our processes as being predictable or unpredictable.

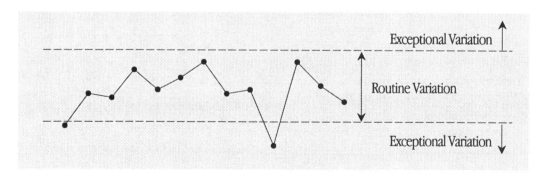

Figure 7.1: Separating Routine Variation from Exceptional Variation

In order to obtain signals of exceptional variation we will compute limits for the running record of our data. As shown in Figure 7.1, the idea is to establish limits that will allow us to distinguish between routine variation and exceptional variation.

If we compute values that place the limits too close together we will get *false alarms* (or false signals) when routine variation causes a point to fall outside the lines by chance. This is the first type of mistake we could make. We can avoid this mistake entirely by computing limits that are far apart.

But if we have the limits too far apart we will *miss some signals* of exceptional variation. This is the second type of mistake we could make. We can minimize the occurrence of this mistake only by having the limits close together.

The trick is to strike a balance between the consequences of these two mistakes, and this is exactly what Walter Shewhart did when he created the *control chart.** In his book, *Economic Control of Quality of Manufactured Product*, Shewhart came up with a way of computing limits to separate routine variation from exceptional variation so that you will have very few false alarms. Shewhart's choice of limits will bracket approximately 99% to 100% of the routine variation. As a result, whenever you have a value outside the limits you can be reasonably sure that the value is the result of exceptional variation.

7.2 Two Types of Action

So what does it mean when your current value is outside the limits and is the result of exceptional variation? How can you make use of this information? To answer this we return to the fact that every process is subject to dozens of cause-and-effect relationships.

When a process displays predictable variation, that variation may be thought of as the result of many different cause-and-effect relationships *where no one cause is dominant over the others*. While every process is subject to many different cause-and-effect relationships, predictable processes are those in which the net effect of the multiple causes is a sort of static equilibrium. Deming's terminology for this condition was *common cause variation*.

On the other hand, when a process displays unpredictable variation, that variation must be thought of as consisting of the sum of the common cause variation plus some *additional* cause-and-effect relationships. Since the sum is unpredictable, we must conclude that the additional cause-and-effect relationships dominate the common cause variation, and therefore that it will be worth our while to identify these additional cause-and-effect relationships. For this reason Shewhart called these dominant causes *assignable causes* (also known as special causes).

If we characterize the routine variation of a predictable process as noise, then the exceptional variation of an unpredictable process would be like signals buried within the noise, and a process behavior chart allows us to detect these signals because it filters out the noise.

---

* Shewhart called routine variation "controlled variation," and exceptional variation was "uncontrolled variation." Out of this terminology Shewhart's charts came to be called control charts. However, because of the baggage associated with the word "control" this name can be quite misleading. Therefore we shall use the more descriptive name of process behavior charts to describe this versatile technique.

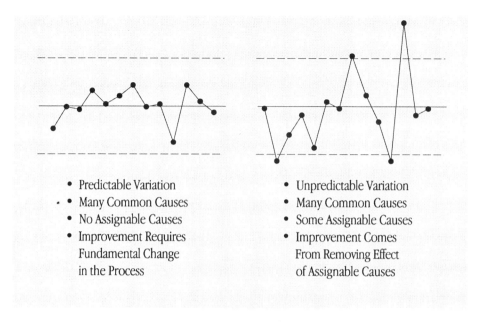

- Predictable Variation
- Many Common Causes
- No Assignable Causes
- Improvement Requires
  Fundamental Change
  in the Process

- Unpredictable Variation
- Many Common Causes
- Some Assignable Causes
- Improvement Comes
  From Removing Effect
  of Assignable Causes

Figure 7.2: Two Types of Processes

This is how the characterization of a process as predictable or unpredictable can be the key to improving that process. If a process is predictable no one cause-and-effect relationship will stand out as the place to start. But if a process is unpredictable, the process behavior chart will allow you to detect the presence of assignable causes, so you can improve the process by working to remove the impact of these assignable causes.

Sometimes these assignable causes are external to the process—upsets due to circumstances beyond our control. At other times these assignable causes are internal to the system—former common causes that have, for whatever reason, become dominant over the other common causes.

When we identify and remove an assignable cause that was external to the process, we are, in most cases, merely returning the process to its previous condition. However, when we identify and remove the effect of an assignable cause that is internal to the process we will be improving both the process and the process outcomes. It is in the latter case that process behavior charts become the locomotive of Continual Improvement.

Thus, the path to process improvement depends upon what type of variation is present.

- If a process displays predictable variation, then the variation is the result of many common causes and it will be a waste of time to look for assignable causes. Improvement will only come by changing a major portion of the process.

- If a process displays unpredictable variation, then in addition to the common cause variation there is an extra amount of variation that is the result of one or more assignable causes. Improvement will come by finding and removing the assignable causes. Changing a major portion of the process will be premature.

Thus, the distinction between the two types of variation leads to two different routes to process improvement. When a process is unpredictable, looking for assignable causes will be a high payback strategy because the assignable causes are, by definition, dominant. On the other hand, looking for common causes of routine variation will be a low payback strategy because no single common cause is dominant. And a process behavior chart is the operational definition of an assignable cause. No guesswork is needed. Simply plot your data, compute the limits, and start to interpret the chart. Whenever points fall outside the limits, go look for the assignable causes. As you find the assignable causes, and as you take appropriate actions to remove the effects of these assignable causes from your process, you will be improving your process.

7.3 The Basic Process Behavior Chart: The *XmR* Chart

The simplest type of process behavior chart is the *chart for individual values and a moving range*. Since this is such a mouthful, I will call this chart an *XmR Chart*. So how do we create this chart? The first example will use the data from the first two rows of Table 6.1, which are reproduced in Table 7.1. These values are counts of the number of yellow beads, in samples of 50 beads each, drawn from a box containing over 5000 beads.

Table 7.1: Number of Yellow Beads Out of 50 Beads

11 4 6 4 5 7 5 4 7 12 4 2 4 5 6 4 2 2 5 9 5 6 5 9

We begin with a running record of these 24 counts. The average of these 24 values is 5.54. We show this value as a central line for the plot. The use of a central line provides a visual reference to use in looking for trends in the values. In this case, there is no evidence of a trend in Figure 7.3.

Figure 7.3: Time-Series Plot of Yellow Bead Data

In order to compute limits that are appropriate for these data—limits which will filter out the noise of the routine variation—we will need to measure the routine variation. To do this we will compute *moving ranges* for these data. The moving ranges are the differences between successive values.

Since moving ranges are used to measure variation, we do not care what the sign of the difference might be. Thus, if you get a negative value for a moving range, you change the sign and record a positive value. By convention, moving ranges are never negative. They are always taken to be positive or zero.

The first value is 11. The second value is 4. Thus, the first moving range is the difference between these two values, which is 7.

$$\begin{array}{lccc} \textit{values} & 11 & 4 & 6 \\ \textit{moving ranges} & & 7 & 2 \end{array}$$

The second count is 4. The third count is 6. The second moving range is thus 2. Continuing in this way the 23 moving ranges of Table 7.2 are found.

Table 7.2: Number of Yellow Beads Out of 50 Beads

values	11	4	6	4	5	7	5	4	7	12	4	2	4	5	6	4	2	2	5	9	5	6	5	9
moving ranges		7	2	2	1	2	2	1	3	5	8	2	2	1	1	2	2	0	3	4	4	1	1	4

These moving ranges are incorporated into the chart on a separate running record directly under the running record of the original values. The central line for this new plot will be the average of the 23 moving ranges, which is 2.61. The combined plots are shown in Figure 7.4.

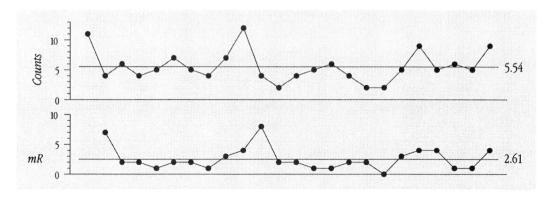

Figure 7.4: Time-Series Plots of Yellow Bead Data and Moving Ranges

The purpose of computing the moving ranges was to characterize the routine variation. The *average moving range* provides a simple summary of this routine variation, and it will be used in the computation of the limits for the two plots in Figure 7.4.

For the moving range portion of the chart (referred to as the *mR* Chart), the *Upper Range Limit* will be found by multiplying the average moving range by a scaling factor of 3.27.

$$\textit{Upper Range Limit} = \textit{URL} = 3.27 \times \overline{mR} = 3.27 \times 2.61 = 8.53$$

This Upper Range Limit is plotted as a dashed horizontal line on the mR Chart. The scaling factor of 3.27 is a fixed value used to convert the average moving range directly into the Upper Range Limit.

The limits for the individual values portion of the chart (the X Chart) are called *Natural Process Limits*. They are centered on the central line. The distance from the central line to either of these limits is computed by multiplying the average moving range by another fixed scaling factor. Thus the *Upper Natural Process Limit* is found by multiplying the average moving range by 2.66, and then adding the product to the central line of the X Chart. Likewise, the *Lower Natural Process Limit* is found by multiplying the average moving range by 2.66, and then subtracting the product from the central line of the X Chart.

$$Upper\ Natural\ Process\ Limit\ =\ UNPL\ =\ \bar{X}\ +\ (\,2.66\ \text{x}\ \overline{mR}\,)\ =\ 5.54\ +\ (\,2.66\ \text{x}\ 2.61\,)\ =\ 12.48$$

$$Lower\ Natural\ Process\ Limit\ =\ LNPL\ =\ \bar{X}\ -\ (\,2.66\ \text{x}\ \overline{mR}\,)\ =\ 5.54\ -\ (\,2.66\ \text{x}\ 2.61\,)\ =\ -1.40$$

Of course, since these individual values are counts, a negative *LNPL* is meaningless—counts cannot be negative. Therefore, we will have a one-sided X Chart with a boundary condition (zero) on the bottom and a Natural Process Limit on the top.

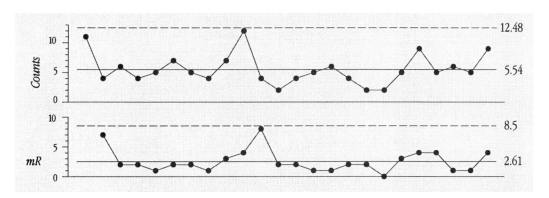

Figure 7.5: The *XmR* Chart for the Yellow Bead Data

The complete *XmR* Chart for these data is shown in Figure 7.5. The limits in Figure 7.5 define bands of routine variation for both the individual values and the moving ranges. As long as the counts vary between 0 and 12, and as long as the moving ranges vary between 0 and 8, there is no evidence of exceptional variation. The variation here can be explained as pure noise. There is no evidence of any signals. When a process is predictable the Natural Process Limits define what to expect in the future. From Figure 7.5 we should expect this process to continue to produce counts that cluster around 5.5, and vary from 0 to 12.

Figure 7.6 shows the remaining 168 counts from Table 6.1 plotted against the limits of Figure 7.5. Inspection of this chart will show that the limits obtained from the first 24 values bracket the remaining values and provide a reasonable prediction of what to expect from this process.

Figure 7.6: *X* Chart for 192 Counts of Yellow Beads

Thus the process behavior chart allows you to:

1. *characterize a process as predictable or unpredictable,*

2. *identify points that represent exceptional variation,*

3. *predict the average level to expect from a predictable process in the future, and*

4. *characterize the amount of routine variation to expect from a predictable process in the future.*

7.4 An *XmR* Chart for Accounts Receivable

A large company with a diversified customer base tracked their accounts receivable data on an *XmR* Chart. The relevant data for one year are shown in Table 7.3, where the amounts are in millions of dollars. Since the accounts receivable vary as the sales level varies, Table 7.3 also shows the total sales for the past three months. Instead of tracking the accounts receivable in dollars, they tracked the accounts receivable as a percentage of the sales for the past three months. This adjustment of one number by another is common with all sorts of business data.

Table 7.3: Accounts Receivable for Year One

Month	A/R	Sales	A/R as % of Sales	mR	Month	A/R	Sales	A/R as % of Sales	mR
January	129.7	233.2	55.6		July	126.2	234.8	53.8	1.9
February	133.0	243.1	54.7	0.9	August	127.6	232.7	54.8	1.0
March	135.8	247.2	54.9	0.2	September	121.6	227.6	53.4	1.4
April	133.1	242.7	54.8	0.1	October	126.7	222.2	57.0	3.6
May	135.8	238.7	56.9	2.1	November	131.5	221.4	59.4	2.4
June	133.9	240.5	55.7	1.2	December	139.4	220.7	63.2	3.8

The average for the accounts receivable percentages is 56.18 percent. We use the monthly percentages to obtain the moving ranges (shown as the *mR* values in Table 7.3). The average of the 11 moving ranges is 1.69.

Using these values we compute the limits for an *XmR* Chart to be:

$$UNPL = \bar{X} + 2.66\, \overline{mR} = 56.18 + (2.66 \times 1.69) = 60.68$$

$$LNPL = \bar{X} - 2.66\, \overline{mR} = 56.18 - (2.66 \times 1.69) = 51.68$$

$$URL = 3.27\, \overline{mR} = 3.27 \times 1.69 = 5.53$$

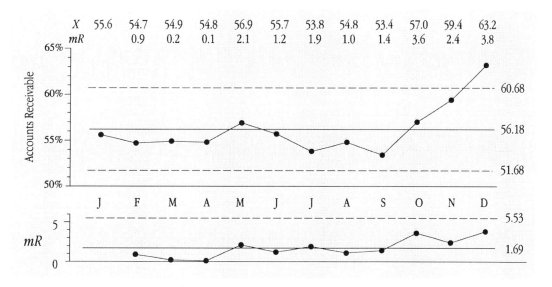

Figure 7.7: *XmR* Chart for Accounts Receivable Values

The *XmR* Chart in Figure 7.7 makes three things immediately apparent:

1. The accounts receivable have averaged about 56 percent of the three-month sales values.
2. Allowing for routine variation these monthly values could climb up to 60 percent, or drop to 52 percent, *without signaling any change in the accounts receivable process.*
3. The December value of 63 percent is a signal of exceptional variation. There has been a change in the accounts receivable process, and it was a change for the worse. (While this change was *detected* in December, it could have begun to occur earlier. When trying to identify assignable causes it is often helpful to go back to the last time the running record crossed the central line. Here the change may have begun as early as October.)

Not only do you know these facts about the accounts receivable process, but you have the chart to use in communicating these facts to others. Since (in this case) a change from 56 percent to 63 percent amounts to an extra 16 million dollars being tied up in working capital each month, this was a fact worth communicating.

The process behavior chart allows you
to separate the probable noise from the potential signals,
so you can concentrate on the signals, where interesting things are happening,
and can ignore the noise, where nothing much is going on.

7.5 Exercises

EXERCISE 7.1:

The Institute for Social Research at the University of Michigan reported that, for the years 1980 to 1983, the percentages of high school seniors who smoked daily were, respectively:

21.3%, 20.2%, 20.9%, and 21.0%

Create an *XmR* Chart for these data.

Computation Worksheet: 1980 –1983

$$\text{Average Value} = \bar{X} = \underline{\hspace{1.5cm}}$$
$$\text{Average Moving Range} = \overline{mR} = \underline{\hspace{1.5cm}}$$
$$2.66 \times \overline{mR} = \underline{\hspace{1.5cm}}$$
$$UNPL = \bar{X} + 2.66\,\overline{mR} = \underline{\hspace{1.5cm}}$$
$$LNPL = \bar{X} - 2.66\,\overline{mR} = \underline{\hspace{1.5cm}}$$
$$URL = 3.27 \times \overline{mR} = \underline{\hspace{1.5cm}}$$

(When only four values are used to compute limits you will find that the four baseline values will always fall within the limits. This is an unavoidable consequence of the computations. While it is desirable to use more than four points in the baseline period, it is not always possible. When you have a limited amount of data, you may obtain reasonable and useful limits from baselines having as few as four points, and such limits may be used to evaluate future points to see if a change has occurred in the process.)

EXERCISE 7.2:

For the years of 1984 to 1993 it was reported that the percentages of high school seniors who smoked daily were: 18.8, 19.6, 18.7, 18.6, 18.1, 18.9, 19.2, 18.2, 17.3, and 19.0 respectively. Create an *XmR* Chart for these data.

Computation Worksheet: 1984 –1993

$$\text{Average Value} = \bar{X} = \underline{\hspace{2cm}}$$

$$\text{Average Moving Range} = \overline{mR} = \underline{\hspace{2cm}}$$

$$2.66 \times \overline{mR} = \underline{\hspace{2cm}}$$

$$UNPL = \bar{X} + 2.66\,\overline{mR} = \underline{\hspace{2cm}}$$

$$LNPL = \bar{X} - 2.66\,\overline{mR} = \underline{\hspace{2cm}}$$

$$URL = 3.27 \times \overline{mR} = \underline{\hspace{2cm}}$$

Making Sense of Data

EXERCISE 7.3:

Thirty presenters at a technical conference were evaluated by those who attended their sessions. Among the questions asked was the following:

	excellent	very good	average	below average	poor
5. Overall Evaluation of Presentation	☐	☐	☐	☐	☐
(point values used for pseudo-averages	5 pts	4 pts	3 pts	2 pts	1 pts)

Using the point assignments shown above a pseudo-average was computed for each presenter. The following table shows each presenter's initials, the number of evaluations filled out, their pseudo-average for Item 5, and the moving ranges. The average of the pseudo-averages is 3.50 and the average moving range is 0.49. Place these values on an *XmR* Chart and interpret the chart.

presenter	D.A.	B.B.	C.C.	R.C.	J.G.	K.H.	G.J.	T.J.	H.K.	M.K.
no. of eval.	30	28	35	23	22	12	26	31	29	30
pseudo-averages	3.37	4.57	3.77	3.57	3.50	2.34	3.35	4.87	3.14	3.23
moving Ranges		1.20	0.80	0.21	0.07	1.16	1.00	1.52	1.73	0.10

presenter	U.K.	N.L.	W.L.	K.M.	S.M.	S.N.	T.N.	T.O.	S.P.	C.R.
no. of eval.	35	31	19	29	28	31	21	32	21	29
pseudo-averages	3.69	3.42	3.68	3.31	3.14	3.48	3.62	3.50	3.67	3.38
moving Ranges	0.45	0.27	0.26	0.37	0.17	0.34	0.14	0.12	0.17	0.29

presenter	T.R.	D.S.	M.S.	N.S.	P.S.	J.T.	N.T.	O.T.	R.T.	O.W.
no. of eval.	16	27	30	26	25	34	25	27	28	22
pseudo-averages	2.46	3.67	3.33	3.65	3.56	3.65	3.32	3.67	3.57	3.59
moving Ranges	0.92	1.21	0.33	0.32	0.09	0.09	0.33	0.35	0.10	0.02

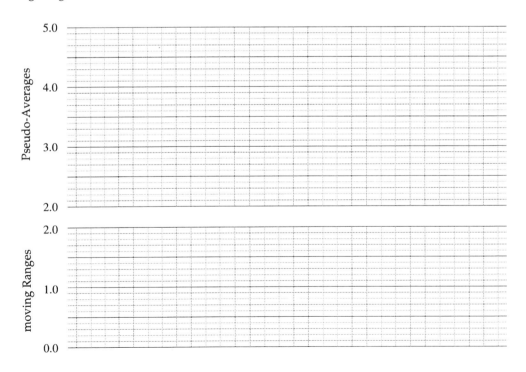

106

Chapter Eight

Interpreting the Process Behavior Chart

The previous chapter outlines the computations and construction of an *XmR* Chart. This chapter will focus on how to interpret these process behavior charts. To this end I shall begin with a characterization of data coming from a predictable process.

8.1 What Do Predictable Processes Look Like?

Table 6.1 contains the counts of the number of yellow beads in 192 samples of 50 beads each. In the previous chapter we used the first 24 of these values to obtain limits of 12.48 to −1.40. (Since these values are counts, and counts cannot be less than zero, the lower limit was replaced by the boundary value of zero.) If we plotted all 192 counts on an X Chart, and added a histogram on the end, we would get Figure 8.1.

Figure 8.1: *X* **Chart and Histogram for the Number of Yellow Beads in 192 Samples of 50 Beads Each**

The white band shown in Figure 8.1 is symmetric about the central line. The top of this white band is half-way between the central line and the Upper Natural Process Limit. (If we had a Lower Natural Process Limit, the bottom of the band would be half-way between the central line and the *LNPL*.) Thus, the white band defines the middle 50% of the region within the limits.

Inspection of Figure 8.1 shows that the bulk of the values fall in the middle 50% of the region within the limits. Experience suggests that when the process is predictable approximately 85 percent of the values will fall within the white band. In this case 165 out of 192, or 86%, fall in this zone.

Conversely, only about 15% of the values should fall close to the upper limit or close to the lower boundary when the process is predictable. This means that when you are looking at a process behavior chart you should expect the time-series to visually *fill up the middle* portion of the regions between the limits, with only occasional values falling near the limits.

For a two-sided chart, with both upper and lower limits, there should be relatively few values in the upper 25% of the region between the limits, and relatively few values in the lower 25% of the region between the limits. With a one-sided chart, where a boundary condition falls within the computed limits, the values may pile up against the boundary, but there should still be relatively few values near the one limit.

8.2 Detecting Strong Signals and Weaker Signals

A process behavior chart is an operational definition of whether or not your process is subject to the effects of assignable causes. The limits define the ideal, the creation of the chart is the test procedure, and the detection rules for interpreting the chart allow everyone to come to the same conclusion. To this end there are many detection rules that have been developed over the years.

The original detection rule consists of the simplest evidence of an assignable cause—a point outside the limits on either an *X* Chart or an *mR* Chart. Not only is this the simplest signal, but it also indicates that the effect of the assignable cause is large in magnitude. Consider what it takes for a point to fall outside the limits—the assignable cause has to have an impact upon the process which is greater than the sum of all the effects of all the common causes put together. This is why it will be economically worthwhile to seek to identify the assignable causes associated with points outside the limits. Since this is the original detection rule, it is known as Detection rule One.

Detection Rule One: Points Outside the Limits
      A single point outside the computed limits
      on either the *X* Chart, or the *mR* Chart,
      should be interpreted as an indication of
      the presence of an assignable cause which has a *dominant* effect.

Inspection of Figure 8.1 will show why a single point is sufficient—most of the values will be concentrated in the middle one-half of the limits, so that it is very unlikely that a point will fall outside the limits by chance. This one detection rule is sufficient to detect the strong signals. As long as you are finding points outside the limits you have strong signals, and any weaker signals that may exist will be of little interest, making the following rules moot.

The following detection rules, known as run tests, look for weaker signals by using sequences of points. Since run tests only make sense when the sequence of the data makes sense, they cannot be applied to data sets which have an arbitrary ordering. Moreover, for reasons that are beyond the scope of this book, run tests should not be applied to the chart for moving ranges.

The most commonly used run-test is the test for a "run of eight" about the central line. Even though all of the points on an X Chart might fall within the limits, a sequence of eight, nine, or ten successive values that are all on the same side of the central line is generally taken to be evidence of a shift in location. Since sustained shifts are not likely to happen by chance, such a sustained shift is said to be due to an assignable cause.

Figure 8.2: Runs Above and Below the Central Line as Signals of an Assignable Cause

(This rule was originally published as a "run of seven" in 1946. However, since 1956, all of the competent modern sources have rejected the use of seven points in favor of using at least eight successive points on the same side of the central line for this rule. So while many corporate manuals still have the run of seven rule, you should wait for eight in a row before you consider a run about the central line to be a definite signal of a shift.)

If you have an assignable cause which produces a run of eight or more successive values on one side of the central line, and yet none of these points fall outside the limits, it is reasonable to conclude that (1) the assignable cause is sustained in its impact, and (2) the effect of this assignable cause is fairly small. Thus, runs of eight or more about the central line will indicate the presence of a *sustained* but *weak* assignable cause.

Detection Rule Two: Runs About the Central Line
Eight, nine, or ten successive values,
all on the same side of the central line on the X Chart
may be interpreted as an indication of
the presence of an assignable cause which has a *weak* but sustained effect.

The Yellow Bead Data come from a process that is a prototype of a predictable process. If we examine these data using Detection Rule Two we find, as expected, no runs of eight or more about the central line. However, as can be seen in Figure 8.3, there is one run of seven below the central line, and one run of six above the central line. These runs illustrate the

Figure 8.3: Predictable Processes Do Not Tend To Have Runs of Eight About the Central Line

hazard of using fewer than eight values as a signal of a change—you will get false alarms.

Another way that a weak but sustained assignable cause can make its presence known on an X Chart is a "run near the limits:" a sequence of three out of four successive values, in the upper (or lower) 25% of the region between the limits. Since we expect approximately 85% of the values from a predictable process to fall within the middle 50% of the limits, a sequence of three or more points in *one* of the outer 25% zones can reasonably be interpreted as an indication of a shift in process location.

Figure 8.4: Runs Near the Limits as Signals of an Assignable Cause

When an assignable cause results in a run near the limits and yet none of the points fall outside the limits, we can again conclude that (1) the assignable cause is sustained in its impact and (2) the assignable cause has a weak to moderate impact.

Once again, considering the Yellow Bead Data as typical of data coming from a predictable process, we see no runs near the limits in Figure 8.5. While 27 of the 192 values fall outside of the white band, in only one instance do we find two of these 27 values occurring in succession. There are no runs of 3 out of 4 successive values nearer the limits than the central line.

Clearly, since we are interpreting a run near the limits as a signal of a shift, the three values must all fall on the same side of the central line in order for this detection rule to make sense.

Detection Rules One, Two, and Three are easy to use. Without additional computations you can tell in a glance if one of these rules is satisfied.

Detection Rule Three: Runs Near the Limits

Three out of four successive values on the *X* Chart

all within the upper 25% of the region between the limits, or

all within the lower 25% of the region between the limits,

may be interpreted as an indication of the presence

of an assignable cause which has a *moderate* but sustained effect.

Figure 8.5: Predictable Processes Do Not Tend To Have Runs Near the Limits

Whenever one of these rules is satisfied, you will be justified in looking for an assignable cause of exceptional variation. You will probably find that Detection Rules One and Two are sufficient to keep you busy. Rarely will you ever need to use more than Rules One and Two. But when you know Rule Three, you can pull it out and use it whenever you need a little added sensitivity.

In addition to these formal detection rules, there is also a bit of common sense known as the pattern detection guideline. Look for an explanation whenever you find a recurring pattern in the running record: If a pattern repeats itself eight times in a row, you can be sure that you are not looking at routine variation. The persistence of the pattern itself is the signal that something is going on. So if you have a two-point pattern, or a three-point pattern, or any pattern that fits in with the context for the data, and that pattern persists, you should seek to identify the assignable cause behind the pattern.

Detection Rules One, Two, and Three form a coherent set of detection rules that collectively achieve maximum power. Using more detection rules will not boost the sensitivity of the chart, but it will have the effect of increasing the number of false alarms excessively.

Many people have been taught to use a rule for six or seven points going up or down. This rule has repeatedly been found to be of little use except to increase the number of false alarms. It should not be used.

RECOMMENDED DETECTION RULES

Detection Rule One: Points Outside the Limits

A single point outside the computed limits
should be taken as a signal of the presence
of an assignable cause which has a *dominant* effect.

Detection Rule Two: Runs About the Central Line

Eight successive values on the same side of the central line will be taken
as an indication of the presence of an assignable cause which has a *weak*
but sustained effect.

Detection Rule Three: Runs Near the Limits

Three out of four successive values in the upper 25%,
or three out of four successive values in the lower 25%,
of the region between the limits may be taken as a signal of the presence
of an assignable cause which has a *moderate* but sustained effect.

The run tests published in the Western Electric Handbook included two detection rules that are quite similar to Detection Rule Three. These two rules are harder to use than Rule Three because they involve additional computations. Since you may encounter these rules in other places, they are given here in the interest of completeness. These detection rules refer to one-sigma lines and two-sigma lines. Since the computed limits are, by definition, three-sigma limits, these one-sigma and two-sigma lines are respectively one-third and two-thirds of the way from the central line to each of the limits. Examination of the following rules will reveal their similarity to Detection Rule Three.

Detection Rule Four: Runs Beyond Two-Sigma

When two out of three successive values fall
more than two-sigma above the central line,
or more than two-sigma below the central line,
they may be interpreted as a signal of the presence
of an assignable cause which has a *moderate* but sustained effect.

Detection Rule Five: Runs Beyond One-Sigma

When four out of five successive values fall
more than one-sigma above the central line,
or more than one-sigma below the central line,
they may be interpreted as a signal of the presence
of an assignable cause which has a *moderate* but sustained effect.

Detection Rules One, Two, Four, and Five also form a coherent set of detection rules that achieve maximum power. Using more detection rules will not boost the sensitivity of the chart, but will merely increase the number of false alarms by an excessive amount.

8.3 Why Johnnie Can't Breathe

"Teen Use Turns Upward" read the headline for a graph in the June 21, 1994 edition of *USA Today*. The data in the graph were attributed to the Institute for Social Research at the University of Michigan, and were labeled as the "percentage of high school seniors who smoke daily." The percentages for 1980 through 1993 are given in Table 8.1.

Table 8.1: Percentage of High School Seniors Who Smoke Daily

Year	'80	'81	'82	'83	'84	'85	'86	'87	'88	'89	'90	'91	'92	'93
Percentages	21.3	20.2	20.9	21.0	18.8	19.6	18.7	18.6	18.1	18.9	19.2	18.2	17.3	19.0
Moving Ranges		1.1	0.7	0.1	2.2	0.8	0.9	0.1	0.5	0.8	0.3	1.0	0.9	1.7

The article accompanying these data claimed that the jump from 17.3% in 1992 to 19.0% in 1993 was a signal that the "number of smoking 18 to 24-year-olds has leveled off, ending a downward trend that began in 1983."

What can you do to evaluate this claim? You could begin by placing these percentages on an *XmR* Chart with one set of limits, as shown in Figure 8.6.

Figure 8.6: *XmR* Chart for Percentage of High School Seniors Who Smoke Daily, 1980-1993

The average of these 14 percentages is 19.27 percent. The average of the 13 moving ranges is 0.85. Using these values we obtain the limits shown in Figure 8.6:

$$Upper\ Range\ Limit\ =\ URL\ =\ 3.27 \times \overline{mR}\ =\ 3.27 \times 0.85\ =\ 2.78$$

$$Upper\ Natural\ Process\ Limit\ =\ UNPL\ =\ \overline{X} + (2.66 \times \overline{mR})\ =\ 19.27 + (2.66 \times 0.85)\ =\ 21.53$$

$$Lower\ Natural\ Process\ Limit\ =\ LNPL\ =\ \overline{X} - (2.66 \times \overline{mR})\ =\ 19.27 - (2.66 \times 0.85)\ =\ 17.01$$

In Figure 8.6 three of the first four values are closer to the upper limit than the central line (a Detection Rule Three signal), while the last eight values are below the central line (a Detection Rule Two signal). The combination of these two signals suggests that a change has occurred and that there has indeed been a drop in the percentage of high school seniors who smoke daily. Interpreting the chart it would appear that there is a break between the first four years and the last 10 years. Therefore, we might decide to compute limits for each of these segments separately, as was done in the exercises previously.

Figure 8.7: Revised *XmR* Chart for Percentage of Seniors Who Smoke Daily, 1980-1993

Figure 8.7 shows that the "downward trend" of the past 14 years could be explained by a one-time, two percent drop that occurred between 1983 and 1984. Those who are interested in preventing teenagers from smoking should try to learn what happened to the Class of '84. An understanding of this assignable cause could prove useful in anti-smoking campaigns. Many explanations of the "downward trend" may be offered. However, no matter how logical, no matter how eloquent, no matter how appealing, no explanation can be considered to have any validity unless it can account for the sudden change between '83 and '84.

But what about the "jump" from 17.3 percent in 1992 to 19 percent in 1993? The *XmR* Chart in Figure 8.7 shows no evidence of any change in the teen-age use of tobacco over the ten year period from 1984 to 1993! The change from 1992 to 1993 is well within the bounds of routine variation.

So what would it take to indicate a change? A single point outside the limits on either the X Chart or the *mR* Chart would suffice. Three out of four successive values in the upper 25%

of the X Chart would indicate an increase in the use of tobacco. Three out of four successive values in the lower 25% of the X Chart would indicate a drop in the use of tobacco. Eight successive values above, or below, the central line of the X Chart would indicate a change in the use of tobacco. And while you are waiting for such evidence, your best estimate of the fraction of high-school seniors who smoke daily will remain 18.64 percent.

Anyone who tells you otherwise is just blowing smoke.

This ability to use the process behavior chart to gain insight, and then to use that insight to revise the chart, is part of the interactive use of process behavior charts that is the hallmark of Continual Improvement. It is the way of thinking—the learning from the process as a means of improving the process—that characterizes Continual Improvement and sets it apart from improvement programs based on wishes and hopes.

8.4 The Voice of the Customer and the Voice of the Process

Everywhere you look people are being given goals, being asked to shoot for a target, and are being evaluated on their performance relative to some plan. What do all of these plans, goals, and targets have in common? They are all, in some sense, definitions of what the customer wants (especially if we define "customer" to include our bosses). Plans, goals, budgets, and targets, help us to separate the acceptable outcomes from the unacceptable outcomes after the fact. They are the *Voice of the Customer*.

Figure 8.8: "We didn't get down to our goal this year, so we set the goal lower for next year."

Now the Voice of the Customer will let you know when you have an unacceptable outcome, so that you can take action to remedy the situation. But it will not tell you how to avoid the unacceptable outcomes, or how to achieve the acceptable outcomes. So the Voice of the Customer will tell you *when* you are in trouble, but it will not tell you *why* you are in trouble, and it will not tell you how to get out of trouble.

Thus, plans, goals, budgets, and targets will allow you to take action on the outcomes, but they give little help in influencing those outcomes. And this is why the Voice of the Customer is often little more than wishes and hopes.

Process behavior charts, on the other hand, are for taking action on the process—to look for assignable causes when they are present, with an eye toward process improvement, and to refrain from looking for assignable causes when they are absent. The process behavior chart is the *Voice of the Process*. It characterizes every process as being either predictable or unpredictable.

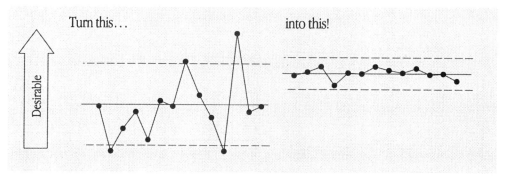

Figure 8.9: The Result of the Effective Use of Process Behavior Charts

When a process is predictable the process behavior chart defines what you can expect in the future. The process average is likely to continue to be the same, and the future values may fall anywhere within the Natural Process Limits defined by the chart.

When a process is unpredictable the process behavior chart helps you to identify those assignable causes that are present, so that you can *take action on the process* to remove the effects of the assignable causes, and thereby improve the process.

Finally, given that we have the Voice of the Customer and the Voice of the Process, it is clearly desirable to have these two voices in alignment.

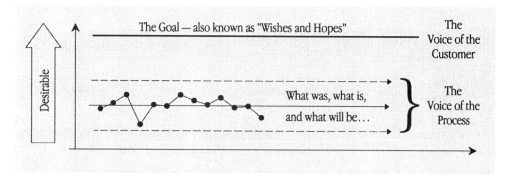

Figure 8.10: The Problem of Aligning the Two Voices

If the voices are not in alignment there are only three things you can do that will bring them into alignment: You can shift the process aim; or you can reduce the process variation; or you can change the goal. Two of these require that you have a way of taking action on your process, and the third requires you to have sophisticated political skills.

Of course, lacking an effective way of taking action on their process, and faced with unacceptable outcomes, many have resorted to the traditional approach: Change the blame, distort the system, or distort the data—whatever it takes. Then they cross their fingers, claim to have fixed the problem, and hope that it will not happen again.

Thus there are three types of action that may be taken with regard to the quality of a product or a service.

1. Specifications (plans, goals, and targets) are for taking action on the outcomes—to separate the acceptable outcomes from the unacceptable outcomes after the fact. They are the *Voice of the Customer*.

2. Process behavior charts are for taking action on the process—to look for assignable causes when they are present, with an eye toward process improvement, and to refrain from looking for assignable causes when they are absent. It is the *Voice of the Process*.

3. Actions to align the two voices are appropriate. However, the lack of a well-defined voice of the process will always be an obstacle to successful alignment.

While it is easy to *say* what you want, the key question is how can you attain these wants? You may well know when the outcome does not meet your requirements, but is this shortcoming a result of the common cause variation or the result of some assignable cause? What is the voice of the process? Is the process predictable, but not capable of meeting your requirements? Or is the shortcoming a result of some breakdown either in the system or in something external to the system? If you attempt to make adjustments before you know the answers to these questions you are doomed to make mistakes.

Plans, goals, and targets have been used for many years. We have even known that we need to align the process with the plans, goals and targets. But it is the ability to listen to the voice of the process that has been missing. Process behavior charts fill this gap.

8.5 Summary

The methodology for moving toward any goal requires that you first understand where you presently are, and that is precisely where the process behavior chart comes into the picture. The process behavior chart helps you in three ways. It defines that level of performance which your process is likely to achieve when it is doing the best it can, it then gives you the information you need to move your process toward that ideal, and finally it allows you to judge just how close you have come to that ideal. Collectively, these three aspects of the process behavior chart define a methodology for Continual Improvement; which is what you need to turn your wants into realities.

Careful consideration of the Three Questions of Chapter One, the Operational Definition of Chapter Three, and the three aspects of the process behavior chart identified above will reveal that, as Walter Shewhart told us long ago, the process behavior chart is an operational definition that allows us to determine whether or not a process is operating up to its full potential.

8.6 Exercises

EXERCISE 8.1:

A trucking company implemented a bonus plan in an effort to boost productivity at certain sites. At the end of a twelve month test period they reported the following accident rates for these sites. The values shown below are the reportable injuries per million man-hours for each month. Place these values on an *XmR* Chart.

Jan.	Feb.	Mar.	Apr.	May	Jun.	Jul.	Aug.	Sept.	Oct.	Nov.	Dec.
43	40	37	33	30	33	34	35	29	33	31	39

Average Value = _____

Average Moving Range = _____

$2.66 \times \overline{mR}$ = _____

$UNPL = \overline{X} + 2.66\,\overline{mR}$ = _____

$LNPL = \overline{X} - 2.66\,\overline{mR}$ = _____

$URL = 3.27 \times \overline{mR}$ = _____

EXERCISE 8.2:

a. Interpreting the *XmR* Chart above, is the "accident process" at these sites predictable?

b. If nothing is changed, what will be the average accident rate for these sites next year?

c. What range of accident rates for these sites should you expect during the next year?

d. How low would a single month's accident rate need to be to indicate a real reduction in the accident rate at these sites?

EXERCISE 8.3:

The same trucking company reported the following accident rates for those sites that did not participate in the productivity bonus plan. Once again, the values shown are the reportable injuries per million man-hours for each month. Create another *XmR* Chart.

Jan.	Feb.	Mar.	Apr.	May	Jun.	Jul.	Aug.	Sept.	Oct.	Nov.	Dec.
35	37	33	32	27	29	31	22	25	30	24	19

Average Value = _____   Average Moving Range = _____

2.66 x $\overline{mR}$ = _____   URL = 3.27 x $\overline{mR}$ = _____

UNPL = $\overline{X}$ + 2.66 $\overline{mR}$ = _____   LNPL = $\overline{X}$ − 2.66 $\overline{mR}$ = _____

EXERCISE 8.4:

a. Interpreting the *XmR* Chart above, is the "accident process" at these sites predictable?
b. If nothing is changed, what will be the average accident rate for these sites next year?
c. If nothing is changed, what range of accident rates for these sites should you expect to see during the next year?
d. How low would a single month's accident rate need to be to indicate a real reduction in the accident rate at these sites?

Chapter Nine

Using *XmR* Charts Effectively

The *XmR* Chart was introduced in the previous chapters. There the computations, basic considerations, and rules for interpretation were outlined. But how do you go from plotting points on a piece of paper to making process improvements? How can something this simple have an impact upon the whole organization? What is the difference between "cubicle wallpaper" and effective charts? And how can process behavior charts become the locomotive of Continual Improvement? To find the answers to these questions read about how others have done it.

9.1 Comparing Groups Using Process Behavior Charts

A trucking company decided to try to increase productivity by putting their workers on a bonus plan. Being conservative, it was decided to test the bonus plan at selected sites for a year before implementing it company wide. At the end of the year-long trial the usual measures of activity were collected and reported for two groups: Group A consisted of those sites where all of the workers were on the bonus plan; Group B consisted of those sites that did not have the bonus plan. Among the various measures reported were some accident data. Table 9.1 shows the accident rates for reportable injuries over a twelve-month period for both groups. The values are the reportable injuries per million man-hours.

Table 9.1: Accident Rates

	Jan.	Feb.	Mar.	Apr.	May	Jun.	Jul.	Aug.	Sept.	Oct.	Nov.	Dec.
Group A	43	40	37	33	30	33	34	35	29	33	31	39
Group B	35	37	33	32	27	29	31	22	25	30	24	19

I ask you, "Are these two groups different?"

You say, "Oh, yes. They clearly have different average accident rates."

I respond, "But they will always have different average accident rates—it is the nature of numerical summaries to vary from time to time and place to place. So you cannot say they are different just because they have different averages."

You say, "But I know they are different."

To which I reply, "How do you know if the difference between the average accident rates is due to a difference between the two groups or just the result of routine variation?"

"Well, I really don't."

"But don't you know how to remove routine variation?"

"You mean by putting the data on an *XmR* Chart?"

"Yes."

"But how will that allow me to compare the two groups?"

"By using two charts you can characterize each group separately, and then use these characterizations to compare the groups."

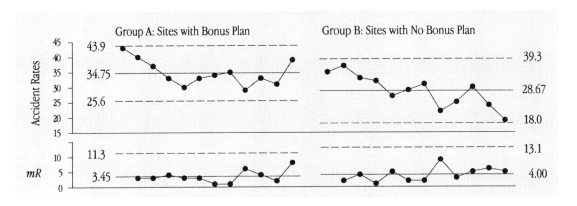

Figure 9.1: *XmR* Charts for Accident Rates

The *XmR* Charts for the two groups are shown in Figure 9.1. Both groups show predictable accident rates. The sites with the bonus plan average about 35 accidents per million man-hours. Routine variation could cause this number to vary anywhere between 25.6 to 43.9 from month to month. The sites without the bonus plan average about 29 accidents per million man-hours. Routine variation could cause this number to vary anywhere between 18.0 to 39.3 from month-to-month.

So, are the two groups different? If we compare the values of one group with the limits from the other group what do we find?

Figure 9.2: Group B Compared to Group A's Limits

In Figure 9.2 the limits for Group A are applied to the values for Group B. The four points for Group B outside the limits for Group A represent a detectable difference between the two groups.

In Figure 9.3 the limits for Group B are applied to the values for Group A. Again we see points outside the limits, indicating a detectable difference between the two groups. Either one of the two conditions above is a license to interpret the difference between the averages as real: The sites with the bonus plan average about six more accidents per million man-hours than do the other sites.

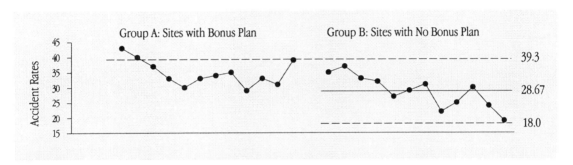

Figure 9.3: Group A Compared to Group B's Limits

If either Figure 9.2 or Figure 9.3 has a point outside the limits of the other group, then there is a detectable difference between the two groups, and if they are supposed to be the same, it will be worthwhile to find out why they are different. The key word here is "detectable." Two groups will always have different averages even when they are the same. It is only when the different averages represent real differences between the two groups that you will want to interpret that difference. And process behavior charts provide the simplest way to detect real differences.

9.2 The "Has a Change Occurred?" Chart

Placing high-level summaries on a process behavior chart will allow you to know when there has been a change in your system. Sometimes these changes are the intended result of actions on the part of the managers. In some cases these changes are the unintended side effects of known changes. And in other cases these changes are complete surprises. In any case, it will always be helpful to know the answer to the question "Has a change occurred?"

The following example shows how a large corporation was able to use Continual Improvement techniques to reduce their working capital by $ 27 million a month. In Section 7.4 we created an *XmR* Chart for the accounts receivable data for Year One. This chart is reproduced in Figure 9.4. Earlier we interpreted the December value as a signal that their accounts receivable system had changed for the worse.

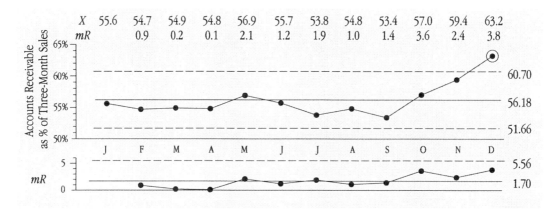

Figure 9.4: *XmR* Chart for Accounts Receivable Values for Year One

The explanation for the change seen in Figure 9.4 is that during the fourth quarter of Year One the accounting systems for North, Central, and South American operations were merged. Since the accounts receivable in Central and South America were slower in being collected this increase was understandable, even if it was undesirable.

Table 9.2 gives the accounts receivable data for Years One and Two in millions of dollars.

Table 9.2: Accounts Receivable for Years One and Two

Year	Month	A/R	Sales	A/R as % of Sales	Year	Month	A/R	Sales	A/R as % of Sales
One	January	129.7	233.2	55.6	Two	January	143.5	235.6	60.9
One	February	133.0	243.1	54.7	Two	February	146.2	240.8	60.7
One	March	135.8	247.2	54.9	Two	March	150.7	257.2	58.6
One	April	133.1	242.7	54.8	Two	April	145.2	253.5	57.3
One	May	135.8	238.7	56.9	Two	May	143.4	251.9	56.9
One	June	133.9	240.5	55.7	Two	June	146.6	252.3	58.1
One	July	126.2	234.8	53.8	Two	July	148.4	254.7	58.3
One	August	127.6	232.7	54.8	Two	August	132.1	259.7	50.9
One	September	121.6	227.6	53.4	Two	September	136.7	256.6	53.3
One	October	126.7	222.2	57.0	Two	October	133.4	254.3	52.5
One	November	131.5	221.4	59.4	Two	November	134.0	264.0	50.8
One	December	139.4	220.7	63.2	Two	December	142.3	268.9	52.9

Figure 9.5 shows that the increase in Accounts Receivable as a percentage of three-month sales, which was detected in December of Year One, persisted for the first seven months of Year Two. However, because they were using the chart to track accounts receivable, and because the chart made the deficiencies in the merged system clear for all to see, the staff had been working during this period to improve the system.

They began by using flowcharts to visualize the systems of the three offices. Of course the three systems were different. Based on the flowcharts of these existing systems they began to create a new system that would not only create consistency between the three offices, but would also streamline the whole system. When they had done this they created

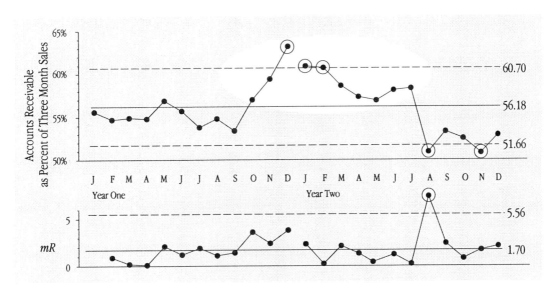

Figure 9.5: *XmR* Chart for Accounts Receivable for Years One and Two

flowcharts of the new process and used these to train the employees at all three offices on how to use the new procedures.

The new system was put into operation in August of Year Two and the effect was immediately seen—both the *X* Chart and the *mR* Chart signal the impact of the new system.

The points for August and November, which fall below the limit on the *X* Chart in Figure 9.5, indicate that this process is doing better at the end of Year Two than it was at the beginning of Year One. They did not just bring the Central and South American operations into line with the North American operations, but they actually improved all three! The accounts receivable dropped from 59% of the three-month sales to 52%. This seven percent drop corresponded to an extra $17.5 million in increased liquidity each month!

So our initial limits, computed using the values for Year One, are sufficient to show three distinctly different modes of operation for the accounts receivable process during Years One and Two. Given this understanding of this process, we might wish to make these three different modes more visible by computing limits for each different mode.

For the first nine months of Year One the average is 54.97%, and the average moving range is 1.11. These values translate into limits of:

$$UNPL = \bar{X} + 2.66\,\overline{mR} = 54.97 + (2.66 \times 1.11) = 57.92$$
$$LNPL = \bar{X} - 2.66\,\overline{mR} = 54.97 - (2.66 \times 1.11) = 52.02$$
$$URL = 3.27\,\overline{mR} = 3.27 \times 1.11 = 3.63$$

For the next ten months the average is 59.04%, and the average moving range (based on the 10 values for October to July) is 1.75. These values translate into limits of:

$$UNPL = \bar{X} + 2.66\,\overline{mR} = 59.04 + (\,2.66 \times 1.75\,) = 63.70$$
$$LNPL = \bar{X} - 2.66\,\overline{mR} = 59.04 - (\,2.66 \times 1.75\,) = 54.39$$
$$URL = 3.27\,\overline{mR} = 3.27 \times 1.75 = 5.72$$

The jump from an average of 55% to an average of 59% corresponded to an extra \$ 10 million being tied up in accounts receivable each month. (Sales are approximately \$ 250 million per quarter and four percent of \$ 250 million is \$ 10 million).

Finally, the last five months of Year Two have an average of 52.08%, and the average moving range is, once again, 1.75. In computing this average moving range only the four values for September through December were used. The large moving range between July and August was not used because it does not represent the routine variation of the process, but rather shows the change between two modes of operation for this process. These values translate into limits of:

$$UNPL = \bar{X} + 2.66\,\overline{mR} = 52.08 + (\,2.66 \times 1.75\,) = 56.74$$
$$LNPL = \bar{X} - 2.66\,\overline{mR} = 52.08 - (\,2.66 \times 1.75\,) = 47.43$$
$$URL = 3.27\,\overline{mR} = 3.27 \times 1.75 = 5.72$$

While it was not absolutely necessary to compute three sets of limits for Years One and Two, the use of these limits helps to define the three modes of operation and to show both the deterioration and the improvement. Figure 9.6 provides a powerful graphic summary for this whole story of improvement. In addition, the three central lines provide the supporting documentation for the estimates of the losses and savings associated with these changes.

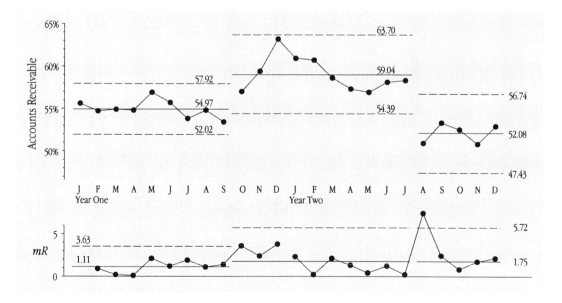

Figure 9.6: Accounts Receivable for Years One and Two

Table 9.3: Accounts Receivable for Years Three and Four

Year	Month	A/R	Sales	A/R as % of Sales	Year	Month	A/R	Sales	A/R as % of Sales
Three	January	146.4	285.7	51.3	Four	January	154.0	297.2	51.8
Three	February	148.9	279.1	53.4	Four	February	152.2	303.6	50.1
Three	March	149.9	289.1	51.8	Four	March	151.2	308.4	49.0
Three	April	154.1	285.7	53.9	Four	April	152.3	301.3	50.6
Three	May	141.6	284.6	49.7	Four	May	147.9	301.4	49.1
Three	June	145.8	281.7	51.8	Four	June	155.6	308.7	50.4
Three	July	149.5	276.1	54.2	Four	July	159.2	321.7	49.5
Three	August	145.5	287.0	50.7	Four	August	163.8	326.1	50.2
Three	September	150.1	283.9	52.9	Four	September	160.2	315.3	50.8
Three	October	142.0	277.1	51.2	Four	October	149.6	305.0	49.1
Three	November	138.1	278.1	49.7					
Three	December	150.3	279.4	53.8					

So what would you forecast for Year Three?

The limits that characterize the process at the end of Year Two are the logical limits to use in forecasting Year Three. If they do not make any further changes in the accounts receivable process, they can expect accounts receivable to average about 52% of the three-month sales. Individual months might have values as high as 56%, or as low as 48%, without being an indication of any change in the accounts receivable process.

The data for Years Three and Four are shown in Table 9.3 and are plotted against the limits from the end of Year Two in Figure 9.7.

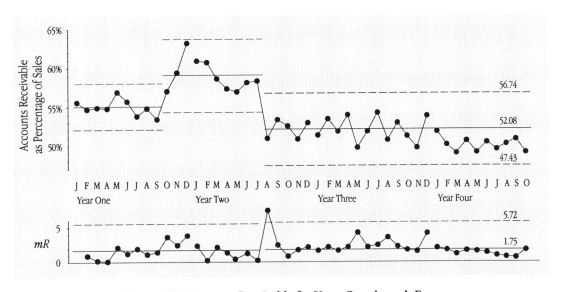

Figure 9.7: Accounts Receivable for Years One through Four

The changes made in August of Year Two resulted in a sustained reduction in the accounts receivable as a percentage of the three-month sales. Since the data for Year Three remain within the limits we do not need to revise or recompute the limits. We continue to use these limits for Year Four, where we see a long run below the central line. This run is evidence that they were successful in making yet another improvement to their collection process—beginning in Year Four, they added interest charges for overdue accounts. The impact of this change is made visible and quantifiable by the *XmR* Chart.

Figure 9.8: The Accounts Receivable Process Was Improved in Year Four

Using the ten months of Year Four to revise the limits we get an average of 50.06% and an average moving range of 1.32. These values yield limits of:

$$UNPL = \bar{X} + 2.66\,\overline{mR} = 50.06 + (2.66 \times 1.32) = 53.57$$
$$LNPL = \bar{X} - 2.66\,\overline{mR} = 50.06 - (2.66 \times 1.32) = 46.55$$
$$URL = 3.27\,\overline{mR} = 3.27 \times 1.32 = 4.31$$

These limits can be placed on the data for Year Four and then extended to characterize what you expect in the future. Interpreting these limits we see that now the accounts receivable are averaging 50% of the sales for the past three months, and the variation in the accounts receivable has been reduced. At the current sales level of $300 million per quarter this two percent reduction in accounts receivable resulted in an additional $6 million reduction in working capital. In all, since the beginning of Year Two, the accounts receivable percentage has been reduced by 9 percentage points, which is currently equivalent to having an additional $27 million of increased liquidity each month.

Notice how it is the interaction between the user and the chart that makes the chart effective. One of the managers in this project said, "The charts were talking to us—telling us what was going on in our system."

—◆—

Using process behavior charts to detect unknown changes in the process, to evaluate planned changes in the process, and to communicate the effects of these changes to others so that the process can be improved for the future, is how the charts become the locomotive of Continual Improvement. Here we see how changes made to an otherwise predictable process resulted first in things getting worse, and then in substantial improvements.

This example also shows how to use the limits to tell the story. In both Figure 9.6 and 9.8 the limits are used to emphasize the changes made and to quantify the impact of these changes. Many beginners nervously ask, "When do I need to revise my limits?" In computing limits the objective is not to "get the right number," but rather to take the right action. As long as the limits provide an adequate description of the process, they are sufficient.

"But how much data do I need before I can calculate limits?"

How much do you have? In the preceding example limits were computed at the end of Year Two using only five values and four moving ranges, because that was all the data that was available that was reasonable to use. In practice it is nice if you can use a dozen or even two dozen values to compute your limits. However, we often have to work with fewer values, and useful limits may be computed using as few as five or six values.

9.3 Why Susie *Can* Breathe

People who suffer from asthma will sometimes be asked to monitor their peak exhalation flow rate (PEFR) scores using a device known as a peak flow meter. To use this device a person will take a deep breath and then exhale into the meter as quickly and forcefully as possible. The value recorded is the peak flow in liters per minute. The lower the peak flow, the greater the obstruction in the airways in the lung and the more severe the asthma condition, with values below 100 being potentially life-threatening. The following is the story of how Dr. Peter Boggs and Fazel Hayati of the Asthma 2000 Group in Shreveport, Louisiana, pioneered the use of a process behavior chart in the treatment of asthma.

The patient was an 11-year-old girl with severe asthma who, prior to the beginning of this story, had been hospitalized three times in the previous year. As part of her treatment program she was asked to collect data on her peak flow rates four times each day. The data used here are the peak flow rates she obtained each morning prior to taking any medication. The first 18 of these values, shown in Figure 9.9, have an average of 183, which is 60% of this patient's predicted normal peak flow rate. In other words, without the congestion of asthma, this girl should be able to produce peak flows in the vicinity of 310. However, an average of 183 does not mean that she will get a value of 183 every day. Some days she does better, and some days she does worse. But do these swings above and below 183 represent changes in this patient's chronic condition?

Figure 9.9: *XmR* **Chart for AM Premedication Peak Flow Rates for Days 1 to 18**

As we have seen in other situations, the easiest and best way of understanding variation is to use process behavior charts. With an average of 183.1 and an average moving range of 52.4 we compute the limits:

$$UNPL = \bar{X} + 2.66\,\overline{mR} = 183.1 + (\,2.66 \times 52.4\,) = 322.5$$
$$LNPL = \bar{X} - 2.66\,\overline{mR} = 183.1 - (\,2.66 \times 52.4\,) = 43.7$$
$$URL = 3.27\,\overline{mR} = 3.27 \times 52.4 = 171.3$$

The patient collected the data, and brought them to the physician who plotted them and created the chart in Figure 9.9. Once this *XmR* Chart was on the table, the obvious question became "What happened on Days 9, 10, 11, and 12?" Here they had a clear and unequivocal run near the limit, indicating a real change in the patient's physiological status.

As it turned out, this four-day period of improved peak flow rates corresponded to a weekend visit by the patient at her aunt's house, while the drop in the peak flow rates that followed corresponded to her first morning back at home.

While standard allergy testing had shown that this patient was allergic to dogs, house mites, and common pollens, and while these allergies had been explained to both the patient and her mother, this clinical knowledge did not have the impact that the simple chart in Figure 9.9 had. Once they had collected their own data, and could see with their own eyes the impact that these allergens had in their own home, they began to make changes. *Both the patient and her mother changed from being objects of treatment to being active participants in that treatment.*

The most important part of any discovery is the ability to communicate that discovery to others. The process behavior chart is a powerful tool for both data analysis and communication. It should be noted that the process behavior chart does not supplant the physician's knowledge or judgment—but it does augment the physician's understanding of the patient's condition. With the real physiological changes that accompany the 200 unit swings shown in Figure 9.9, there will come a point where the physician should and will intervene. This intervention point will be determined by the combination of many different factors, of which the peak flow rate scores are but one element. The process behavior chart can help to evaluate the effectiveness of a course of treatment, but it is naive to assume that it could ever take the place of that synthesis of multiple physiological variables which is the core of the practice of medicine.

But how does this simple chart augment the physician's knowledge? It provides a characterization of the routine variation to be expected until the patient's chronic status is changed. It allows the physician to come up with a more complete assessment of the patient status.

At this point Dr. Boggs was concerned with three main objectives. First, he wanted to increase this patient's average peak flow rate above its current level of 183 (which is only 60% of the patient's normal flow rate). Second, he wanted to change this patient's chronic condition so that the Lower Natural Process Limit would be high enough to remove the potential of severe asthma (a patient is considered to be at risk of severe asthma when Lower Natural Process Limit is below 60% of normal). Finally, he wanted to reduce the daily swings between the morning (premedication) flow rates and the evening (post medication) flow rates. (Since we are only looking at the morning values here these daily swings are not part of the record shown in Figure 9.9.)

Given the compelling evidence of Figure 9.9, the patient and her mother began to work to remove the allergens and irritants from the patient's environment. As they made changes they continued to collect the data and plot it. Figure 9.10 shows that by Day 82 they had made significant progress toward the first objective of raising the average peak flow rate. Over the period from Day 82 to Day 93 the patient had an average flow rate of 209.2, an average moving range of 31.7, and her lower limit had moved up from 44 to 125.

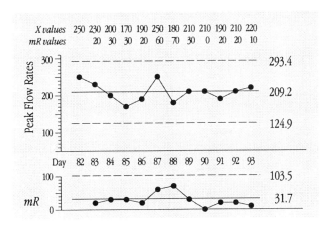

Figure 9.10: *XmR* **Chart for Peak Flow Rates—Days 82 to 93**

The limits from Figure 9.10 characterize an improved status for the patient. As new Peak Flow Rates were obtained they were plotted against the limits of Figure 9.10. On Figure 9.11 we see that by Day 125 they had a run of eight above the central line—evidence that is beyond a reasonable doubt—there has been further improvement in the patient's condition.

Figure 9.11: *XmR* **Chart for Peak Flow Rates—Days 82 to 93 and Days 118 to 132**

Since the objective is to use the limits to characterize the process, and since we have evidence that the process has changed, it is now appropriate to compute new limits to quantify this improvement. These limits are shown in Figure 9.12.

Figure 9.12: *XmR* **Chart for Peak Flow Rates—Days 118 to 132 with New Limits**

These limits show a substantial improvement with respect all three of Dr. Bogg's goals:

1. The average of 244 is approximately 80% of the patient's predicted best. The Natural Process Limits of 180 to 309 can be taken to characterize the patient's current chronic condition. She will routinely vary within these limits unless, or until, her condition is changed in some way.

2. A Lower Natural Process Limit of 180 removes this patient from being routinely at risk of severe asthma. Without some serious change in her chronic condition, she is no longer liable to have episodes with scores below 180. (This is in stark contrast with Figure 9.9 where 11 out of 18 scores were below 180.)
3. The reduced variation shown in Figure 9.12 indicates smaller swings from day-to-day, suggesting greater stability for the patient.

Continued work with this patient and her mother resulted in further improvements as shown in Figure 9.13. Her average peak flow rate was raised to 297, which is 96 percent of her normal score. Her Lower Natural Process Limit was raised to 247, which is comparable to the central line in Figure 9.12, and well above the cutoff for being at risk of severe asthma. Comparing the first and last portions of Figure 9.13 reveals that the patient is now functioning at home the same way that she originally functioned at her aunt's. In addition the variation between her morning (premedication) peak flow rates and her evening (post medication) peak flow rates was cut from over 100 points to only 34 points. This success was the result of the combination of medical knowledge, a clear way of understanding the patient's chronic condition, and the effective communication of this condition in order to obtain compliance on the part of the patient and her mother.

Figure 9.13: *XmR* Chart for Peak Flow Rates after Five Months

In this example we see how the use of the *XmR* Chart allows us to separate routine variation from exceptional variation. It allows us to characterize the current status of a process and to know when a change in that status has occurred. In short, the *XmR* Charts allow us to separate the *probable noise* from the *potential signals* within our data. And this distinction is crucial to understanding and using data effectively.

9.4 A Clinical Report: Peter's Story

This is an example of how process behavior charts were used to (1) evaluate outcomes and (2) assist in making clinical decisions in the treatment of severe, potentially life-threatening self-injurious behavior (*viz.* self-inflicted wounds to the body caused by head-banging and biting the wrists and fingers). The treatment of Peter, a 25 year old man with autistic disorder who functions in the severe range of mental retardation and has been blind since birth, is described from two points of view. First, from the perspective of Dr. Al Pfadt, the behavioral consultant who constructed and analyzed the charts shown here; then from the perspective of Peter's parents. The following material was provided by Dr. Pfadt and his colleagues at the NY State Institute for Basic Research in Developmental Disabilities and is used with the permission of Peter's parents.

Rather than being a story of a dramatic cure, this is the story of incremental improvement, based on the careful collection and analysis of data to discover relationships between presumed causes and observable outcomes.

Peter's self-injurious behavior first emerged during his infancy and has persisted throughout his life. He has had periods of improved functioning and he has suffered disappointing relapses. In a previous, out-of-state, residential placement a variety of aversive behavioral treatment procedures were used, up to and including electric shocks. While these procedures were intended as a form of punishment whenever he engaged in self-injury, they were all unsuccessful in suppressing Peter's dangerous behaviors. Because of this long history of failures, Peter was transferred to the Institute for Basic Research on March 4.

Because of his self-injurious behavior, Peter was routinely kept in restraints consisting of devices resembling handcuffs that tethered his wrists to a belt worn around his waist He also wore a helmet to prevent injury to his head. When they first attempted to remove these restraints Peter became extremely agitated and attempted to injure himself so violently that it was necessary to restore them immediately to protect him from harm. This suggested that the devices functioned as a form of self-restraint that is frequently encountered among individuals who engage in self-destructive behavior. This conceptualization of Peter's behavior also provided the basis for the behavioral component of his treatment plan. Since the restraints appeared to function as a form of self-control, Dr. Pfadt decided not to prohibit their use. Rather, he decided to teach Peter to ask for restraints in a more socially acceptable manner, and then to gradually attempt to develop his tolerance for having the restraints removed periodically for short intervals.

The measure used was the number of minutes per shift that Peter spent out of his restraints. This value could range from a low of 0 minutes to a maximum of 480 minutes. This measure was chosen as an outcome measure for three reasons. First, it reflected Peter's clinical status at the time of admission and provided a focus for his treatment plan, as will be explained later. Second, this measure was objective and was readily obtained by the use of a simple timing device which could be set and reset by staff when restraints were either removed or replaced. Third, without requiring any additional paperwork it satisfied a state requirement—mechanical restraints are prohibited by law unless there is documentation that they are removed every two hours and a safety check performed. These measurements, therefore, provided both a useful indicator of clinical status and a way to comply with a regulation.

The initial success of this strategy was shown by the running record in Figure 9.14. Within the first four days after Peter was admitted to the unit he was spending most of his time out of restraints. By March 8th, the staff were able to remove restraints and keep them off for five consecutive work shifts, although there was a "relapse" when he began to attend his day program.

The start of the day program is an understandably stressful experience for any blind person who must learn to navigate his way around a new environment, even more so for an individual with autistic disorder who may be agitated by changes in routine and exposure to strangers.

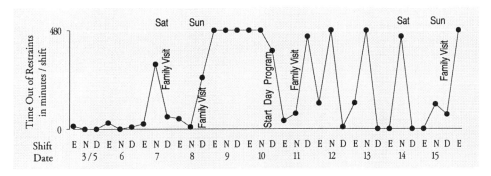

Figure 9.14: Peter's Time Out of Restraints Per Shift, March 4 to March 15

Figure 9.14 shows that with the start of the day program Peter once again was spending his days in restraints. He was, however, spending his nights free of restraints. As he was pressed to perform routines that were spelled out in his treatment plan, this tendency became more pronounced, until, on the 15th, he spent a large portion of the night in restraints. (The routines involved in this part of the program were activities that were intended to increase his functional independence, such as teaching him to brush his teeth. In the past it had appeared that Peter used his self-injurious behavior as a means of ending the frustration attached to learning new routines and independent functioning.)

But how can we be sure that the changes seen in Figure 9.14 are not just routine variation? The only way to be sure is to filter out the routine variation. Using the data for March 4 through March 31 results in Natural Process Limits of 145 minutes to 340 minutes as seen in Figure 9.15. Only six of the 82 values fall within these limits. This is why we are justified in interpreting the running record at face value—Peter is indeed cycling from good periods to bad periods, and these cycles are made manifest on the running record.

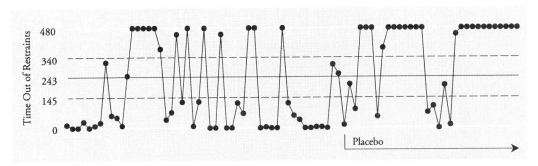

Figure 9.15: *X* Chart for Time Out of Restraints, March 4 to March 31

Initially, good periods were more common during the night shift, as Peter learned to sleep through the night without the need for restraints. The severity of Peter's behavioral outbursts had necessitated the assignment of two staff members to protect him from harm on each work shift and this was accomplished within the unit by means of a rotational assignment of overtime duty that brought virtually the entire roster in the building into contact with him during the course of this period. Some staff worked with Peter more effectively than others and Dr. Pfadt learned to identify their presence (or absence) by carefully inspecting changes in the running record. Other "unexpected" changes also became predictable over time, such as the effect that parental visits had on Peter's behavior, particularly when they didn't occur on weekends as he had come to expect.

As shown in Figure 9.15, a placebo treatment phase was initiated on March 18th in anticipation of the introduction of a new medication (Drug B) in combination with the other medication (Drug A) that Peter was taking when he entered the treatment unit.

This placebo was introduced to minimize the possibility that an expectation of improvement might confound the interpretation of results due to the planned introduction of this new (and still somewhat experimental) medication at a later date. The staff were aware that Peter was taking a placebo in addition to his prescribed medication (this was not a double-blind placebo controlled study). To their surprise, both subjectively and objectively, as seen in Figure 9.15, Peter seemed to improve following the use of one full tablet of the placebo.

Given the sheer volume of points on the shift-by-shift running record they decided to start a summary graph consisting of the weekly averages. The average of the 21 shift-by-shift values for each week would be plotted as one point on this new chart. This provided a higher level summary and allowed everyone to see the big picture more clearly than was possible with the shift-by-shift values. This weekly summary for the first twelve weeks is shown in Figure 9.16, where the improvement on the placebo is shown in Weeks Three, Four, and Five.

Because of this documented improvement while Peter was on the placebo, the staff members insisted that the placebo was helping and initially opposed the plans to have it discontinued. However, according to the protocol, they did discontinue the placebo at the end of Week Five. The running record clearly indicates that Peter's improved level of functioning persisted even though the placebo had been discontinued. An explanation of this placebo effect came they discovered that these supposedly inert tablets contained significant traces of aspirin!

Figure 9.16: Weekly Average Time Out Of Restraints per Shift

Before introducing a new medication (Drug B), the dosage of the original medication was increased during Weeks Nine through Twelve to determine if it was possible to help Peter control his self-injurious behaviors using only a single medication. Increasing the dosage of Drug A did not seem to do much.

These four weeks with the increased levels of Drug A were considered to be the baseline for evaluating the effect of Drug B. In order to obtain limits to use for this evaluation these four weekly averages were used to obtain three moving ranges, and limits for an *XmR* Chart were obtained in the usual manner. This baseline chart is shown in Figure 9.17.

Figure 9.17: Baseline *XmR* Chart for Evaluating Drug B

Four values and three moving ranges are certainly a minimal amount of data to use in computing limits. Such limits will, of necessity, be soft. However, these soft limits were sufficient to detect the changes that followed. Since the objective is to determine when a change has occurred we do not have to have perfect limits. Having Peter wait for six months while they collected 25 to 30 weeks worth of data prior to starting Drug B would have been unconscionable.

Secondly, this is an example of using a high-level summary (the weekly averages) in a chart for individual values. Other types of process behavior charts exist. One of these is the Average and Range Chart. While it might seem natural to use an Average Chart for these weekly averages, it is inappropriate in this case. In part, this is because the individual values have a restricted range of 0 to 480 minutes and many of these values are at the extremes of this restricted range. As a result the usual relationships used by the Average and Range Chart no longer apply.

The new medication (Drug B) was introduced during Week 13. The time out of restraints for each shift was still plotted (as in Figure 9.14) and every week the weekly average was plotted on the X Chart shown in Figure 9.18.

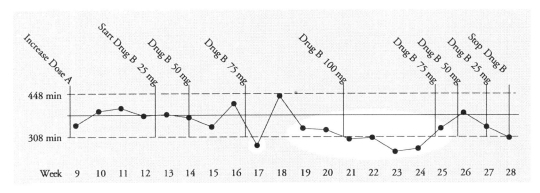

Figure 9.18: *X* Chart for Weekly Averages Used to Evaluate Drug B

The chart in Figure 9.18 was continually up-dated and inspected during this drug trial. leading them to the conclusion that increasing the dosage of Drug B, up to the limit the treatment protocol allowed (100 mg per day), did not result in improved functioning. In fact, the higher doses (i.e., 75 mg and 100 mg) of Drug B were associated with a regression in clinical status. Not only is this seen in the points below the lower limit in Figure 9.18, but it was borne out by the subjective impressions of staff and other objective indicators. Peter was clearly not doing well on Drug B—he inflicted some injuries to his face that required medical interventions (sutures and use of antibiotics to treat an infected wound). The reversal of this regression in clinical status that accompanied the decreased dosages of Drug B confirmed this overall conclusion.

The introduction of Drug C (administered in combination with his original medication) during week 28 (on September 15) produced a dramatic improvement in clinical status. This improvement was shown objectively by the weekly averages in Figure 9.19 and was confirmed by the reports of the staff working with Peter. From Week 33, the use of restraints was virtually eliminated, except for instances that coincided with an ear infection and an episode of cellulitis. Treatment with an antibiotic seems to have resulted in a decrease in agitation and also avoided a large scale relapse, such as was reported in the past when Peter

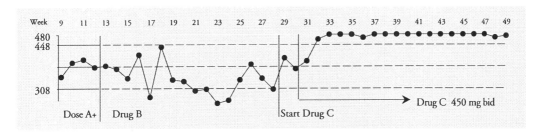

Figure 9.19: *X* **Chart for Weekly Average Time Out of Restraints**

had recurrent ear infections.

Peter's parents, who have struggled with the challenge of managing his self-injurious behaviors for nearly 23 years, wrote the following about this whole decision making process.

> The statistical process of measuring our son's behavior has enabled those who have interpreted the graphs to have a clearer picture of what underlying factors influence the exhibited behaviors. The precise recording and interpretation of the daily processes have pinpointed the incidents that our son is unable to verbalize or relate to his care givers. Through the years it has been difficult to identify and understand those factors that may have contributed to his complex behavior which is manifested by severe battering of his face and biting of his hands.
>
> Many behavior altering programs have been tried with varying responses in improved or worsening behavior. It has always been difficult, in a retrospective approach, to try to sort out those treatment techniques which were effective. This sorting was usually left to subjective analysis and interpretive impressions by observers and involved staff who interacted with our son in his daily management and treatment regimen. It appears that with the mode of precise recording and analysis using the continuous graph formats which was used with our son in this program one could relate his specific behavior at a given point in time to any factor in his daily life that would affect his behavior pattern. This has permitted us to correlate changes in behavior and response to treatment as a total interaction of all the factors. e.g., starting, changing, or terminating medication, parental visits as related to program days and non-program days, different interactions with specific members of staff, etc. A major triggering factor had always been the undetectable onset of illness, e.g., earache, sore throat, or viral infection, which would now be evident on analysis of his behavior chart.
>
> We feel that this is a far more appropriate approach toward the trials of medication in attempts to control the self-injurious behavior. In all the years of our son's behaviors, since the age of three, we have never felt that a treatment program and staff were as totally involved with him as has been the case during the past year.

In summary, the charts provided objective criteria for making data-based clinical decisions which resulted in improved outcomes for the client. Compared with the marked lack of success which characterized prior courses of treatment, the results are nothing less than spectacular. The visual display of the available data provided a clear and unequivocal way of understanding and evaluating both the status of the client and the apparent effectiveness of the treatment. The charts are the voice of the process, and this voice is an important part of any treatment strategy.

9.5 How Do You Use These Charts for Continual Improvement?

Process behavior charts provide an objective way of separating routine variation (probable noise) from exceptional variation (potential signals). The importance of this distinction is made every time we turn on a radio—I have yet to see someone deliberately tune in and listen to static.

Once you and your co-workers have a way to separate potential signals from probable noise, you will find it much easier to agree on what constitutes a signal and, therefore, what deserves attention. At the same time, you and everyone else will spend less time chasing noise, dreaming up explanations of routine variation, and generally spinning your wheels.

Thus, the real secret of the effective use of process behavior charts is in the follow-through. It is how you use the charts to discover what your process can do, or can be made to do. It is how you interact with the chart to understand the behavior of your process. It is how you communicate your process knowledge to others in a way that they can comprehend quickly and easily.

In short, the secret of the effective use of process behavior charts is the way of thinking that goes with them. And you only get this through sound teaching and much practice.

The alternative is described in Chapter Twelve.

Chapter Ten

How to Create Good Charts

The process behavior chart is a very robust analysis technique. It will work with all kinds of data and in all sorts of situations. However, there are some principles for creating the charts that will help you to avoid those few pitfalls that exist.

10.1 What Kind of Data Belongs on an *XmR* Chart?

The XmR Chart is intended
for use with sequences of values
that are logically comparable.

In Section 9.3 the flow rates placed on the *XmR* Chart were the "a.m. premedication flow rates." The patient also collected flow rates in the evening, fifteen minutes after inhaling a bronchodilator (the "p.m. postmedication flow rates"). If we use the symbol X_i to denote the a.m. premedication values, and use the symbol Y_i to denote the p.m. postmedication values, then the *time* series, in a strict sense, would consist of a string of values:

$$X_1, Y_1, X_2, Y_2, X_3, Y_3, X_4, Y_4, ..., X_i, Y_i, ...$$

While these values would be the same measure, obtained by the same instrument, on the same patient, they would be collected under *different* conditions. Dr. Boggs was interested in looking at the time series above because he wanted to know about the daily swings. So he plotted these values in the $XYXY$ order. But while this arrangement of these values is a time series, it cannot be meaningfully placed on an *XmR* Chart because the moving ranges would not provide the proper yardstick for setting meaningful limits. With the $XYXY$ ordering above each moving range would be inflated by the effects of the medication.

So while these data may be arranged in the order XXXX or the order $YYYY$ and then placed on an *XmR* Chart, the $XYXY$ ordering may only be plotted as a time series without the benefit of limits.

When values that are *known* to have come from different cause systems are mixed together on a single running record it is inappropriate to compute limits for that plot. While you can combine different measures on a running record when it makes sense to do so, and while such a running record may be interesting and informative, you cannot combine *different measures* on a single *XmR* Chart. The limits of the *XmR* Chart are appropriate only when the point-to-point variation can be said to characterize the routine variation present in the data. When different measures are combined in a single plot this will no longer be the case, even if the data do constitute a time series. The *XmR* Chart should not be used to compare apples and oranges.

The XmR Chart should not be used
when the moving ranges do not logically represent
the routine variation of the measure being plotted on the X Chart.

Most time series are a sequence of values for a *single* measure, obtained at different points in time, under similar conditions. Such time series are usually appropriate for an *XmR* Chart. Other sequences of values may also be placed on an *XmR* Chart, but only when it makes sense to use the point-to-point variation as the yardstick for constructing the limits. This can be the case when you have data that do not possess a logical time-ordering, and yet are still logically comparable with each other. The data of Table 10.1 fall into this category. They are the Average Call Lengths for each of the 22 operators originally shown in Table 4.1. Since they all came from the same time period, there is no natural way to order these 22 values. Therefore, they have been arranged in an arbitrary order using the Operator ID numbers.

Table 10.1: Operator Average Call Lengths Arranged by Operator ID Number

Op.	TW	BM	TB	JO	SA	GC	FL	NB	SD	DL	PM	FF	MC	CD	LW	SC	TK	RA	AC	JH	LJ	PA
ID#	1	2	3	4	5	6	7	8	9	10	11	12	13	14	15	16	17	18	19	20	21	22
Avg.	10.5	8.1	11.6	11.5	16.7	8.8	6.2	10.4	9.0	10.4	10.9	12.1	8.1	5.3	13.4	11.7	8.0	8.2	11.7	9.0	11.8	7.3
mR		2.4	3.5	0.1	5.2	7.9	2.6	4.2	1.4	1.4	0.5	1.2	4.0	2.8	8.1	1.7	3.7	0.2	3.5	2.7	2.8	4.5

Figure 10.1: *XmR* Chart for Operator Average Call Lengths Ordered by ID Number

The moving ranges in Table 10.1 still capture the routine variation between operators, and so limits based on these moving ranges will filter out the routine variation, allowing us to see if any operators are distinctly different from the rest. The resulting *XmR* Chart is shown in Figure 10.1.

While Operator 5 has the highest Average Call Length and Operator 14 has the lowest Average Call Length, their values are within the bounds of routine variation. Based on these data, these two operators cannot be said to be detectably different from the rest.

When arbitrary orderings are used you cannot apply any of the run-based detection rules when interpreting the chart. Only Detection Rule One is appropriate for such a chart.

But would we get the same result with a different ordering? If we arrange the data of Table 10.1 alphabetically according to the operator's last names we get the arrangement shown in Table 10.2. The resulting *XmR* Chart is shown in Figure 10.2. While the points are shuffled, and the limits change slightly, the story remains the same.

Table 10.2: Operator Average Call Lengths Arranged by Operator Name

Op.	PA	RA	SA	NB	TB	AC	GC	MC	SC	CD	SD	FF	JH	LJ	TK	DL	FL	BM	PM	JO	LW	TW
ID#	22	18	5	8	3	19	6	13	16	14	9	12	20	21	17	10	7	2	11	4	15	1
Avg.	7.3	8.2	16.7	10.4	11.6	11.7	8.8	8.1	11.7	5.3	9.0	12.1	9.0	11.8	8.0	10.4	6.2	8.1	10.9	11.5	13.4	10.5
mR		0.9	8.5	6.3	1.2	0.1	2.9	0.7	3.6	6.4	3.7	3.1	3.1	2.8	3.8	2.4	4.2	1.9	2.8	0.6	1.9	2.9

Figure 10.2: *XmR* **Chart for Operator Average Call Lengths Ordered Alphabetically**

The one thing to avoid when using an ordering that is not a natural time ordering is an ordering that depends upon the values themselves. An arbitrary ordering is acceptable only when it is independent of the *X* values. To illustrate why this is the case, consider what happens when the Average Call Length Data are arranged in ascending order prior to being placed on the *XmR* Chart. These ordered values are shown in Table 10.3, and the resulting chart is shown in Figure 10.3.

Table 10.3: Operator Average Call Lengths in Ascending Order

ID#	14	7	22	17	13	2	18	6	9	20	8	10	1	11	4	3	16	19	21	12	15	5
Avg.	5.3	6.2	7.3	8.0	8.1	8.1	8.2	8.8	9.0	9.0	10.4	10.4	10.5	10.9	11.5	11.6	11.7	11.7	11.8	12.1	13.4	16.7
mR		0.9	1.1	0.7	0.1	0.0	0.1	0.6	0.2	0.0	1.4	0.0	01	0.4	0.6	0.1	0.1	0.0	0.1	0.3	1.3	3.3

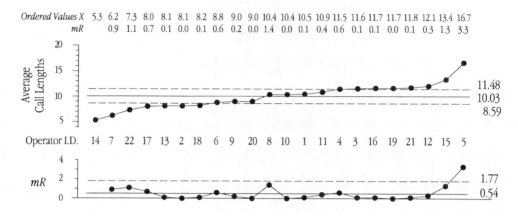

Figure 10.3: *XmR* Chart for the Ordered Average Call Lengths

The limits in Figure 10.3 are much tighter than those in the two preceding charts. This tightening of the limits is due to the arrangement of the values in ascending order. When the moving ranges are based upon *ordered values* they will not characterize the routine variation of the Average Call Lengths. Since the moving ranges in Figure 10.3 do not provide a logical yardstick to use in comparing the Average Call Lengths, we end up with limits on the *XmR* Chart that are highly artificial as well as being inappropriate for characterizing routine variation.

THE MOVING RANGE CHART

Finally, what do we learn from the Moving Range Chart? The construction and use of the Moving Range Chart is recommended for two reasons. First, a moving range which falls above the Upper Range Limit may be taken as an indication of a potential break in the time series—some sudden shift which is so large that it is unlikely to have occurred by chance. Second, the use of the Moving Range Chart is a simple way to signal to others that you do know the correct way of computing the limits. Since there are many who do not know the difference between the right and wrong ways of computing limits for individual values, and since the right ways all depend upon the moving ranges, the use of an *mR* Chart will differentiate you from the uninformed.

When placing individual observations on a process behavior chart there are only two correct ways of computing the limits. Up to this point all of the examples and exercises have illustrated the computations that use the *average moving range*. In the next section the computations that use the *median moving range* will be illustrated.

10.2 Using the Median Moving Range

In general, the limits based on the average moving range will be the best limits to use with your *XmR* Chart. This is because the average moving range is very efficient in its use of the data. Because the average moving range provides a stable estimate of dispersion, you will end up with good limits even when a few of the ranges fall above the upper range limit. But when a large number of ranges get inflated by signals, or when a few ranges are excessively large, they can inflate both the average moving range and the limits.

Medians are less efficient than averages, but they are also less susceptible to extreme values. So if your average moving range might have been unduly inflated by some exceptionally large moving ranges, you might wish to consider using the median moving range instead. Except for the computation of the median moving range and the use of different scaling factors the computations will proceed in the same manner as before. These will be illustrated using the data of Table 10.4.

Table 10.4 shows the monthly earnings for one company that always began its monthly report with a sentence like: "January's pretax earnings of $2.5 million were $4.4 million better than our forecast." While these numbers sound good, it takes the perspective of context and time to fully comprehend just what they mean. And the simplest way to gain this perspective is to use an *XmR* Chart.

Table 10.4: Actual Earnings for One Year in Millions of Dollars

Month	J	F	M	A	M	J	J	A	S	O	N	D
Actual Earnings	2.5	2.3	16.3	6.3	7.6	16.3	7.1	7.8	7.8	9.9	10.5	- 4.8
Moving Ranges		0.2	14.0	10.0	1.3	8.7	9.2	0.7	0.0	2.1	0.6	15.3

Simply reading over these numbers is enough to give you a sense that this company's earnings are fairly erratic. Also the moving ranges are either very small or very large, indicating big swings in the earnings. If we look at a stem-and-leaf plot of these moving ranges we get:

Figure 10.4: Stem-and-Leaf Plot of Moving Ranges from Table 10.4

The plot in Figure 10.4 shows six small moving ranges and five large moving ranges, with nothing in the middle. While the average moving range is 5.64, there are no values close to 5.64.

On the other hand the median moving range is 2.1. The appearance of Figure 10.4 along with the discrepancy between the average moving range and the median moving range, combine to suggest that the average moving range has been inflated. Therefore, we shall use the median moving range to compute limits for the *XmR* Chart.

- The Upper Natural Process Limit for the X Chart is found by multiplying the median moving range by the scaling factor of 3.14 and then adding the product to the average (or median) of the individual values:

$$UNPL = \bar{X} + (3.14 \times \widetilde{mR}) = 7.47 + (3.14 \times 2.1) = 14.07$$

- The Lower Natural Process Limit for the X Chart is found by multiplying the median moving range by the scaling factor of 3.14 and then subtracting the product from the average (or median) of the individual values:

$$LNPL = \bar{X} - (3.14 \times \widetilde{mR}) = 0.87.$$

- The Upper Range Limit for the *mR* Chart is found by multiplying the median moving range by the scaling factor of 3.86:

$$URL = 3.86 \times \widetilde{mR} = 3.86 \times 2.1 = 8.12$$

The scaling factors of 3.14 and 3.86 used in these calculations are the appropriate constants developed specifically for computing limits for an *XmR* Chart using a median moving range.

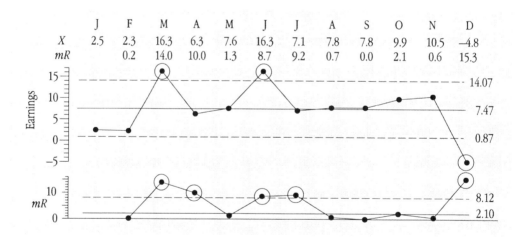

Figure 10.5: *XmR* Chart for Earnings Per Month

The chart in Figure 10.5 shows that the earnings for this company are erratic and changing from month to month. Their sales levels and expenses are changing to such an extent that even this high level summary does not fall within the computed limits. Here the computed limits do not predict the future earnings. The earnings for this company simply do not display that long-term consistency which is the essence of a predictable process. To forecast earnings with any credibility you will need to be able to anticipate the exceptional values.

If we use the average moving range of 5.64 the limits would be 2.3 times wider than the limit shown in Figure 10.5. When there is a substantial difference in the limits, it will generally be best to use the limits based on the median moving range.

EPISODE TREATMENT GROUPS

Another example comes from a large Health Maintenance Organization. A consulting firm has developed a model for defining equivalent illness classifications across patients and across providers. This model adjusts for the age of the patient, the diagnosis, the complications during a treatment episode, any accompanying illnesses suffered by the patient, and the operations performed that might reflect on the severity of the episode. The resulting Episode Treatment Groups (ETGs) are supposed to stratify the collection of patient and provider interactions into equivalence classes, where all the interactions in a given group are comparable with respect to all the factors mentioned above. In other words, each ETG should be homogeneous, allowing the hospital or HMO to compare providers within an ETG. Of course the HMO is interested in the total cost of an episode of treatment. The assumption behind this whole classification scheme is that episodes belonging to the same ETG should have similar diagnoses, similar degrees of severity, and similar total costs. Table 10.5 contains the total episode costs for 35 patients classified in the same ETG and served by one provider. These costs are arranged by the starting date of each episode of treatment, and cover one calendar year for this provider.

Table 10.5: Total Costs for ETG 678 for Provider 760

X	260	130	189	1,080	175	200	193	120	33
mR	—	130	59	891	905	25	7	73	87
X	293	195	571	55,698	209	1,825	239	290	254
mR	260	98	376	55,127	55,489	1,616	1,586	51	36
X	93	278	185	123	9,434	408	570	118	238
mR	161	185	93	62	9,311	9,026	162	452	120
X	207	153	209	243	110	306	343	244	
mR	31	54	56	34	133	196	37	99	

Even a cursory examination of the values in Table 10.5 will show that they cannot be considered to be similar. While the average cost is $2,149, this value does not provide a reasonable estimate of location since 33 of the 35 values fall below this average. Here we will use the median of the X values as the central line. Likewise, the average moving range of 4030.2 exceeds 30 of the 34 moving ranges, making it a poor estimate of location. Here we will need to use the median moving range to compute limits.

The median cost for this ETG for this provider is $238. The median moving range is $125. Both of these medians have been influenced by the extreme values, and are probably somewhat inflated, but they have not been as severely contaminated as the averages. In spite of this possible inflation, the medians will provide useful limits that will approximate the amount of variation that can be attributed to routine differences between episodes.

$$UNPL = \tilde{X} + (\,3.14 \times m\tilde{R}\,) = 238 + (\,3.14 \times 125\,) = \$\,630$$

$$LNPL = \tilde{X} - (\,3.14 \times m\tilde{R}\,) = 238 - (\,3.14 \times 125\,) = -\$\,154 \quad \text{(use boundary of 0)}$$

$$URL = 3.86 \times m\tilde{R} = 3.86 \times 125 = \$\,482$$

Four individual values and eight moving ranges fall above these limits. The chart is shown in Figure 10.6. So what can we make of this result? This ETG classification scheme has not successfully identified a homogeneous set of episodes. Four out of 35 means that 11 percent of these episodes do not belong in this group. A similar analysis of hundreds of providers for another ETG category showed about 12 percent exceptions. Thus, there is not only a lack of homogeneity for this one category, but for other categories as well.

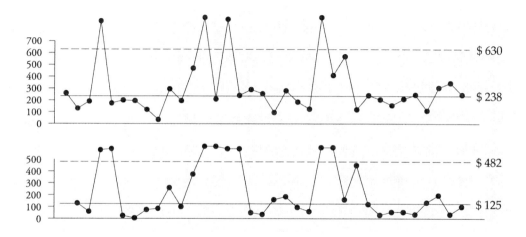

Figure 10.6: Total Costs for Episode Treatment Group 678 and Provider 760

This lack of homogeneity is a problem because hundreds of hospitals and HMOs use these ETGs to compare providers. Given that the records within a given ETG are not homogeneous, what number can they use for comparisons? Could they use the average cost of $2149 for Provider 760 for ETG 678? While this may be the average of the 35 costs of Table 10.5, this average has a numerator where 74 percent of the total comes from just one case. Change the value of that one case and you will see a dramatic change in the average cost.

When the data are not homogeneous
the average is not an appropriate summary statistic.

But can you use the median of $238? With 11 percent contamination, which is what the four excessive values amount to, even this value is inflated and can only provide a rough characterization of location for these costs. We used the median to construct our limits, but since the data are not homogeneous the median is only an imperfect summary.

Can you use the fact that this provider had 11 percent exceptional values? When this was done for one ETG category, across hundreds of providers, there was no detectable difference between the providers (see Exercise 13.1). This consistency of the percentage of exceptional values suggests that it is the model for creating the ETGs that is at fault. The exceptional costs are uniformly spread out across all the providers, leading to the inescapable conclusion that the ETG system does not deliver the homogeneous groupings that it promises.

Virtually every statistical technique for making comparisons between groups, items, or categories is built on the assumption that the data within each category are homogeneous. When this is demonstrably and globally not true, all comparison techniques become arbitrary and capricious. And when your comparison technique is arbitrary and capricious, your results will be no better.

Think about what the preceding paragraph means with respect to the uncritical use of confidence intervals and tests of hypotheses to make comparisons....

10.3 Charting Adjusted Data

Here we return to the monthly earnings data reported in Table 10.4. Each month the earnings value was compared to a forecast value. Presumably these forecasts took into account the foreseeable ups and downs in the revenue stream and the foreseeable expenses. Therefore, even though the raw earnings values do not show a steady-state predictability from month to month, we might like to know if the forecasts do a reasonable job of capturing the peaks and valleys.

If the forecasts are of any real value they should do a better job of predicting the earnings than simply using the central line from Figure 10.5. To see if they improve things, we shall adjust the actual earnings by the forecast value and plot the differences on an *XmR* Chart. These adjustments are shown in Table 10.6.

Table 10.6: Forecast Earnings and Actual Earnings

Month	J	F	M	A	M	J	J	A	S	O	N	D
Actual Earnings	2.5	2.3	16.3	6.3	7.6	16.3	7.1	7.8	7.8	9.9	10.5	–4.8
Forecast Earnings	–1.9	2.8	12.7	3.9	5.6	9.9	6.7	4.7	5.6	7.0	8.9	–0.4
Actual – Forecast	4.4	–0.5	3.6	2.4	2.0	6.4	0.4	3.1	2.2	2.9	1.6	–4.4

The average of these differences is 2.01, and the average moving range is 2.96. Since the median moving range of 2.7 is close to the average moving range we do not see the discrepancy observed on the previous page. Therefore, we shall use the average moving range to compute the limits for this *XmR* Chart.

Figure 10.7 tells us several things about this company's earnings forecasts. First of all, the central line for the X Chart shows that their earnings average about $2.0 million better than their forecasts. In other words, the best estimate of their earnings will be the published forecast plus two million. Whether this is deliberate or unconscious, there is a two million dollar bias in the forecast values, and the chart documents this bias. (It always sounds better to

	J	F	M	A	M	J	J	A	S	O	N	D
X	4.4	−0.5	3.6	2.4	2.0	6.4	0.4	3.1	2.2	2.9	1.6	−4.4
mR		4.9	4.1	1.2	0.4	4.4	6.0	2.7	0.9	0.7	1.3	6.0

Figure 10.7: *XmR* Chart for Earnings Minus Forecasts

exceed your forecast earnings than to fall short.)

Second, since all of the points fall within the limits, their earnings vary around this average in a predictable manner.

Third, the interpretation of the limits on the *X* Chart would suggest that for any given published forecast you could predict that the earnings would be in the interval:

[forecast + $ 10 million] to [forecast − $ 6 million]

That is, their earnings could exceed their published forecasts by as much as $ 10 million, or they could fall short by as much as $ 6 million.

Fourth, with an uncertainty of ± $ 8 million (compared with the uncertainty of ± $ 6.5 million in Figure 10.5) the forecasts have not reduced the routine variation even though they did correctly anticipate the exceptionally high and low months.

"These limits are far too wide to be useful." Are they? It is not the limits that are at fault but rather the noise in the data. The limits in Figure 10.7 are based upon the data given. *These limits are wide simply because these data are full of noise.* The process behavior chart limits are the Voice of the Process. Whether or not you like the Voice of the Process does not matter to the process.

But the uncertainty in the forecasts indicated by these limits is greater than their average earnings. Figure 10.5 shows their average earnings for this year to be around $ 7.5 million per month, while the uncertainty in Figure 10.7 is plus or minus $ 8 million. How can they use numbers that are this uncertain?

The answer is that they must use these numbers very carefully. If they do not know how weak their forecasts are, they will be tempted to interpret them as being more precise than they actually are, and thereby confuse noise with signals. No matter what method or technique you may use to obtain a forecast, it is the noise in the data that will limit how good that forecast can possibly be. The number you use may be the best number available, but it can still be overwhelmed by noise. You cannot begin to use a number properly until you know its limitations. Process behavior charts explicitly show those limitations. Other techniques hide these limitations by sweeping them under the rug.

As illustrated here, the art of using process behavior charts may require that you plot something other than the original data. Adjusted data, when used in association with the original data, may provide more insight than can be obtained from the original data alone.

10.4 Exercises

EXERCISE 10.1:

The moving ranges in Table 10.1 are, respectively:

2.4, 3.5, 0.1, 5.2, 7.9, 2.6, 4.2, 1.4, 1.4, 0.5, 1.2, 4.0, 2.8, 8.1, 1.7, 3.7, 0.2, 3.5, 2.7, 2.8, and 4.5

Create a Stem and Leaf Plot and use it to find the Median Moving Range.

first pass

```
0 |
1 |
2 |
3 |
4 |
5 |
6 |
7 |
8 |
```

ordered values

```
0 |
1 |
2 |
3 |
4 |
5 |
6 |
7 |
8 |
```

Making Sense of Data

EXERCISE 10.2:

The average of the X values in Table 10.1 is 10.03. Use the median moving range found in Exercise 10.1 and compute limits for an *XmR* Chart.

Compare these limits with those shown in Figure 10.2. Is there any practical difference?

Computation Worksheets:	EXERCISE 10.2	EXERCISE 10.3

Average Value = _____   Average Value = _____

Median Moving Range = _____   Median Moving Range = _____

$3.14 \times \widetilde{mR}$ = _____ $3.14 \times \widetilde{mR}$ = _____

$UNPL = \bar{X} + 3.14\,\widetilde{mR}$ = _____ $UNPL = \bar{X} + 3.14\,\widetilde{mR}$ = _____

$LNPL = \bar{X} - 3.14\,\widetilde{mR}$ = _____ $LNPL = \bar{X} - 3.14\,\widetilde{mR}$ = _____

$URL = 3.86 \times \widetilde{mR}$ = _____ $URL = 3.86 \times \widetilde{mR}$ = _____

EXERCISE 10.3:

The percentages of high school seniors who smoked daily for the years 1984 to 1993 are: 18.8, 19.6, 18.7, 18.6, 18.1, 18.9, 19.2, 18.2, 17.3, and 19.0 respectively. The moving ranges for these values are: 0.8, 0.9, 0.1, 0.5, 0.8, 0.3, 1.0, 0.9, and 1.7.

Find limits for an *XmR* Chart using the median moving range.

Compare these limits with those in the latter portion of Figure 8.7.

Is there any practical difference?

EXERCISE 10.4:

The median moving range for the data of Exercise 7.3 is 0.32. Recompute the limits for the *XmR* Chart of Exercise 7.3. How do these limits change your interpretation?

EXERCISE 10.5: Use the following Stem and Leaf Plots to find the median for the 35 X values and the median for the 34 mR values from Table 10.5.

Stem and Leaf Plot for the X values		Stem and Leaf plot for the mR values	
0	33 93	0	07 25 31 34 36 37 51 54 56 59 62 73 87 93 98 99
1	10 18 20 23 30 53 75 85 89 93 95	1	20 30 33 61 62 85 96
2	00 07 09 09 38 39 43 44 54 60 78 90 93	2	60
3	06 43	3	76
4	08	4	52
5	70 71		
		8	91
10	80	9	05
18	25	15	86
		16	16
94	34		
		90	26
556	98	93	11
		551	27
		554	89

EXERCISE 10.6:

Use the mR Chart in Figure 10.7 to identify the median moving range.
Compute limits for Figure 10.7 using the median moving range.

Computation Worksheets: EXERCISE 10.6   EXERCISE 10.7

Average Value = _____   Average Value = _____

Median Moving Range = _____   Median Moving Range = _____

$3.14 \times \widetilde{mR}$ = _____ $3.14 \times \widetilde{mR}$ = _____

$UNPL = \bar{X} + 3.14\,\widetilde{mR}$ = _____ $UNPL = \bar{X} + 3.14\,\widetilde{mR}$ = _____

$LNPL = \bar{X} - 3.14\,\widetilde{mR}$ = _____ $LNPL = \bar{X} - 3.14\,\widetilde{mR}$ = _____

$URL = 3.86 \times \widetilde{mR}$ = _____ $URL = 3.86 \times \widetilde{mR}$ = _____

EXERCISE 10.7: The average of the 82 values shown in Figure 9.15 is 242.6. The median moving range for these data is 30 minutes. Confirm the limits shown in Figure 9.15.

EXERCISE 10.8: Use an *XmR* Chart to determine if there is a detectable weekly cycle in the number of ATM transactions each day. The values from the January Report, shown on page 65, are reproduced below (rounded to the nearest multiple of 10). The average value is 7562 and the median moving range is 135.

W	T	F	S		S	M	T	W	T	F	S		S	M	T	W
7550	7510	7630	7640		7760	7290	7440	7620	7580	7510	7720		7900	7170	7290	7460
—	40	120	10		120	470	150	180	40	70	210		180	730	120	170

T	F	S		S	M	T	W	T	F	S		S	M	T	W	T	F
7500	7570	8030		7860	7370	7350	7630	7540	7550	8130		7750	7050	7350	7470	7590	7610
40	70	460		170	490	20	280	90	10	580		380	700	300	120	120	20

Chapter Eleven

What Makes the *XmR* Chart Work?

This chapter may not be of immediate interest to the beginner. It is included here because there are many questions which inevitably arise when people start using process behavior charts. When these questions arise, it is helpful to have access to some explanation of what makes the charts work. The purpose of this chapter is to provide these explanations. Therefore, you should read the following sections when you have questions about the background of the process behavior chart technique. So treat the following sections like selections in a cafeteria line to be picked up or skipped over as appropriate.

11.1 The Logic Behind Process Behavior Charts

The logic behind process behavior charts is shown in Figure 11.1. In order to justify the use of summary statistics to compute the limits, we begin with the tentative assumption that the process is predictable.

Next, based upon the summary statistics, a prediction is made concerning how the process should behave. In particular, this prediction comes in the form of calculated limits which define the expected amount of routine variation for the data.

Finally, the observed values are compared with the predicted limits. There are two possible outcomes for this comparison:

1. If the observations are consistent with the predictions, then the process may be predictable. At least there is no solid evidence to contradict the assumption of predictability for the process.

2. If the observations are inconsistent with the predictions, the process is unpredictable. This is due to the nature of the way the limits were computed. The inconsistency between the observations and the predictions is almost surely due to an incorrect assumption of predictability rather than a violation of the principles behind the calculation of the limits.

Thus, evidence of unpredictability is strong evidence which can safely be used as the basis for action. The absence of such evidence is not as conclusive, but since no action is

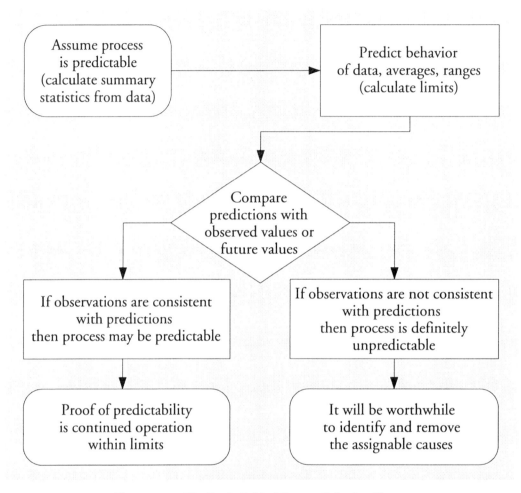

Figure 11.1: The Logic Behind Process Behavior Charts

required, the process should be left alone until such a time when the process behavior charts indicate that the process has changed.

It will always be a mistake to look for an assignable cause prior to detecting a change in the process. No matter how eloquent the explanation, action taken in the absence of a detectable signal from the data is essentially based upon nothing more than a wishful interpretation of noise. Wishes and hopes make for neat fairy tales, but they are a lousy basis for taking action upon your operations, processes, and systems. This is why it is imperative to learn how to separate potential signals from probable noise. Process behavior charts are the primary tool for filtering out the probable noise which is present in every data set.

11.2 Why Three-Sigma Limits?

Shewhart chose to draw the line between routine variation and exceptional variation according to the formula:

Average ± 3 Sigma

which is why the Natural Process Limits for the individual values, the Upper Range Limit, and those limits which we will encounter later may all be referred to as *three-sigma limits*. They are all specific applications of the generic formula above. But why did Shewhart decide to use this formula instead of some other? To find Shewhart's rationale we have to go to his first book, *Economic Control of Quality of Manufactured Product*. Some excerpts which explain his thinking follow:

> "Hence we must use limits such that through their use we will not waste too much time looking unnecessarily for trouble."

We do not want to have an undue number of false alarms—that is, we do not want values to fall outside the limits by accident. Since you are supposed to look for an assignable cause whenever a point falls outside the limits, an excessive number of false alarms would undermine your credibility and discredit the technique.

> "The method of attack is to establish limits of variability...such that, when [an observation] is found outside these limits, looking for an assignable cause is worthwhile."

We do not want to detect each and every little change in the process. It is just those assignable causes whose impact is great enough to justify the time and expense of investigation that we are interested in detecting and removing. We want to detect the strong signals.

> "If more than one statistic is used, then the limits on all the statistics should be chosen so that the probability of looking for trouble when any one of the chosen statistics falls outside its own limits is economic."

Multiple statistics generate multiple opportunities for false alarms, so we need to be very conservative in what we call a potential signal.

> "...we usually choose a symmetrical range characterized by [*t*-sigma] limits."

A symmetric interval is generic and safely conservative. The term *sigma* denotes a standard unit of dispersion.

> "Experience indicates that $t = 3$ seems to be an acceptable economic value."

Theory suggests that three-sigma limits should filter out virtually all of the probable noise, and experience indicates that three-sigma limits are sufficiently conservative for use in practice.

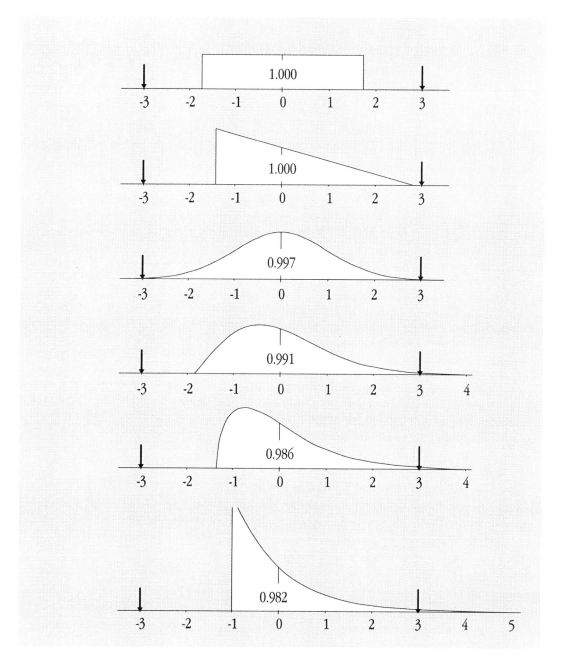

Figure 11.2: The Coverage of Three-Sigma Limits

"Hence the method of establishing allowable limits of variation in a statistic depends upon theory to furnish the expected value and the standard deviation [sigma] of the statistic, and upon empirical evidence to justify the choice of [three-sigma] limits."

Three-sigma limits are not used because they correspond to some theoretical probability. They are used because while they are consistent with theory, they have also been thoroughly proven in practice to be sufficiently conservative. However, since it is hard to draw pictures to convey the weight of the empirical evidence, we shall have to resort to the use of theory to show just how conservative and effective three-sigma limits happen to be. To this end, Figure 11.2 shows six curves, each of which represents a theoretical probability model. These six curves were selected to represent a broad range of shapes. The three-sigma limits are shown in each case, and the proportion of the area that falls within the three-sigma limits is shown on each curve. There are four lessons to learn from Figure 11.2:

The first remarkable thing we can learn from Figure 11.2 is that in each case the three-sigma limits cover virtually all of the routine variation. This means that we do not have to have a "normally distributed" process in order for the limits to work. Three-sigma limits are completely general, and work with all types of process behaviors. When a process is predictable, no matter what the shape of the histogram, virtually all of the routine values will fall within the interval defined by the formula: Average ± 3 Sigma. This is why process behavior charts, with their three-sigma limits, will yield very few false alarms.

The second thing we can learn from Figure 11.2 is what it tells us about points that fall outside the three-sigma limits—they are much more likely to be due to a dominant assignable cause than to any common cause. So when a point falls outside the limits you will be justified in looking for an assignable cause.

The third thing we can learn from Figure 11.2 is what happens with very skewed distributions. The three lower curves have lower limits that look like they will be very ineffective. A process with such a skewed histogram would have to shift to the left by a huge amount before any values would fall below the lower limit. While this is a fair interpretation of the three bottom curves shown in Figure 11.2, the reality is somewhat different. In practice, skewed distributions occur when the data pile up against a boundary or barrier. This barrier would be on the left in Figure 11.2. Such a barrier precludes any substantial shift toward the lower limit, and effectively makes the lower limit irrelevant. The chart will be a one-sided chart, with the only real potential for change being a shift to the right. And it is the long right-hand tails that get covered by the three-sigma limits in these cases. So with skewed data the chart places the protection just where you need it. (Of course, three-sigma limits work equally well when the data are skewed to the left.)

The fourth thing we can learn from Figure 11.2 is that we do not need to be overly concerned about the exactness of our computations. We do not have to get the exact three-sigma limits—anywhere in the vicinity will suffice. In those extreme situations where the curves go all the way out to the three-sigma limits, they are very flat when they get there. If our calculations should err a little bit, and we end up with 2.5 sigma limits, or 3.5 sigma limits, we will still be filtering out virtually all of the noise, and anything we detect will be a potential signal.

Table 11.1: The Number of Yellow Beads in Each of 192 Drawings of 50 Beads Each

Counts																								Average	$\overline{mR}$
11	4	6	4	5	7	5	4	7	12	4	2	4	5	6	4	2	2	5	9	5	6	5	9	5.54	2.61
8	6	5	7	3	2	5	8	6	7	6	5	5	4	2	7	11	5	6	4	5	7	6	2	5.50	2.17
8	3	6	5	5	5	4	8	5	7	7	8	6	6	3	5	7	4	6	6	4	6	3	6	5.54	1.91
9	4	4	3	4	6	7	5	10	5	7	3	5	4	5	10	4	8	5	4	3	2	4	4	5.21	2.39
4	7	6	6	4	5	4	8	4	8	3	8	6	4	6	4	6	3	9	4	5	2	3	7	5.25	2.74
7	2	8	4	7	7	6	5	6	5	9	3	8	3	9	4	4	7	4	5	6	6	3	6	5.58	2.91
3	4	4	6	4	6	5	6	6	10	1	7	8	4	4	4	8	7.	5	4	3	8	6	4	5.29	2.22
4	6	4	10	5	5	1	6	7	6	8	9	6	5	7	3	4	6	9	2	8	7	6	4	5.75	2.70

Table 11.1 shows the 192 counts of yellow beads from Table 6.1 arranged into sets of 24 values, along with the average and the average moving range for each set. Figure 11.3 shows the eight corresponding X Charts. While the limits vary from one set to another, the message remains the same: This process is predictable.

Figure 11.3: Computed Three-Sigma Limits Filter Out Routine Variation

Three-sigma limits filter out virtually all of the probable noise. The objective is not to compute the limits with high precision, but rather to use the limits to characterize the process as being either predictable or unpredictable. In spite of the differences between the eight sets of limits in Figure 11.3, they all tell the same story.

Figure 11.4 shows 600 values obtained from a chemical process. After every 100 batches they would compute a new set of limits using the last 100 values. Thus, each of the six sets of limits shown were obtained from the data plotted against those limits. No matter which segment you choose to examine you will find points outside the limits. While the six different sets of limits vary, the interpretation of the chart remains the same: This process is being operated in an unpredictable manner.

Figure 11.4 illustrates a very important point. Even though the limits shown were computed using the data from the unpredictable process, in every case the limits were good enough to detect the unpredictable behavior of the underlying process. Correctly computed three-sigma limits allow you to detect signals of unpredictable behavior even when the limits

Figure 11.4: Computed Three-Sigma Limits Detect Potential Signals

are computed using the data from the unpredictable process.

When we compute three-sigma limits from our data we do not have to worry about whether or not we found the "right" value. Anywhere in the ballpark will suffice. The objective is not to find the right number, but rather to take the right action.

Three-sigma limits are not used because they correspond to some theoretical probability. They are used because they are consistent with theory and have been thoroughly proven in practice to be sufficiently conservative. They filter out the probable noise and reveal the potential signals. Three-sigma limits work. Accept no substitutes.

11.3 The Wrong Way to Compute Limits

Introductory classes in statistics commonly teach you to use a measure of dispersion known as the standard deviation statistic (which was introduced in Section 6.2):

$$ s = \sqrt{ \frac{1}{n-1} \sum_{i=1}^{n} (X_i - \bar{X})^2 } $$

If you survived your statistics class you probably know that this measure is rarely computed by hand since it can be easily obtained from spreadsheet programs and hand-held calculators at the push of a button. This statistic is frequently included in numerical summaries of collections of data, and is even provided automatically by many different software programs. So why did we not make use of this common measure of dispersion when we computed limits for the *XmR* Chart? Because the assumption behind the computation of a global standard deviation statistic is inconsistent with the question being asked by the *XmR* Chart.

The *XmR* Chart examines a collection of values to see if they might have come from one underlying and unchanging process, or if they show evidence of process changes.

The standard deviation statistic, *s*, is a global statistic, commonly computed using all the data. The assumption behind this computation is that the data can be logically considered to be one large homogeneous collection of values, all obtained from the same underlying and unchanging process.

Thus, while the *XmR* Chart *examines* the data for evidence of nonhomogeneity, the global standard deviation statistic, *s*, *assumes* the data to be completely homogeneous.

> **When the data are not homogeneous**
> **the global standard deviation statistic**
> **is not an appropriate summary statistic.**

The correct ways of computing limits for an *XmR* Chart, illustrated in Chapters Seven and Nine, did not make use of the global standard deviation statistic because of this limitation. To see the effect of using the global standard deviation statistic when the data are not homogeneous consider the data of Table 11.2, which have an average of 32.05, and a global standard deviation statistic of $s = 9.69$.

Table 11.2: Twenty Nonhomogeneous Values

25	26	23	24	46	43	41	44	25	23	22	26	43	44	42	45	25	24	24	26

Figure 11.5: 3 *s* Limits for the Twenty Nonhomogeneous Values

If we naively multiply the *s*-statistic by 3.0, and then add and subtract the result to the average we will end up with the "3*s* limits" of 2.98 to 61.12 shown in Figure 11.5. Using Detection Rules One, Two, and Three with Figure 11.5 we do not find any detectable signals of the nonhomogeneous nature of these data, even though the running record looks like a crankshaft.

Correctly computed limits will allow you to detect the nonhomogeneous behavior of the data in Table 11.2. You will get the chance to see this for yourself in Exercises 11.1 and 11.2.

11.4 But How Can We Get Good Limits From Bad Data?

In order for the process behavior chart approach to work it has to be able to *detect* the presence of assignable causes even though the limits may be computed from data which are *affected* by the assignable causes. In other words, we have to be able to get good limits from bad data. This requirement places some constraints on how we perform our computations.

In order to get good limits from bad data with an *XmR* Chart you will have to use the moving ranges to characterize the short-term, point-to-point variation. The formulas then use this short-term variation to place limits on the long-term variability. This is why limits for an *XmR* Chart *must* be computed using either the average moving range or the median moving range. You cannot use any other measure of dispersion to compute limits for an X Chart.

Specifically, you cannot use global measures of dispersion to compute limits. This precludes the use of the standard deviation statistic computed on a single pass through all of the data. Whenever the data are affected by assignable causes a global measure of dispersion will always be severely inflated, resulting in limits that will be too wide and a process behavior chart that will be misleading.

So do not attempt to use any do-it-yourself formulas. Use the formulas and the scaling factors shown in the next section, and if a stranger, or even a friend, offers you another way of computing limits, just say no!

11.5 So Which Way Should You Compute Limits?

When data occur one value at a time it will usually be logical to place them on an *XmR* Chart. The two-point moving range will be used to measure the routine variation, and this variation will be summarized using either the average moving range or a median moving range.

When using the average moving range the formulas for the central lines and limits of an *XmR* Chart are:

$$UNPL_X = \bar{X} + 2.660\ \overline{mR}$$
$$CL_X = \bar{X}$$
$$LNPL_X = \bar{X} - 2.660\ \overline{mR}$$
$$URL_R = 3.268\ \overline{mR}$$
$$CL_R = \overline{mR}$$

When using a median moving range the formulas for the central lines and limits of an *XmR* Chart are:

$$UNPL_X = \bar{X} + 3.145 \; \widetilde{mR}$$
$$CL_X = \bar{X}$$
$$LNPL_X = \bar{X} - 3.145 \; \widetilde{mR}$$
$$URL_R = 3.865 \; \widetilde{mR}$$
$$CL_R = \widetilde{mR}$$

The formulas shown here all use the average of the individual values as the central line. This was done in the interest of simplicity. As illustrated in the previous chapter, you may, at your discretion, use the median of the individual values as the central line for the X Chart.

While the limits above are sometimes referred to as the *control limits for X* and the *upper control limit for R*, in the interest of clarity I have chosen to call them Natural Process Limits and the Upper Range Limit.

Of course, because of the nature of the scaling factors, you cannot mix them. You have to use the scaling factors that are specific to your summary measure of dispersion. If you use an average moving range to compute limits, you have to use the factors 2.660 and 3.268. If you use a median moving range to compute limits, you have to use the factors 3.145 and 3.865. As was shown in the previous chapters, rounding these scaling factors off to 2.66, 3.27, 3.14, and 3.86 is acceptable.

But how can you choose between these two computational approaches? Both are right. In the end it comes down to a matter of judgment and personal choice. The objective of the computations is to obtain values that will bracket approximately 99 percent to 100 percent of the routine variation, and both approaches will do this.

The average moving range will generally be easier for people to use because they already know how to find an average. To use the median moving range you will have to know how to find a median. While this is not hard, it is new to many and therefore creates an extra barrier to the use of the charts.

The average moving range is more efficient in its use of the data than is the median moving range. However, in the presence of one or more very large ranges the average moving range is subject to being more severely inflated than the median moving range. When this happens the median moving range will frequently yield the more appropriate limits.

The limits based upon an average moving range will begin to "solidify" when 17 or more values are used in the computation. Limits based upon a median moving range will begin to "solidify" when 23 or more values are used in the computation. Fewer data may be used with either approach, but the limits will be progressively "softer" as the amount of data used decreases.

So you may choose to always use an average moving range, or you may choose to always use a median moving range, or you may choose to switch between them depending upon the characteristics of the data.

11.6 Where Do the Scaling Factors Come From?

In Figure 11.1 the first box says "calculate summary statistics from data," while the second box says "calculate limits." In practice this is just what we do: We leap from the summary statistics to the limits in a single step by the use of the scaling factors such as 2.66, etc. The reason for this is simple—process behavior charts were first used in a day when there were no hand-held calculators, no desk-top computers, and no spreadsheet programs. When people were doing the computations by hand all short-cuts were appreciated. And that is exactly what values like 2.66 are—computational short-cuts. These values accomplish two operations in one computation.

THE ORIGIN OF THE 2.660 SCALING FACTOR

The first operation is to convert the summary statistic for dispersion into a measure of dispersion that is appropriate for the data. That is, we need to convert, say, the average moving range into a measure of dispersion for the individual values. If we denote the individual values by the symbol, X, then we could denote this measure of dispersion for the X values as $Sigma(X)$. The formula for this conversion is:[*]

$$Sigma(X) \; = \; \frac{\overline{mR}}{d_2}$$

When working with moving ranges the effective subgroup size is $n = 2$. (This is because each moving range is a two-point moving range, based on pairs of successive values.) With an effective subgroup size of two, the value for d_2 is 1.128 (see Table 1 in the Appendix).

The second operation is to compute the three-sigma distance. Thus we get:

$$3 \; Sigma(X) \;\; = \;\; 3 \; \frac{\overline{mR}}{d_2} \;\; = \;\; \frac{3 \; \overline{mR}}{1.128} \;\; = \;\; 2.660 \; \overline{mR}$$

And so 2.660 is the scaling factor that converts the average moving range into an estimate of the distance between the central line and the limits on an X Chart.

THE ORIGIN OF THE 3.145 SCALING FACTOR FOR MEDIAN MOVING RANGES

An alternative formula for $Sigma(X)$ is:

$$Sigma(X) \; = \; \frac{\widetilde{mR}}{d_4}$$

With an effective subgroup size of $n = 2$, the value for d_4 is 0.954, giving:

---

[*] See footnote on Table One of the Appendix for a more complete explanation of *Sigma(X)*.

$$3 \ Sigma(X) \quad = \quad \frac{3 \ \widetilde{mR}}{0.954} \quad = \quad 3.145 \ \widetilde{mR}$$

And so 3.145 is the scaling factor that converts the median moving range into an estimate of the distance between the central line and the limits on an X Chart.

THE ORIGIN OF THE 3.268 SCALING FACTOR

In a similar manner, it was established long ago that:

$$Sigma(R) \quad = \quad \frac{d_3 \ \overline{mR}}{d_2} \quad or \quad \frac{d_3 \ \widetilde{mR}}{d_4}$$

With and effective subgroup size of $n = 2$ we find in Table 1 of the Appendix that $d_2 = 1.128$, $d_3 = 0.8525$, and $d_4 = 0.954$. So the three-sigma Upper Range Limit will be:

$$Average(R) + 3 \ Sigma(R) \quad = \quad \overline{mR} + 3 \ \frac{0.8525 \ \overline{mR}}{1.128} \quad = \quad (\ 1 \ + \ 2.268\ ) \ \overline{mR} \quad = \quad 3.268 \ \overline{mR}$$

And so 3.268 is the scaling factor that converts the average moving range into an estimate of the upper limit for the mR Chart.

THE ORIGIN OF THE 3.865 SCALING FACTOR FOR MEDIAN MOVING RANGES

When the median moving range is used to compute limits the estimate of the average for the distribution of the moving ranges becomes:

$$Average(R) \quad = \quad \frac{d_2 \ \widetilde{mR}}{d_4}$$

and so we get:

$$Average(R) + 3 \ Sigma(R) \quad = \quad \frac{d_2 \ \widetilde{mR}}{d_4} + 3 \ \frac{d_3 \ \widetilde{mR}}{d_4} \quad = \quad \frac{d_2 \ + \ 3 \ d_3}{d_4} \ \widetilde{mR} \quad = \quad 3.865 \ \widetilde{mR}$$

And so 3.865 is the scaling factor that converts the median moving range into an estimate of the upper limit for the mR Chart.

When you use these scaling factors you are computing the appropriate three-sigma limits. It is automatic. The scaling factors incorporate the multiplier of 3.0 along with the appropriate adjustment terms to convert the raw statistic into the desired limit. Each scaling factor is specific to a particular application and a particular choice for the dispersion statistic.

11.7 Chunky Data

Most problems with process behavior charts are fail-safe. That is, the charts will err in the direction of hiding a signal rather than causing a false alarm. Because of this feature, when you get a signal, you can trust the chart to be guiding you in the right direction.

There is only one exception to this fail-safe feature of the process behavior charts, and that is chunky data. Data are said to be chunky when the distance between the possible values becomes too large. Measuring a person's height to the nearest yard would result in chunky data—an increment of one yard is so large that it will obscure the variation from person to person. Excessive round-off is one way to create chunky data. Using measurement units that are too large is another way.

The effect of chunky data upon a process behavior chart will be illustrated by starting with a set of values that are fairly predictable, and then rounding these values off to make them chunky.

The *XmR* Chart for the values in Table 11.3 is given in Figure 11.6. (The values in Tables 11.3 and 11.4 should be read row by row.) None of the values in Figure 11.6 fall outside the limits.

Table 11.3: Fifty Values from a Fairly Predictable Process

214.0	214.3	213.7	213.4	213.5	213.8	214.3	214.3	214.5	214.6
213.9	213.4	214.7	214.8	214.9	214.3	214.1	213.7	213.8	214.0
214.2	214.2	214.5	213.5	213.6	213.6	214.4	214.3	213.6	213.7
214.2	214.7	213.7	214.2	213.8	214.3	213.7	214.5	213.7	213.8
214.1	214.2	214.7	214.0	214.0	214.2	213.7	213.4	214.0	213.2

Figure 11.6: *XmR* Chart for Fifty Values from a Fairly Predictable Process

Next the values from Table 11.3 were rounded off to the nearest whole number. These rounded values are shown in Table 11.4 and were used to create the *XmR* Chart in Figure 11.7. There we see ten individual values and one moving range outside their limits.

Table 11.4: Fifty Values from a Fairly Predictable Process Rounded to Whole Numbers

214	214	214	213	214	214	214	214	214	215
214	213	215	215	215	214	214	214	214	214
214	214	214	214	214	214	214	214	214	214
214	215	214	214	214	214	214	214	214	214
214	214	215	214	214	214	214	213	214	213

Figure 11.7: *XmR* **Chart for Fifty Rounded Values from a Fairly Predictable Process**

The only difference between these two charts is the size of the increments for the values. The points outside the limits in Figure 11.7 have nothing to do with the behavior of the underlying process. They are the result of chunky data.

> *Chunky data can result in points that fall outside the limits*
> *even when the underlying process is predictable.*

Fortunately, when this problem exists it is easy to identify. The way to identify chunky data begins with an inspection of the values to determine the size of the increment present. You want to determine just how close together two of the values could be—what is the measurement unit used. You may do this by examining the values or the moving ranges since they will both display the same sized increments. In Table 11.3 the values are recorded to one decimal place. In Table 11.4 the values are given to the nearest whole number.

Next you will need to determine how many possible range values there are between zero and the Upper Range Limit. Since the ranges will display the same sized increments as the individual values, you can begin with zero and count by increments until you get a value above the *URL*. If the number of possible range values (including zero) within the limits is three or less, then you have chunky data.

In Figure 11.6 the *mR* Chart has an *URL* of 1.31. With an increment of 0.1, there are a total of 14 possible values for the ranges below the limit. In Figure 11.7 the *URL* is 1.00. With an increment of 1.0, there are only two possible values (namely 0 and 1) within the limits of this *mR* Chart.

> *For the XmR Chart, your data can be said to be chunky if there are three or fewer possible values below the Upper Range Limit. When this happens the limits for the X Chart will be distorted. In order to be safe from the distorting effects and artificial signals created by chunky data, you need to have a minimum of four possible values below the Upper Range Limit.*

Thus Figure 11.6 is free of the effects of chunky data, while Figure 11.7 suffers the effects of chunky data. We therefore cannot safely interpret the signals on Figure 11.7 as being due to assignable causes in the process—the points outside the limits are a consequence of using chunky data to construct the chart.

Of course, when you have chunky data but do not find points outside the limits it is safe to say that the process is behaving predictably. Chunky data simply increases the likelihood of false alarms.

The procedure for checking for chunky data consists of three steps:

1. Determine the increment displayed by the individual values.
2. Determine the Upper Range Limit.
3. Determine the number of possible values for the ranges within the limits. If this number is below the threshold your data are chunky.

> *For Average and Range Charts (see Chapter Sixteen) with subgroups of size n > 2, the data will be said to be chunky when the Range Chart has four or fewer possible values within the limits.*

> *For Average and Range Charts with subgroups of size n = 2, the data will be said to be chunky when the Range Chart has three or fewer possible values below the Upper Range Limit.*

When you have chunky data the remedy is to use smaller increments in the values. If you cannot do this then you will not be able to compute appropriate limits for your process behavior chart—you are effectively limited to using a running record.[*]

By What Method?

What Do You Want to Accomplish?

How Will You Know?

---

[*] For a more complete explanation of this problem see *Understanding Statistical Process Control, Second Edition*, by Wheeler and Chambers, Section 9.1.

11.8 Exercises

EXERCISE 11.1:

Twenty nonhomogeneous values from Table 11.2 are reproduced below.

Create an *XmR* Chart for these data with limits based on the average moving range. How does this chart detect and indicate the nonhomogeneity of these data?

X	25	26	23	24	46	43	41	44	25	23	22	26	43	44	42	45	25	24	24	26
mR		1	3	1	22	3	2	3	19	2	1	4	17	1	2	3	20	1	0	2

EXERCISE 11.2:

Twenty nonhomogeneous values from Table 11.2 are reproduced below.

Create an *XmR* Chart for these data with limits based on the median moving range.

How does this chart detect and indicate the nonhomogeneity of these data?

Do we have chunky data here?

X	25	26	23	24	46	43	41	44	25	23	22	26	43	44	42	45	25	24	24	26
mR		1	3	1	22	3	2	3	19	2	1	4	17	1	2	3	20	1	0	2

EXERCISE 11.3:

Remember that the objective of a process behavior chart is to filter out the routine variation, so that we can spot any exceptional variation that is present.

a. Did the global standard deviation statistic used for Figure 11.5 differentiate between routine variation and exceptional variation?

b. Would you characterize the moving ranges as local or global measures of dispersion?

c. How do the moving ranges separate the routine variation from the exceptional variation?

d. Why does the median moving range do a better job of detecting the nonhomogeneity in the data set used in Exercise 11.1 and 11.2?

EXERCISE 11.4:

Figure 11.6 was characterized as a fairly predictable process.
What potential signal exists in Figure 11.6?
Is this a strong signal or a weak signal?

Chapter Twelve

Avoiding Man-Made Chaos

12.1 Creating Man-Made Chaos

Today in countless organizations around the world, individuals will be given pages of numbers and told to analyze the data and prepare a report. Perhaps you have been given this job. What did you do? What do you think most of these people will do? In our experience, most people simply look up what was done last time—and then repeat it. Only the details and the data are updated—the format for the report is the same from month to month, quarter to quarter, and year to year.

As an illustration, I will use the quarterly sales data for six regions. The report for the Fourth Quarter of Year Four might consist of a list of the sales figures, along with such interpretative guides as the percentage change from the previous quarter and the percentage change from the same quarter last year.

Table 12.1: Quarterly Sales Volumes for Fourth Quarter of Year Four

	Sales Volumes	Percent Change from Last Quarter		Percent Change from Same Quarter Last Year		Performance Index
Region F	670	21.6%	very good	65.4%	very good	+ + + +
Region D	802	14.4%	good	25.3%	very good	+ + +
Region E	462	27.3%	very good	8.5%	good	+ + +
Region C	1,196	–18.4%	very bad	5.6%	good	–
Region B	878	–11.9%	bad	–12.1%	bad	– –
Region A	952	–8.3%	bad	–26.5%	very bad	– – –

Once these values have been collected and the comparison percentages computed, the question is what to do next. Since the regions are different sizes it is inappropriate to rank them according to sales amounts. But the percentages might be compared.

We could rank these regions according to the percent changes from the previous quarter. This approach would yield the ranking E, F, D, A, B, C. The winner would be Region E, with its 27.3 percent gain, and the loser would be Region C with its 18.4 percent drop.

But we could also rank the regions using the percent changes from the same quarter last year, which would result in the ordering F, D, E, C, B, A. Clearly Region F with its 65.4 percent gain should be singled out for special praise, while Region A with its 26.5 percent drop should be closely examined.

But which ordering should they use? In order to solve the dilemma this company created a performance index. The performance index combined the two percentages for each region by characterizing each percentage as very good (++), good (+), bad (–), or very bad (– –), and then adding up the pluses and minuses and using the results to rank the regions. The ranking in Table 12.1 is based upon this performance index as shown in the last column.

Clearly Regions F, D and E won the esteem sweepstakes this quarter. For their "superior performance" these three regions were awarded plaques to place on their office walls. Regions A and B received reprimands. And the manager for Region C kept his head down and stayed quiet. Since this was the way it had always been, everyone accepted that this was the way it should be. You learned to "take your beatings like a man" or else you got out of sales.

Three months later this whole game was played out again. The story is summarized in Table 12.2. Obviously Regions A and B took their reprimands to heart! They moved from the cellar to the top of the list for the next quarter. While Regions A and B got commendations, Region E received the only reprimand handed out this quarter.

Table 12.2: Quarterly Sales Volumes for First Quarter of Year Five

	Sales	Percent Change from Last Quarter		Percent Change from Same Quarter Last Year		Performance Index
Region A	1041	9.3%	good	36.1%	very good	+ + +
Region B	939	6.9%	good	6.4%	good	+ +
Region C	1330	11.2%	very good	–1.6%	bad	+
Region D	749	–6.6%	bad	8.3%	good	0
Region F	588	–12.3%	very bad	26.2%	very good	0
Region E	420	–9.1%	bad	–5.7%	bad	– –

Region E took its reprimand to heart and, in the Second Quarter of Year Five, moved up in the rankings. Region F moved from next to bottom to the top of the list. Clearly this system of assigning blame works! But let off the pressure and things fall apart. Regions B and C slid from near the top of Table 12.2 down to the bottom of Table 12.3.

Table 12.3: Quarterly Sales Volumes for Second Quarter of Year Five

	Sales	Percent Change from Last Quarter		Percent Change from Same Quarter Last Year		Performance Index
Region F	699	18.9%	very good	30.4%	very good	+ + + +
Region D	762	1.7%	good	5.4%	good	+ +
Region E	454	8.1%	good	–0.2%	bad	0
Region A	1020	–2.0%	bad	1.2%	good	0
Region B	834	–11.2%	very bad	–2.0%	bad	– – –
Region C	1003	–24.6%	very bad	–25.9%	very bad	– – – –

For the Third Quarter of Year Five, Region C moved out of the reprimand zone, but Region B fell to the bottom. So while Region A was reprimanded, Region B was threatened. Meanwhile Regions F and D received commendations, and Regions E and C tried to avoid attention.

Table 12.4: Quarterly Sales Volumes for Third Quarter of Year Five

	Sales	Percent Change from Last Quarter		Percent Change from Same Quarter Last Year		Performance Index
Region F	743	6.2%	*good*	34.8%	*very good*	+ + +
Region D	807	5.9%	*good*	15.1%	*good*	+ +
Region E	447	–1.5%	*bad*	23.1%	*very good*	+
Region C	1197	19.4%	*very good*	–18.3%	*very bad*	0
Region A	976	–4.3%	*bad*	–5.9%	*bad*	– –
Region B	688	–17.5%	*very bad*	–31.0%	*very bad*	– – – –

The report for the last quarter of Year Five is shown in Table 12.5. Regions A and C received commendations, while Regions D and E were reprimanded. And so the cycle continues—"win some, lose some, and some get rained out."

Table 12.5: Quarterly Sales Volume for Fourth Quarter of Year Five

	Sales	Percent Change from Last Quarter		Percent Change from Same Quarter Last Year		Performance Index
Region A	1,148	17.6%	*very good*	20.6%	*very good*	+ + + +
Region C	1,337	11.7%	*good*	11.8%	*very good*	+ + +
Region B	806	17.2%	*very good*	–8.2%	*bad*	+
Region F	702	–5.5%	*bad*	4.7%	*good*	0
Region D	781	–3.2%	*bad*	–2.6%	*bad*	– –
Region E	359	–19.7%	*very bad*	–22.3%	*very bad*	– – – –

Consider the net effect of all of this "data analysis." Table 12.6 summarizes the actions taken. Over the course of these five quarters all six regions have received one or more commendation plaques to place on the office wall. Yet, in the same period of time, all the regions except Region F have managed to receive one or more reprimands!

Table 12.6: Summary of Management Actions Based On Sales Figures

Table	Quarter	Commended	Reprimanded
12.1	IV, Yr. 4	F, D, E	A, B
12.2	I, Yr. 5	A, B	E
12.3	II, Yr. 5	F, D	B, C
12.4	III, Yr. 5	F, D	A, B
12.5	IV, Yr. 5	A, C	D, E

This kind of management amounts to nothing more than the use of "carrots and sticks." Yet that is all that this type of "data analysis" will permit. When the analysis is flawed, the actions will, of necessity, also be flawed.

Notice what has happened here.

- Data were used to create a quarterly report.

- These quarterly reports were full of descriptive and comparative values.

- Not knowing what else to do, these values were used to generate a ranking.

- The ranking was used to define "winners" and "losers."

- The winners celebrated and the losers commiserated.

- After the hangovers disappeared, the whole cycle began again.

All of which results in ***man-made chaos***.

12.2 Description Is Not Analysis

The conflicting messages of the commendations and reprimands described in the previous section constitute man-made chaos. This chaos is the result of the faulty interpretation of numbers. It is based upon the idea that "two numbers which are not the same are different." This concept is simple, straightforward, and wrong. In fact, it is wrong on several levels.

First of all, there is the distinction between the measure itself and the thing measured. If we measured the same thing repeatedly, with sufficient precision, we would commonly obtain different values. Even in the realm of accounting this is true because every accounting value is dependent upon the assumptions or categorizations that were required for the computation. Change the assumptions and categorizations in rational and reasonable ways, and the figures will change. Thus, in practice, there is a certain amount of variation *in every measure*.

Next, there is the problem of measuring something at different points in time. Over time, not only may the assumptions and categorizations change, but the raw inputs will definitely change. The people doing the work may change. Even the rules of how to compute the measure may change. Thus, in practice, there is a certain amount of variation *over time* in every measure.

Finally, there is the problem of comparing measures of different things. When different regions are compared using common measures there is the problem of whether or not the measures were collected and computed the same way. If the assumptions and decisions necessary to collect the raw data and to compute the measures are not all exactly the same, then it is unrealistic to assume that the measures for the different regions are comparable. Even if the two regions performed exactly the same, they would not necessarily get the same values on a given measure. Thus, in practice, there is a certain amount of variation from *place to place* in every measure.

Given these multiple sources of variation in our measures, we should always make a distinction between the numbers themselves and the properties which the numbers represent. Of course, this is precisely what is not done when numbers are used to create rankings. The rank ordering of the values is transferred over to the items represented by those values, regardless of whether or not the items being ranked actually differ. No allowance is made for variation.

Yet we see rankings everywhere. For example, U.S. cities are scored on various extrinsic features and then these scores are ranked and the winners and losers are announced. Some cities are identified as "most livable," and others are listed as "least livable." Such rankings are usually the result of not knowing what else to do with the numbers. This syndrome may be characterized by, "What can we do with our numbers?—Well, we can place them in order. Maybe that will show us something."

Whenever actions are taken based upon the assumption that any numerical difference is a real difference, those actions will ultimately be arbitrary and capricious. This is an inevitable consequence of the fact that the above assumption ignores the effects of variation. Variation is random and miscellaneous, and it undermines all simple and naive attempts to interpret numbers. And yet our lives are governed by such interpretations of numbers. Any time the value of some measure changes, people are required to identify the source of that change, and then to take steps to keep it from happening again. We hear calls for accountability, the explanation of all "variances," and tighter control. The result is man-made chaos.

Descriptive summaries may be interesting, but they should never be mistaken for analysis. Analysis focuses on the question of why there are differences. Just because two numbers are different, however, does not mean that they represent things which are different. This discrepancy between the numbers and those things which the numbers represent is the essence of the uncertainty of interpreting data. Even when nothing else changes, the numbers will. This is why descriptive summaries, by themselves, are inadequate to provide the insight needed for a meaningful analysis. They may be used as part of an analysis, but you cannot interpret the descriptive summaries at face value.

Any effective analysis must separate that variation which is due to noise from that which may be attributed to signals. Routine variation due to common causes must be filtered out before we can identify any exceptional variation due to assignable causes which may be present.

In this language, the problem with the typical "analysis" shown in Tables 12.1 to 12.5 is a failure to make any allowance for noise. All differences are interpreted as signals, with the consequence that reprimands and commendations are handed out at random each quarter.

In the next section we will examine each region using *XmR* Charts.

12.3 Charts for Each Region

Region E

Region E Summary

then

then

now

Unacceptable!

Region E was ranked at the bottom of the list for the Fourth Quarter of Year Five, as shown in Table 12.5. Their sales had dropped 19.7% from the previous quarter and were down 22.3% from the same quarter last year. Needless to say, Region E received a reprimand for the Fourth Quarter of Year Five.

But this executive summary does not tell the full story, as we can see by placing the sales values for Region E on an X Chart.

Figure 12.1: *X* **Chart for Quarterly Sales for Region E**

First of all, there is no evidence that sales in Region E are growing, and there is no evidence that the sales are dropping. Even though the sales for the last quarter were down, this is within the bounds of what can be expected. Each of the previous three years has had comparable low quarters. Basically, the sales for Region E appear to be highly variable from quarter to quarter, and this variation dominates this time series. The limits in Figure 12.1 show that routine variation can amount to as much as 107 units on either side of the average of 420 (based upon a median moving range of 34).

So what about the 19.7% drop in sales from the previous quarter? What about the 22.3% drop in sales from the same quarter last year? What insights do these percentages provide? While it is never good to hear that sales have dropped, the question remains as to whether or not this drop represents a change to the system. Since the sales value of 359 is within the limits, it is within the realm of routine variation. While the sales were down, they are not low enough to indicate a change to the system.

What should we forecast for the First Quarter of Year Six? The central line value of 420 will be the best forecast. Unless the system changes, and it has not shown any evidence of change during the past five years, the best forecast for *each* quarter of Year Six will be 420.

Region D

Region D was ranked next to the bottom of the list in Table 12.5. Their sales had dropped 3.2% from the previous quarter and were down 2.6% from the same quarter last year. Because of these disappointing results, Region D received a reprimand for the Fourth Quarter of Year Five.

But this executive summary is wrong, as we can see when we place the sales values for Region D on an *X* Chart.

Figure 12.2: *X* **Chart for Quarterly Sales for Region D**

The *X* Chart for the sales for Region D shows a definite upward trend. While the horizontal limits of Figure 12.2 make the trend clear, they do not adequately characterize this process. Here is a case where we need *trended limits*. To fit such limits to these data we begin by finding a trend line.

To establish a trend line for Region D we divide the data into two halves and compute the averages: The first ten quarters have an average of 588.2, while the last ten quarters have an average of 725.2. The first of these half-averages is plotted at the mid-point of the first ten quarters—time period 5.5 (see the "plus mark" on Figure 12.3). The second of these half-averages is plotted at the mid-point of the last ten quarters—time period 15.5 (the second plus mark). Then these two points are connected to form a trend line, as shown in Figure 12.3.

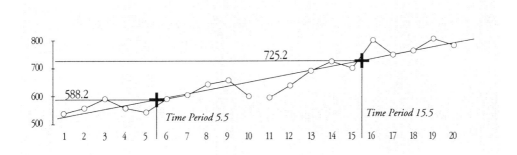

Figure 12.3: Trend Line for Quarterly Sales for Region D

From these two half-averages we can estimate the trend. The difference between the two half-averages, divided by the number of time periods between them, will be the estimated increment per time period:

$$\text{Trend per quarter} = \frac{725.2 - 588.2}{10 \text{ quarters}} = 13.7 \text{ units per quarter}$$

Since the limits in Figure 12.2 are 93.5 units on either side of the central line, we place trended limits 93.5 units on either side of the half-average points to get the chart shown in Figure 12.4.

Figure 12.4: Trended Limits for *X* Chart for Quarterly Sales for Region D

Recall that Region D received a reprimand for their performance during the Fourth Quarter of Year Five. And just what was the basis for this reprimand? Looking at Figure 12.4 you have to wonder. The sales in the Fourth Quarter of Year Five were right on the trend line, and sales throughout Year Five had been progressing according to the estimated trend.

The reason for the reprimand was a drop in the percent differences. These percent differences were low for the Fourth Quarter of Year Five because sales were up in both the Fourth Quarter of Year Four and the Third Quarter of Year Five. Thus, Region D earned their reprimand not because the last quarter was bad, but because they had had two good quarters in the past! So what insight is gained by comparing this quarter's sales with the sales in previous quarters? What do such descriptive percentages accomplish? They only serve to confuse the numerically illiterate.

The trend line value for the First Quarter of Year Six (time period 21) is computed to be the average value at time period 15.5 plus 5.5 periods at 13.7 units per period:

$$725.2 + (5.5 \times 13.7) = 800.6$$

This would be a reasonable forecast value for Region D. The trended limits place bounds on this forecast. Sales of 894 (800.6 + 93.5) or above in the First Quarter of Year Six would be exceptional. Sales of 707 (800.6 − 93.5) or below would also be exceptional. Sales levels in between would be unremarkable except to verify the continuation of the historical trend. Forecast values for the following quarters would increase by 13.7 units each quarter.

Region B

Region B Summary

then

now

then

Mixed Results

Region B was not singled out for attention in Table 12.5. While their sales had increased 17.2% from the previous quarter, earning them a "very good," their sales were down 8.2% from the same quarter last year, earning them a "bad." Because of this mixed performance, Region B did not receive either a reprimand nor a commendation for the Fourth Quarter of Year Five.

Figure 12.5: *X* Chart for Quarterly Sales for Region B

However, the *X* Chart shows that the quarterly sales for Region B are definitely declining, and have been doing so for the past five years. So while the executive summary did give Region B a break from the beatings, it did not reveal the nature of the problem with the sales in this region.

To fit a trend line we once again split the data into halves. The first ten quarters have an average of 1173.3, while the last ten quarters have an average of 878.5. This gives an estimated trend of:

$$\text{Trend per quarter} \ = \ \frac{878.5 - 1173.3}{10 \text{ quarters}} \ = \ -29.48 \text{ units per quarter}$$

The limits are 272.2 units on either side of the central line in Figure 12.5. Setting limits the same distance on either side of the half-averages yields the chart in Figure 12.6.

Visually, the graph in Figure 12.6 shows that we should forecast the sales for Region B to be about 700 units next quarter. The wide limits indicate that there is a lot of noise in these sales values. Sales could be as good as 972 units, or as low as 428 units, without indicating that the downward trend has changed. Of course, the main questions are: Why does this trend exist? and Can anything be done about it? If not, get ready to close Region B.

Figure 12.6: Trended Limits for *X* Chart for Quarterly Sales for Region B

In the past two examples we have not made any adjustment in the width of the limits when we placed them around a trend line. Shouldn't we make some adjustment for the trend? In most cases there will not be enough of a change to warrant the effort.

For example, we estimated that the sales for Region B were dropping by almost 30 units per quarter. This trend would affect the moving ranges in the following manner: Every time the sales go down from one quarter to the next this trend would increase the size of the moving range by 30 units; but every time the sales go up from one quarter to the next this trend would decrease the size of the moving range by 30 units. In this case, eleven moving ranges would be 30 units too large, and 8 moving ranges would be 30 units too small. If we adjusted each moving range by adding or subtracting the appropriate amount, and then recomputed the average moving range, the result would be 97.7 instead of 102.3. This adjustment would result in limits that are 5% narrower than those shown in Figure 12.6. While slightly narrower limits might increase the sensitivity of the chart in Figure 12.6, they will not remedy the situation, and if the trend is not changed, the width of the limits will be a moot point. The objective is insight, with an eye toward improvement, rather than calculating the "right" numbers.

Therefore, I recommend placing limits on either side of the trend line using the factors given in the previous chapters: 2.660 times the average moving range, or 3.145 times the median moving range. This will provide the needed insight without undue complexity.

Some readers may wonder why we are using such a simple approach to finding the trend line. "Wouldn't a regression line work better?" Regression is the accepted approach for fitting a line to the data in a scatterplot where one variable, *Y*, is thought to be dependent upon the other variable, *X*. But here there is no sense in which these trends in sales "depend" upon the time period. The relationships here are not cause-and-effect, but rather coincidental. When this is the case we can use the simple method of half-averages with confidence that we will obtain reasonable trend lines without undue complexity.

Region C

Region C Summary

now

then   then

Good Job!

Region C was ranked next-to-the-top in Table 12.5. Their sales had increased 11.7% from the previous quarter and were up 11.8% from the same quarter last year. As a result of this "superior performance" Region C received a commendation plaque for this quarter.

We shall begin by looking at the first four years of data for Region C. The X Chart shown in Figure 12.7 has limits based upon the median moving range of 84.

Figure 12.7: *X* **Chart for Quarterly Sales for Region C, Years One to Four**

Overall, Figure 12.7 suggests a trend. The first seven values are below the central line. Six of the last seven values are above the central line. And one point falls above the upper limit. Given these multiple indications we might decide to estimate a trend line for these data.

Using the first four years to determine the trend, the first eight quarters have an average of 1110.8, while the last eight quarters have an average of 1270.6. The mid-point of the first eight quarters is time period 4.5. The mid-point of the last eight quarters is time period 12.5. Plotting 1110.8 at time period 4.5, and plotting 1270.6 at time period 12.5 yields a trend line which has an estimated trend of:

$$\text{Trend per quarter} \ = \ \frac{1270.6 - 1110.8}{8 \text{ quarters}} \ = \ 19.98 \text{ units per quarter}$$

Placing the limits ± 264.2 on either side of this trend yields the trended chart in Figure 12.8.

So while the sales for Region C had been increasing about 20 units per quarter, that is no longer the case. We detect a change for the worse in the Second Quarter of Year Five. The change could have begun as early as the last quarter of Year Four. Furthermore, while sales have bounced back the last two quarters, they are still below the trend line. Horizontal limits will be more appropriate for the near future for Region C. So while Region C got a plaque for "superior performance," their sales have flattened out and show no sign of returning to the former trend. Once more, the executive summary got the story wrong.

Figure 12.8: Trended Limits for *X* Chart for Quarterly Sales for Region C

Using the last five quarters to determine an average value, and placing limits ± 264.2 units on either side of this average value, we get the chart in Figure 12.9. This chart suggests a forecast value of 1213 per quarter for Year Six.

Figure 12.9: Final *X* Chart for Quarterly Sales for Region C

When using a process behavior chart to make forecasts the limits from the chart will provide a worst case/best case forecast. Since approximately 85 percent of the observations from a predictable process will fall within the middle 50% of the limits, we could also make a most likely forecast:

Most Likely Forecast = Central Line ± 1.5 *Sigma(X)*.

For Region C, we could forecast that the most likely values for the First Quarter of Year Six would be 1213 ± 132, or approximately 1100 to 1350. The worst case/best case forecast would be 1213 ± 264, or approximately 950 to 1500.

Region A

Region A Summary

now

then

then

Excellent Work!

Region A was the top-ranked region in Table 12.5. Their sales had increased 17.6% from the previous quarter and were up 20.6% from the same quarter last year. As a result of this "superior performance" Region A received a commendation plaque for this quarter.

But once again, a longer-term perspective tells a different story. (The limits below were obtained using the median moving range.)

924 928 956 1222 748 962 983 1024 991 978 1040 1295 765 1008 1038 952 1041 1020 976 1148

1200 — 1194.9

1000 — 999.95

800 — 805.0

Figure 12.10: *X* **Chart for Quarterly Sales for Region A**

The *X* Chart for Region A shows several interesting things. While the overall level of sales for Region A has not changed during the past five years, the values outside the limits signal changes in the system that generated the sales. Back in Year One there was pressure to make the year look good. In response to this pressure, salesmen got their customers to buy ahead and stockpile the product. And it worked. Year one looked good. Unfortunately, the sales in the First Quarter of Year Two were so low that merely returning to normal looked like a dramatic improvement. At the end of Year Three this whole sorry episode was repeated, with the same result. Now, at the end of Year Five, this biannual disaster is happening once again. The only remarkable thing about the Fourth Quarter of Year Five is that they failed to go above the upper limit. You should not look for a strong First Quarter for Year Six. In fact, a reasonable forecast would probably be about 800. If history repeats itself, the remaining three quarters of Year Six should average about 1000. Each of these forecasts have a most likely range of ± 100 and a worst case range of ± 200.

So what is the value of the knowledge that the sales for Region A increased 17.6% from the previous quarter and 20.6% from the same quarter last year? Even though these numbers appear to be very good news, properly interpreted, they are harbingers of doom to come. Once more the local, limited comparisons mislead rather than inform.

Region F

Region F was ranked fourth in the list shown in Table 12.5. Their sales had dropped 5.5% from the previous quarter, but were up 4.7% from the same quarter last year. This mixed performance left Region F in the middle of the list, where it did not receive any special attention following the Fourth Quarter of Year Five.

Once again the X Chart tells a different story.

Figure 12.11: *X* Chart for Quarterly Sales for Region F

The limits in Figure 12.11 were based upon the median moving range value of 41. Clearly there is a trend in these data, so we should think about trended limits. But how shall we compute a trend line? If we use all five years and split the data into two groups of ten quarters each, like we have done with other regions, then we would get half-averages of 466.0 and 573.1, which would result in a trend of:

$$\text{Trend per quarter} = \frac{573.1 - 466.0}{10 \text{ quarters}} = 10.7 \text{ units per quarter}$$

However, the graph shows that Year Three was a complete disaster, and nowhere near this trend.

A second way of computing a trend line would be to use only the last three year's data. The first six quarters of this three-year period have a half-average of 436.8 while the last six quarters have a half-average of 658.8. These values result in a trend of:

$$\text{Trend per quarter} = \frac{658.8 - 436.8}{6 \text{ quarters}} = 37.0 \text{ units per quarter}$$

While such a trend would indeed be nice, it may be a bit optimistic to assume that this rate of growth will continue in the future.

A third way of computing a trend line for these data would be to use selected years as the basis for the trend. For example, we could use Year One and Year Five to construct a trend. The average for Year One is 442.8. This value would be plotted at the mid-point of year one (time period 2.5). The average for Year Five is 683.0. This value would be plotted at the mid-point of Year Five (time period 18.5). Since these two values are separated by 16 quarters, the trend would be:

$$\text{Trend per quarter} = \frac{683.0 - 442.8}{16\ \text{quarters}} = 15.0\ \text{units per quarter}$$

This third estimate of a trend line avoids the depressing effect of the drop from Year Two to Year Three. At the same time it avoids the excessive optimism of using only the last three years. Which is why it is used in Figure 12.12. If the sales in Region F do better than this, the chart will tell us and we can then revise our trend line. There is always an element of judgment required to use process behavior charts.

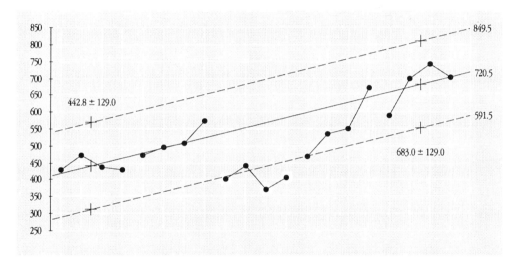

Figure 12.12: Trended Limits for *X* Chart for Quarterly Sales for Region F

Using the trend line in Figure 12.12, our forecast for the sales in Region F for the next quarter would be 720.5. The Most Likely Forecast is 655 to 785, and the Worst Case/Best Case Forecast is 590 to 850.

12.4 So What If We Combined All Six Regions?

Figure 12.10 shows the quarterly sales for Region A to be unpredictable during the past five years. Figure 12.5 shows the quarterly sales for Region B to be unpredictable during the past five years. Figure 12.7 shows the quarterly sales for Region C to be unpredictable during the past five years. Figure 12.2 shows the quarterly sales for Region D to be unpredictable during the past five years. And Figure 12.11 shows the quarterly sales for Region F to be un-predictable during the past five years.

So what should we expect when we place the total sales for each quarter on an *XmR*

Chart? This *X* Chart is shown in Figure 12.13, with limits based upon the average moving range of 221.7. No point is even close to falling outside the limits even though five of the six regions had one or more points outside the limits on their *X* Charts.

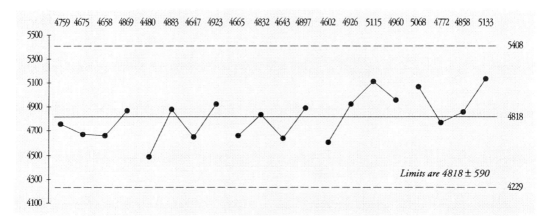

Figure 12.13: *X* Chart for Quarterly Sales for All Six Regions Combined

Time series which consist of the sum of many different components will tend to be more predictable than their components—the whole is more predictable than the parts. As the individual components of a time series are accumulated the noise also accumulates. With each additional component there is more room for the values to average out, leaving a time series that is globally predictable even though the individual components are unpredictable. That this happens should not be surprising. The signals present in the individual component series are added in with nonsignals before they are plotted on the aggregate chart. This dilution of the signals is the reason that Figure 12.13 does not have points outside the limits or long runs about the central line. The chart in Figure 12.13 correctly indicates that the aggregate sales are predictable, and the wide limits do indicate the amount of noise contained in these values. So if you encounter wide limits do not be dismayed. They simply mean that your data contain a lot of noise, which is to be expected with highly aggregated time series.

Figure 12.14: Trended Limits for *X* Chart for Quarterly Sales for All Six Regions Combined

With such highly aggregated time series the decision to use a trend line will be a matter of judgment. Figure 12.14 shows the results of fitting a trend to the data of Figure 12.13. The half-averages are 4739 and 4897, giving an estimated trend of approximately 16 units per quarter.

12.5 How Then Can We Compare Regions?

Once we have used the process behavior charts to make forecasts for the first quarter of Year Six we can use these forecasts to characterize what we expect from each region. Since these forecasts are based upon the actual performance in each region they form a much more appropriate basis for making comparisons than the traditional percent differences.

Table 12.7: Forecast Sales by Region for the First Quarter of Year Six

	Forecast	Most Likely Range	Worst Case/Best Case
Region A	805	707 to 903	610 to 1000
Region B	760	625 to 895	490 to 1030
Region C	1213	1081 to 1345	949 to 1477
Region D	809	762 to 856	715 to 903
Region E	420	366 to 474	313 to 527
Region F	720	655 to 785	591 to 849

Table 12.7 combines the simple forecasts with the most likely forecasts and the worst case/best case forecasts for each region. Recalling that a bar chart is the appropriate chart for making comparisons across categories, these forecasts are shown as bars in Figure 12.15. In constructing this graph a horizontal line was used to mark the simple forecasts, a white box to show the most likely range, and a shaded box with a dashed outline to show the worst case/best case forecasts.

Figure 12.15 summarizes Table 12.7 and makes it is easy to see which regions are similar and which ones are different. Specifically, Regions A, B, and D are all likely to have about the same amount of sales revenue in the next quarter. Region F should have close to the same amount of revenue as Regions A, B, and D. Region C still has the largest sales volume, while Region E has the smallest sales volume. And the sales volumes in Regions B and C show more variability than is seen in the other regions.

These forecasts are different from the usual blue sky numbers that are routinely used in many businesses. These values are not goals. They are not wishes and hopes. They are simple projections of what can be reasonably expected based upon the past performance of each region. Unless something unusual happens, these intervals are very likely to bracket the actual sales figures for the next quarter. The rationale for each of these forecasts is based on the interpretation of the process behavior chart for each region.

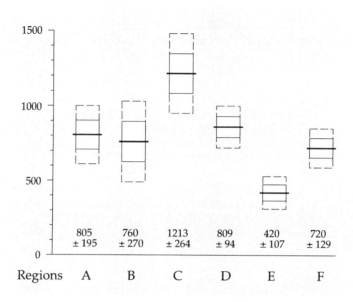

Figure 12.15: Forecast Sales for the First Quarter of Year Six

This approach of using a bar chart to compare the different regions will become less effective as the number of regions increases. When the number of categories exceeds 20 it will usually be more effective to identify the exceptional categories and treat the others as one large, reasonably homogeneous group. Of course the way to do this is to place some summary characteristic for each category on an *XmR* Chart, as was done in Figures 10.1 and 10.2 and in Exercise 7.3. Those categories with points outside the limits are exceptional, and are different from the rest. Those categories with points inside the limits are part of the large, reasonably homogeneous group.

12.6 Avoiding Man-Made Chaos

As seen above, description is not analysis. Description may allow you to make comparisons, some of which may even be meaningful, but it will not provide the needed insight into the system that produced the descriptive values. In fact, the usual descriptive measures tend to make the underlying system invisible. This is why description will not provide a basis for prediction. It only deals with what is past, without providing any clue to what may happen in the future.

Yet the essence of management is prediction, and while prediction requires knowledge, explanation does not. Description may be the basis of explanation, but analysis is required for knowledge. Which is why a new approach to presenting and interpreting data is needed. The old ways simply do not do the job.

The use of process behavior charts for presenting and interpreting data represents a new paradigm in data analysis. While the technique is simple, the revolution in thinking is profound. Therefore, you must begin by practicing the technique in order to learn the new way of thinking.

While it may be interesting to compare the sales volumes for different regions, such a comparison is mere description, not analysis. Differences between the values for the different regions may be informative, just as it is sometimes informative to compare apples and oranges, but the limitations of such comparisons must be respected. Because the regions are different it is unrealistic to expect the measures from different regions to be the same. The sales volumes for one region simply do not provide the proper context for interpreting the sales volumes for another region. When it comes to analysis, the only meaningful comparisons are comparisons of a measure with itself over time.

No data have any meaning
apart from their context.

In order to properly use any number, you must understand the limitations of that number. Among these limitations are:
- the qualifications which apply to the collection of the raw data,
- the inconsistencies that occur in the way the data are collected, and
- the assumptions made when the raw data are transformed into the number reported.

Without an appreciation of these limitations you are likely to think that numbers are more objective than they truly are.

This tendency to think that numbers have some magic objectivity begins with the subliminal suggestions of elementary school—the multiplication table is very straightforward. Therefore, anything which may be expressed with numbers must also be very straightforward. Unfortunately, this is not the case. Not only are there the issues of just how certain values should be classified (Does this belong in inventory or supplies?), but also the very quality of the numbers may be questionable. This is especially true when data are obtained from multiple sources.

When data have been collected for one purpose, it is very hard to use those data for a different purpose. Data that are routinely collected may be little more than someone's best guess, based upon a cursory examination of the present, a knowledge of the past, and skewed by unstated assumptions. In order to have good data for a given purpose you will usually have to collect the data for that specific purpose. And even then there will always be noise present in the values.

While all data contain noise,
some data contain signals.
Before you can detect a signal within any data set
you must first filter out the noise.

Process behavior charts provide us with a way to filter out the noise that is present in all data. They help us to separate the routine variation from the exceptional variation. Since our actions will be different for these two types of variation, this distinction is critical for every analysis.

> *You have to detect a difference*
> *before you can estimate that difference,*
> *and only then can you assess*
> *the practical importance of that difference.*

Regions are different. No data are needed to support this claim. It is self evident. Data may be used to describe the differences, but not all the differences in the numbers are due to differences between the regions. Since cross-region comparisons are essentially "apples to oranges," it is difficult to determine how to filter out the noise in such descriptive uses of data. However, when a measure is compared with itself over time, process behavior charts provide a way to separate the routine variation from the signals of exceptional variation.

The old approach to data analysis consisted of the accumulation of descriptive measures, the construction of descriptive graphs, and the ranking of regions based upon the descriptive numbers. The result was a pile of bar graphs and pie charts.

The conventional approach to improvement has been to tinker with your good processes and to replace or redesign your bad processes. In contrast to this, process behavior charts provide the insight you need to improve both good and bad processes. When a process is unpredictable it will be worthwhile to eliminate assignable causes of excessive variation. When a process is predictable any improvements will require fundamental changes in the process. While this is directly contrary to much conventional wisdom, it has been proven to work time and time again, in all types of endeavors, all over the world.

It is this paradigm shift provided by process behavior charts that is the foundation of Continual Improvement. When managers do not understand how to listen to the Voice of the Process, their efforts for improvement will be misdirected, resulting in increased costs, wasted effort, lower morale, and loss of business.

12.7 A Triumph of Computation Over Common Sense

A measure used by the Postal Service to create man-made chaos on a monthly basis is known as Delivery Collection Efficiency Achievement (*DCEA*). Those operating units that are fortunate enough to have a *DCEA* that is above average are commended, while those with a *DCEA* that is below average are reprimanded.

The *DCEA* value depends upon four other measures. For simplicity I will denote these four quantities by the symbols X, Y, Z, and H.

X = Total Cased Delivery Volume (in feet)

Y = Delivery Days (in period)

Z = Possible Deliveries

H = Hours (for the operating unit)

The formula for *DCEA* which is in my possession has one parenthesis missing. This missing parenthesis creates some ambiguity in the exact formula, but regardless of where the parenthesis is placed the *DCEA* values will suffer from the problems below. By placing the parenthesis in the most reasonable position and simplifying the expression, the equation for *DCEA* can be written as:

$$DCEA = 5.61439 \left[\frac{X}{YZ}\right]^{0.35922} \left[0.203466\ YZ + \frac{X}{H}\right]$$

If we interpret X to represent the production volume of the operating unit, and if we think of Y and Z as the area of opportunity within which this activity occurred, then perhaps it might make sense to divide X by the product of Y and Z. However, when this ratio is raised to the 0.35922 power all vestiges of rationality are lost. Raising the ratio to the 0.35922 power is approximately the same as finding the cube root of that ratio. If this ratio has units attached, then how are you going to interpret the cube root of those units? If this ratio is dimensionless, then why do you need to find the cube root? On this basis alone, raising this ratio to the 0.35922 power is either nonsense or unnecessary.

This then leaves the second term, which is the sum of two terms. The first of these is a fraction of our "area of opportunity," the product of Y and Z, while the second is a simple measure of productivity—volume over hours. The units for the first term will be [days times deliveries] while the units for the second term will be [feet per hour]. If we are going to combine the first term with this second term into a meaningful measure, *both terms must have the same units*. This difference in the units completely undermines any vestiges of rationality for these numbers.

Thus, the *DCEA* is nothing more than numerical jabberwocky—complex nonsense intended to impress the numerically illiterate. Such meaningless numbers may be computed, but they cannot be called *measures* since they do not, in any real sense, measure anything. If you cannot express in words what a computed value represents, then you have left the realm of common sense.

Making Sense of Data

12.8 Exercises

EXERCISE 12.1: The sales values for Region E for the first ten quarters were:

    397,   391,   414,   407,   415,   442,   384,   448,   441,   366

The sales values for Region E for the next ten quarters were:

    470,   426,   445,   455,   363,   462,   420,   454,   447,   359

(a) Plot the sales values on the X Chart.

Exercise 12.1 (continued)

   (b) Compute the half-averages and plot the trend line on the X Chart.

   (c) Compute the 19 moving ranges and find the average moving range.

   (d) Find the Upper Range Limit.

   (e) Multiply the average moving range by 2.66, and use this value with the half averages to obtain trended limits for the X Chart.

   (f) What single value would you use as a forecast for time period 21?

   (g) What range of possible values would you expect for time period 21?

EXERCISE 12.2:

The percentages of "high school seniors who smoke daily" are shown below for the years 1980 through 1993.

Year	80	81	82	83	84	85	86	87	88	89	90	91	92	93
Percentages	21.3	20.2	20.9	21.0	18.8	19.6	18.7	18.6	18.1	18.9	19.2	18.2	17.3	19.0
Moving Ranges		1.1	0.7	0.1	2.2	0.8	0.9	0.1	0.5	0.8	0.3	1.0	0.9	1.7

The article accompanying these data claimed that the jump from 17.3% to 19.0% was a signal that the "number of smoking 18 to 24-year-olds has leveled off, ending a downward trend that began in 1983." We will examine this last statement by computing a trend line for these data and placing limits on either side of the trend line.

(a) Plot the percentages and moving ranges on the following page.

(b) Compute the average percentage for the six years 1980, 1981, 1982, 1983, 1984, and 1985, and plot this half-average at the mid point of this six-year period (halfway between 82 and 83).

(c) Compute the average percentage for the six years 1987, 1988, 1989, 1990, 1991, and 1992, and plot this half-average at the mid point of this six-year period (halfway between 89 and 90).

(d) Draw a trend line connecting the half-averages.

(e) Use all thirteen values to compute the average moving range and then multiply by 3.268 to find the Upper Range Limit. Plot this limit and the central line on the mR Chart.

(f) To construct trended limits compute values that are ± 2.66 times the average moving range on either side of the half-averages, plot these points, and connect them to get Upper and Lower Trended Natural Process Limits.

(g) In order for the 1993 value to signal the end of a downward trend it would have to fall outside the trended limits. Does the value for 1993 fall outside the limits?

EXERCISE 12.3:

An HMO uses the following data to compare physicians. Each of the physicians below had between 20 and 40 cases during the past year which have been classified as belonging to Episode Treatment Group 265: Ischemic Heart Disease (except Congestive Heart Failure w/o Acute Myocardial Infarction). The values reported are the median costs for each physician. The values are ordered by physician ID number. The average of the 24 median costs is 893 and the average moving range is 337. Construct an X Chart that will allow a comparison between these 24 physicians.

Provider	104	140	147	376	378	411	564	643	664	668	698	703
Cost	938	677	953	1172	642	1346	577	1110	472	608	1220	1304

Provider	704	706	708	714	719	725	740	741	747	776	977	1021
Cost	1035	731	1268	1332	925	810	931	922	376	713	500	871

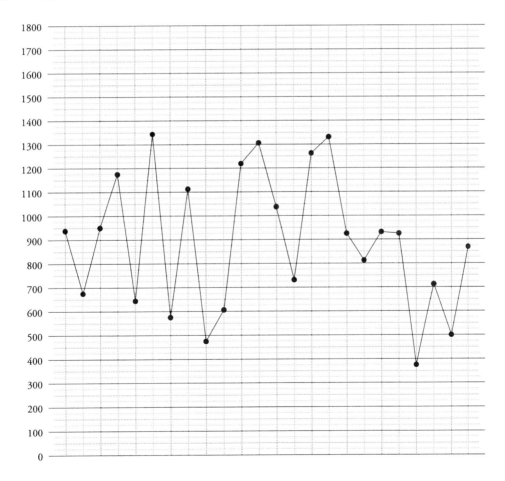

Can any providers be singled out as being different from the rest?

Making Sense of Data

EXERCISE 12.4:

As part of their job a group of men are required to maintain a certain skill level. To this end they are routinely given a skills test and scored on their performance. The following table gives the results for 46 of these individuals. The ordering is alphabetical by last name. Compute limits for the X Chart below to determine if anyone is performing at a different skill level than the rest of the group. The average score is 72.76, and the average moving range is 1.77

Person	A1	A2	C1	C2	C3	E1	E2	F1	F2	F3	H1	H2
Score	73.25	72.25	75.5	71.5	72.0	72.0	71.75	74.25	72.25	73.25	72.25	74.5
mR	—	1.0	3.25	4.0	0.5	0.0	0.25	2.5	2.0	1.0	1.0	2.25

Person	J1	J2	K1	L1	L2	L3	L4	L5	M1	M2	M3	N1
Score	73.0	71.75	70.5	71.5	71.5	71.5	73.75	71.75	73.5	73.5	73.5	75.75
mR	1.5	1.25	1.25	1.0	0.0	0.0	2.25	2.0	1.75	0.0	0.0	2.25

Person	N2	O1	O2	O3	P1	P2	P3	R1	R2	S1	S2	S3
Score	74.75	71.75	75.0	73.5	75.25	72.25	72.75	71.25	75.25	73.0	71.5	71.25
mR	1.0	3.0	3.25	1.5	1.75	3.0	0.5	1.5	4.0	2.25	1.5	0.25

Person	S4	T1	T2	W1	W2	W3	W4	W5	W6	Z1
Score	72.0	74.75	70.75	74.0	74.75	72.75	71.0	67.5	71.75	73.75
mR	0.75	2.75	4.0	3.25	0.75	2.0	1.75	3.5	4.25	2.0

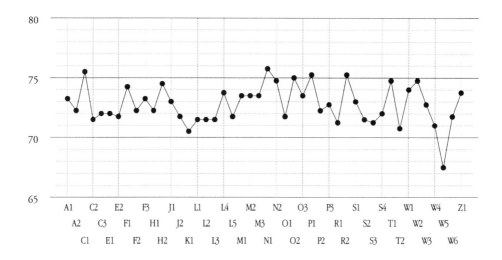

198

Chapter Thirteen

Charts for Count Data

13.1 Counts and Measurements

Traditional charting techniques make a distinction between data that are based upon measurements and data that are based upon counts. With measurement data you choose the number of decimal places recorded. With counts you will be using the counting numbers {0, 1, 2, 3, 4, ...} and so no decimal places are recorded. For the purpose of creating a process behavior chart the traditional distinction between counts and measurements is not necessary. Therefore, throughout this book the term "measures" is used as a generic reference to "some general characteristic of a process." A *measure* may consist of *counts* or it may consist of *measurements*.

Figure 13.1: Two Types of Measures

The main reason for making a distinction between measurements and counts is that counts are slippery. Anyone with fingers and toes knows how to count, and yet this apparent simplicity can get you into trouble. Obtaining the count is only half the job. In addition to the count, you also need to know the *area of opportunity* for that count. In fact, it is the area of opportunity that *defines how to interpret the count*.

What is the area of opportunity for a count? It is the region within which the counts occur. It has to do with what is being counted, how it is being counted, and what possible restrictions there might be upon the count. Until you know the area of opportunity for a count you do not know how to interpret that count.

But before we consider areas of opportunity for counts, it might be advisable to character-ize some measures that are being used today. The list on the next page consists of counts, measurements, and ratios of the two. This list is based upon a list appearing in Peter Scholtes' book, *The Leader's Handbook*.

TYPE OF MEASURE		MEASURE
count	•	Number of complaints (by type or category)
measurement	•	Sales volume in dollars
count	•	Number of employees leaving
measurement	•	Hours per quarter spent in training
count	•	Absences (by type, by area)
measurement	•	Overtime
count	•	Number of orders coming from a particular advertising medium
measurement	•	Cycle time (order to delivery)
count	•	Grievances (by type, by area)
measurement	•	Cycle time for special requests
count	•	Accidents (by type, by area)
measurement	•	Time between policy changes
count	•	Number of suggestions made
measurement	•	Dollar volume of transactions this week
count	•	Number of transactions per week
measurement	•	Time spent performing rework
count	•	Number of transactions requiring rework/special processing
measurement	•	Inventory levels (in dollars)
count	•	Errors in order fulfillment
measurement	•	Direct cost of errors in order fulfillment
count	•	Sales volume in units
measurement	•	Earnings (by type, location, and sector)
count	•	Payroll errors (by type, by area)
measurement	•	Cash flow
ratio of counts	•	Proportion of customers who are repeat customers
ratio of counts	•	Proportion of customers who were referred to you by other customers
ratio of counts	•	Proportion of browsers who purchase something
ratio of counts	•	Proportion of suggestions implemented
ratio of counts	•	Proportion of transactions completed on time
ratio of counts	•	Proportion of transactions requiring rework
ratio of measurements	•	Proportion of time spent in rework
ratio of measurements	•	Proportion of sales coming from a particular sector
ratio of measurements	•	Percent over budget or under budget
measurement	•	Forecast sales
measurement	•	Actual sales
measurement	•	Actual sales minus forecast sales
measurement	•	Expenses (by type)
measurement	•	Cycle time for filling job vacancies (by type, by area)
measurement	•	Accounts receivable
ratio of measurements	•	Accounts receivable as percentage of sales
count / measurement	•	Transactions per teller-hour

13.2 Areas of Opportunity

There are two different types of count data; counts of items having some attribute and counts of events. The difference between these two types of counts consists of differences in what is being counted and differences in the nature of the areas of opportunity.

Counts of Items

When you are characterizing each item in a set of **n** items according to whether or not that item possesses some attribute, and counting the number of items with that attribute, your measure will be a *count of items*.

Counts of items have a finite counting number, **n**, as their area of opportunity—the value you obtain may be any counting number from 0 to **n**. You may count those items having the attribute or you may count those items not having the attribute, but in the end, each item either does or does not count.

Examples of this type of counts are:

Number of orders generated by a particular advertisement
Number of employees retiring
Absences (by type, by area)
Number of transactions requiring rework/special processing
Number of orders filled incorrectly
Number of incorrect payroll checks

Notice that for each count listed above, you can count the items with the attribute listed, or you can count the items *not* having the attribute listed. In other words, you could insert the word "not" into each description above and still have a meaningful statement.

Counts of items are actually "counts of items having some attribute," and we can change the definition of the attribute at our discretion. This is not the case with counts of events.

Counts of Events

Since you cannot have half of an event, events are countable—you must use the counting numbers to keep track of events. However, unlike attributes where you can count the *presence* or *absence* of the attribute, you cannot count the *nonevents*.

Examples of counts of events are:

Number of complaints (by type)	Grievances (by type, by area)
Number of suggestions made	Accidents (by type, by area)
Number of transactions per week	Sales volume in units

The easiest way to tell the difference between counts of events and counts of items having some attribute is to ask yourself if it makes sense to insert a negation in the definition. We cannot count the number of noncomplaints, yet we can count the number of employees retiring or *not* retiring. We cannot count the number of nonaccidents, but we can count the number of orders correctly or incorrectly filled.

The area of opportunity for a *count of events* is the region within which the events occurred. This region might be a finite region of space and time, or a finite region of product, or a finite number of manhours worked.

When working with counts of events the definition of the area of opportunity can be vague. In fact, for a given count, it may be defined in different ways. The area of opportunity for the number of transactions might be the number of hours the business was open, or it might be the number of manhours worked. Either could serve as the area of opportunity for this count. The key to defining the area of opportunity for counting events is that it must be some finite region of space, or time, or production, or activity, which serves to define the region within which the events occur.

Counts of Items or Events

Some counts could be either a count of items or a count of events depending on how you define the count and the area of opportunity. Errors in order fulfillment could belong to either category. If you count all types of errors, so that a single order could have more than one error, then this might be considered a count of events. However, if you count the number of orders with errors, you have a count of items.

If you count the number of sales per week, you are counting events. If you count the number of visitors to the store who made a purchase, you are counting items.

Finally, we can occasionally treat counts of items as if they are counts of events. This happens when the counts are small relative to **n**, so that **n** does not actually place a practical upper bound on the values for the counts. An example of this might be the number of absences for a given company on a given day. The actual number of absences will (usually) be so much smaller than the possible number that it will not matter much whether we consider this count to be a count of items or a count of events.

When working with counts it is critical to know the size of the area of opportunity for each count. The distinction between counts of items and counts of events is important only to the extent that it will help you to carefully define your areas of opportunity.

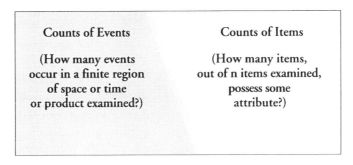

Counts of Events	Counts of Items
(How many events occur in a finite region of space or time or product examined?)	(How many items, out of n items examined, possess some attribute?)

Figure 13.2: Two Types of Counts

Now why does all this matter? Why should you be concerned about areas of opportunity and whether a count is a count of items or a count of events? This all becomes important when the area of opportunity varies from time-period to time-period. As long as the area of opportunity stays approximately the same from period to period, we can compare the counts directly. However, when the size of the area of opportunity for a count changes appreciably from period to period, we can no longer compare the counts—we have to compare the *rates*. And a rate is obtained by dividing a count by its area of opportunity.

For example, consider comparing the number of transactions on successive days of the week. The number of transactions per day might vary considerably while the number of transactions per visitor to the store might be comparable from day to day. In other words, the variation of the count might be due to the variation in the area of opportunity. This type of variation is not what we want to track, for if it was, we would be directly measuring the area of opportunity as a variable of interest.

So, in order to use count data effectively, you need to ask the following questions:
• What is being counted?
• What is the area of opportunity for these counts?
• Are the areas of opportunity approximately the same for successive counts?

Failure to consider these questions may result in useless data. Consider the problem of tracking complaints. How do you count complaints? Do you count the number of complaints you receive each month? Or do you count the number of customers who complained? What do you do when one customer complains six times—give him the phone number of your competition? Careful instruction, careful distinctions, and clear communication of those distinctions will be needed before you can begin to collect useful count data.

A pediatrics unit reported the number of "concerns per month." Their data are shown in Table 13.1.

Table 13.1: **Number of Concerns Each Month for a Pediatric Unit**

J	F	M	A	M	J	J	A	S	O	N	D	J	F	M	A	M	J	J	A	S
20	22	9	12	13	20	8	23	16	11	14	9	11	3	5	7	3	2	1	7	6

Questions about these data might be:
• What is a "concern?" How is it defined? Are these complaints? Or are these internally generated counts? Where is the border between a concern and a nonconcern?
• Why does the number of concerns drop? Did they get better? Or did half the physicians (those considered to be "troublemakers") leave the practice?
• The hospital administrator is using these numbers to challenge the orthopedics unit to improve—is that valid?

For our purposes, let us assume that "concerns" is just an antiseptic term for complaints. We could characterize the area of opportunity for the count of complaints in several ways. We could consider the area of opportunity to be the number of office visits. Or we could consider the area of opportunity to be the number of procedures performed, or the number of manhours worked by primary care-givers. Which should we use? You get to choose. Any will work, but you need to plan in advance, and this information needs to be reported along with the data.

Then there is the matter of what constitutes a complaint. Does a complaint about a chilly reception room count? What you count and how you count it are matters of choice, but they are choices you need to make before you begin to collect the data! Your choice of the area of opportunity will determine the ways that you can use the counts to understand your process.

I did not put the data of Table 13.1 on a graph because I do not know the context for these counts. Without context we are unable to make sense of our numbers no matter what type of graph we may choose to use. Without a knowledge of the areas of opportunity we do not even know if the counts can be directly compared.

13.3 Collecting Good Count Data

Do not despair. You can collect useful count data. But it is never quite as easy as it sounds. The essence of the problem of count data is two-fold: What should be included in your count? and What is the area of opportunity that you might use to adjust the counts to make them comparable?

You should begin with a written description of what is to be included in your count and the threshold for being included. Give examples. Be as specific as possible.

Next, you should consider what area of opportunity is appropriate for your count. This area of opportunity must bear some clear relationship to the count and must be something that can be measured or counted. The test here is rationality. There must be some logical connection between the size of the area of opportunity and the size of the count. For any one count there may be several different possible ways to characterize the area of opportunity, and for this reason alone, the choice must be made initially. Of course, as time grants you more insight, you may need to change the area of opportunity for a given count, but that is no excuse for overlooking this important step at the beginning.

If you do not choose an appropriate area of opportunity for your count, then you will almost certainly have people collect data in different, and inconsistent, ways.

- Do you count on-the-job accidents (a count of events) or the number of injured persons (a count of items)? Either would probably work, but these two counts are basically different in their structure.

- Say that you track the ways your customers heard about you. You might count the number of customers referred to you by other customers. What should be the area of opportunity? The total number of customers in your customer base, or the number of customers who made a purchase this month? Either would work, but one will be much easier to obtain. In fact, to get useful data you might have to shift from counting customers to counting transactions as an approximate area of opportunity.

- You might track the sales generated through your website. The number of website orders divided by the number of website visits would be a proportion based upon counts. But the proportion of your sales that came from these website orders would be a ratio of measurements.

There is no simple, cut-and-dried formula for obtaining good count data. The process is a mixture of planning and common sense, with some thought given to how to adjust for variable areas of opportunity.

If you do not know the area of opportunity for a count,
you do not know how to interpret that count.

13.4 Charts for Counts

When a sequence of counts,

$X_1, X_2, X_3, \ldots,$

has areas of opportunity denoted by

$a_1, a_2, a_3, \ldots,$

and when these areas of opportunity are all approximately the same size,

you may place the counts directly on an

XmR Chart.

When the areas of opportunity are approximately the same size the counts may be compared directly on an *XmR* Chart. The *X* portion of the chart will enable us to compare our counts regardless of whether we have counts of items or counts of events. At the same time the *mR* Chart will directly measure the dispersion present in the data and allow us to compute empirical limits that are appropriate for these counts.

As long as the average count is greater than 1.0 the *XmR* Chart will provide a satisfactory way of placing count data on a process behavior chart. When the average count falls to the region of 1.0 or below, the *XmR* Chart for counts will display the problem identified in Chapter Eleven as chunky data. This problem undermines your ability to use the moving range to compute the limits for the counts. When you have an average count of 1.0 or less you are working with rare events or rare attributes, and you may wish to consider the alternative ways of charting rare events and rare attributes shown in Section 14.7.

ORDERS WITH ERRORS

The supervisor of a telephone order service center audits 100 orders each day. Each order is characterized by whether or not it contains an error. The numbers of orders found to have one or more errors in the daily audits for 21 working days are shown on the *XmR* Chart in Figure 13.3. The average of these 21 counts is 19.2. The median moving range is 4.0.

Figure 13.3 shows one value above the Upper Natural Process Limit and a run of 11 successive values below the central line. These are both indications that this process is not predictable. Moreover, with an average of 19 out of 100, the error rate is far too high. Thus, the chart tells us that this process is unpredictable and unacceptable. The fact that it is unacceptable means that we should want to change this process. The fact that it is unpredictable means that there is hope that this error rate can be reduced.

Figure 13.3: *XmR* **Chart for Number of Orders with Errors**

The fact that each sample consisted of 100 orders is what made it possible to place the counts directly on the *XmR* Chart in this example. In general, whenever the areas of opportunity are approximately the same, you can make direct comparisons between the counts. Traditionally, areas of opportunity are considered to be approximately the same when the largest area is no greater than 1.5 times the smallest area.

Alternatively, if the ratio:

$$\frac{\text{Minimum Area of Opportunity}}{\text{Average Area of Opportunity}}$$

is 80 percent or greater, and the ratio:

$$\frac{\text{Maximum Area of Opportunity}}{\text{Average Area of Opportunity}}$$

is 120 percent or smaller, then the areas of opportunity are approximately the same.

13.5 Charts for Rates Based On Counts

When a sequence of counts,

$$X_1, X_2, X_3, \ldots,$$

has areas of opportunity denoted by

$$a_1, a_2, a_3, \ldots,$$

and when these areas of opportunity are different in size,

the rates $\dfrac{X_1}{a_1}, \dfrac{X_2}{a_2}, \dfrac{X_3}{a_3}, \ldots$ *will be directly comparable,*

and these rates may be placed on an XmR Chart.

Counts which have different sized areas of opportunity are not directly comparable. Therefore, when your counts have different sized areas of opportunity you have to convert the counts into rates before making comparisons. A count is converted into a rate by dividing the count by its own area of opportunity.

An example of rates on an *XmR* Chart was given in Figure 8.6. There, for any given year, the percentage of high school seniors who smoke daily is based upon the ratio of the number who smoke to the number questioned. The number questioned is the area of opportunity, and since this number varied from year to year, the counts were converted into proportions prior to making comparisons. When it does not make sense to compare the counts, we compare the rates instead.

Another example is given by the data obtained when a manager tracked the number of orders requiring premium freight. Each day she noted how many orders were made, **n**, and how many of these were shipped by premium freight, X. The proportions, *p*, are the number of expedited orders for a day divided by the total number of orders for that day. The data are shown in Table 13.2 and the *p* values are plotted on an *XmR* Chart in Figure 13.4. The average of the proportions is 0.245, and the average moving range is 0.033.

Figure 13.4 shows a predictable process in which about 25 percent of the transactions are expedited. On any given day it could go as high as 33 percent or dip as low as 16 percent without indicating any process change.

Table 13.2: The Proportion of Orders Shipped by Premium Freight

Date	X	n	p	mR	Date	X	n	p	mR	Date	X	n	p	mR	Date	X	n	p	mR
1	27	102	.265	—	8	28	99	.283	.037	15	19	101	.188	.036	22	21	94	.223	.020
2	31	146	.212	.053	9	37	143	.259	.024	16	33	140	.236	.048	23	32	139	.230	.007
3	70	280	.250	.038	10	47	235	.200	.059	17	68	292	.233	.003	24	65	229	.284	.054
4	54	207	.261	.011	11	46	185	.249	.049	18	44	207	.213	.020	25	46	170	.271	.013
5	69	322	.214	.047	12	70	271	.258	.009	19	74	257	.288	.075	26	75	290	.259	.012
6	101	410	.246	.032	13	105	469	.224	.034	20	124	511	.243	.045	27	117	407	.287	.028

Figure 13.4: *XmR* Chart for Proportion of Orders Shipped by Premium Freight

When we place counts or rates on an *XmR* Chart we still have to satisfy the requirements of rational subgrouping. This means that the counts or rates must come from a system or process where it makes sense to use the moving range to measure dispersion.

Moreover, when *rates* based on counts are placed on an *XmR* Chart, you will still need to have an average *count* that is greater than 1.0 in order for the moving ranges to yield appropriate limits. As noted earlier, the computations for the *XmR* Chart will break down when the average count falls below 1.0.

13.6 Some Cautions About Ratios Involving Counts

We work with the counts themselves whenever the areas of opportunity are approximately the same size because it is simpler to do so. When the areas of opportunity are appreciably different from period to period we convert the counts into rates. But ratios are more complex than simple measures and present their own difficulties.

When a ratio contains a count in the numerator that ratio will only be able to take on certain values:

$$\frac{0}{a}, \frac{1}{a}, \frac{2}{a}, \frac{3}{a}, \frac{4}{a}, \frac{5}{a}, \ \ldots$$

So while you may compute these ratios to any number of decimal places, they are not really numbers from a continuum. Instead they possess a certain discreteness which is obscured by the computation of the ratio.

When a ratio contains counts in *both* the numerator and the denominator, the distance between the discrete values for the ratio will be determined by the count in the denominator.

$$\frac{0}{n}, \frac{1}{n}, \frac{2}{n}, \frac{3}{n}, \frac{4}{n}, \frac{5}{n}, \dots$$

Say for example, you are counting the success rates for a particular procedure at four local hospitals. You could count the number of times in the past year each hospital has performed the procedure, and you could count the number of successful procedures (if you are careful to define what constitutes a success). Then you divide the latter number by the former to obtain the success rate for each hospital. The four hospitals have success rates of 100%, 86%, 80%, and 60%. So who is best?

> Hospital One (100%) performed this procedure 1 time during the past year.
> Hospital Two (86%) performed this procedure 7 times during the past year.
> Hospital Three (80%) performed this procedure 50 times during the past year.
> Hospital Four (60%) performed this procedure 5 times during the past year.

If you had to undergo this procedure, where would you want to go?

When we express a ratio as a percentage it is natural to think "by the hundred." In fact that is exactly what *per centum* means in Latin. So when you report a percentage you are essentially reporting a rate in "parts per hundred." While this makes sense when your denominator is a count that is at least 40 or greater, it can be misleading when the area of opportunity is a small count.

To understand this, consider what would happen to the percentages above if each hospital had one fewer successful procedures during the past year. Hospital One would go from 100% to 0%. This is the minimum change for Hospital One. Clearly, we do not know the success "percentage" for Hospital One to the parts-per-hundred level. Hospital Two would go from 86% to 71%, a 15% change. So while the percentages lull you into thinking in terms of parts per hundred, your minimum change here is 15%. Hospital Three would go from 80% to 78%, while Hospital Four would go from 60% to 40%. Thus, it is only with Hospital Three that we know the success rate to a level of precision that approaches the parts-per-hundred level.

Expressing numbers in percentages, or ratios, implies to your reader that a certain amount of continuity exists. When the ratio involves small counts this implied property is absent.

When you have to work with ratios where the denominators are small counts you should report *both* the numerator and denominator values along with each ratio (similar to what was done in Table 13.2). When the data are displayed directly on the chart these values should also be on the chart. This is the only approach that has any integrity. Failure to do this invites your readers to over-interpret the ratios.

So there are two problems with ratios involving counts.

- *Counts in the numerator create a discreteness for the possible values.*
- *Counts in the denominator limit how close together these possible values can be.*

When all of the counts in the denominator are sufficiently large (say 40 or more), the possible values will be fairly close together, and the discreteness of the ratios can be ignored in practice. But when some of the counts in the denominator are small (say 20 or less), the ratios (commonly computed to at least two decimal places) will be much more discrete than they look. I shall refer to this problem of small counts in the denominator as *chunky ratios*.

Count data with unequal areas of opportunity will result in chunky ratios when all three of the following conditions exist:

- The counts are counts of items.
- The areas of opportunity, n_i, vary by more than $\pm 20\%$ from the average, $\bar{n}$.
- Some of the areas of opportunity, n_i, are counts that are smaller than 20.

When you attempt to place chunky ratios on a process behavior chart you will have wide limits. This is simply a manifestation of the fact that chunky ratios contain little information. The small areas of opportunity which create the chunky ratios will also result in process behavior charts that are very insensitive. This insensitivity will make you want to avoid working with chunky ratios if at all possible.

13.7 Summary

When working with count data you will need to know the areas of opportunity for the counts in order to make sense of the data. For completeness these areas of opportunity must be reported along with the counts.

When the areas of opportunity are approximately the same size from period to period you may place the counts directly on an *XmR* Chart.

When the areas of opportunity vary more than $\pm 20\%$ from the average size of the areas of opportunity you should convert the counts into rates before plotting them on a process behavior chart. This is done by dividing each count by its own area of opportunity. These rates may then be placed on an *XmR* Chart.

The one real restriction on the use of the *XmR* Chart with data based on counts is the restriction of chunky data. This problem is seen with data based on counts whenever the average count falls to 1.0 or below. But then, when the average count falls below 1.0 you have rare events or rare attributes, and it will generally be more satisfactory to measure the area of opportunity between rare events than to try to count the rare events themselves. More will be said about this in the next chapter.

13.8 Exercises

EXERCISE 13.1:

The following table lists 24 providers who had between 20 and 40 cases in Episode Treatment Group 265 during the past year. When the costs for each case were placed on an *XmR* Chart a total of 95 out of 685 cases had excessive costs. In the following table the number of cases treated and the number of cases with excessive costs are listed for each provider. Use these data to create an appropriate *X* Chart that will compare these 24 providers to see if any providers have more, or less than their share of excessive costs.

(When making cross-sectional comparisons using an arbitrary ordering we will use the moving ranges to compute the limits, but since the *mR* Chart itself has no real interpretability in this situation it is best not to show it.)

Provider	104	140	147	376	378	411	564	643	664	668	698	703
No. Cases	30	40	37	34	20	30	40	21	21	24	30	29
No. Excessive	8	7	5	7	2	5	4	3	5	3	2	8
Proportion	0.27	0.18	0.14	0.21	0.10	0.17	0.10	0.14	0.24	0.13	0.07	0.28

Provider	704	706	708	714	719	725	740	741	747	776	977	1021
No. Cases	22	29	37	22	23	32	34	24	20	29	20	37
No. Excessive	4	4	4	4	2	5	3	1	1	3	1	4
Proportion	0.18	0.14	0.11	0.18	0.09	0.16	0.09	0.04	0.05	0.10	0.05	0.11

EXERCISE 13.2:

Verify the limits shown in Figure 13.3 using the values shown for the average and the median moving range.

EXERCISE 13.3:

Verify the limits shown in Figure 13.4 using the values shown for the average and the average moving range.

Chapter Fourteen

Traditional Charts for Count Data

Count data have traditionally been placed on special process behavior charts. This chapter will explain these special charts and outline when they may be used. Since all of the charts in this chapter may be considered to be special cases of the X Chart, and since the *XmR* Chart provides a universal way of placing count data on a process behavior chart, it is not necessary for the beginner to work through this chapter. While this chapter is included here for completeness, in practice it may be skipped over. If you already know about the charts described in this chapter, you may find the comparisons between the *XmR* Chart and the traditional charts of interest.

14.1 Charts for Binomial Counts: the *np*-Chart

The *np*-chart is a chart for individual counts where those individual counts satisfy two special conditions:

Binomial Condition 1: The count is a count of items. That is, each count is the count of the number of items, out of **n** items, that possess some attribute.

Binomial Condition 2: Let **p** denote the probability that a single item possesses the attribute. *The value of* **p** *must remain constant* for each of the **n** items in a single sample. (Among other things, this means that the items possessing the attribute do not cluster or clump together. Also, whether or not one item possesses the attribute will not affect the likelihood that the next item will possess the attribute.)

When these two conditions are met, the counts can be said to be characterized by the binomial probability model, and this model may be used to compute the limits for the counts according to special formulas. However, if the second condition does not hold, then the use of the binomial probability model will be incorrect.

Counts which satisfy the two conditions above, and which have areas of opportunity that are approximately constant, can be placed on an *np*-chart.

- The plot for the *np*-chart will be the running record of counts.

- The central line for the *np*-chart will be the average count, which can be denoted as either:

$$CL_{np} = \bar{X} \quad \text{or} \quad \mathbf{n}\bar{p}$$

where the average proportion of items with the attribute is defined by:

$$\bar{p} = \frac{\text{total number of items in baseline samples with attribute}}{\text{total number of items examined in baseline samples}}$$

- Since the binomial model establishes a relationship between location and dispersion we do not compute moving ranges, or any other measure of dispersion for an *np*-chart. Instead we use $\bar{p}$ to compute our three-sigma distance according to the formula:

$$\text{Estimated three-sigma distance for binomial counts} = 3\sqrt{\mathbf{n}\bar{p}(1-\bar{p})}$$

- So our Upper Limit for the *np*-chart will be:

$$UL_{np} = \mathbf{n}\bar{p} + 3\sqrt{\mathbf{n}\bar{p}(1-\bar{p})}$$

- And our Lower Limit for the *np*-chart will be:

$$LL_{np} = \mathbf{n}\bar{p} - 3\sqrt{\mathbf{n}\bar{p}(1-\bar{p})}$$

- The upper limit will be meaningful only when it is less than the area of opportunity, **n**. If the computed upper limit exceeds **n**, then there is no upper limit. Likewise, when the computed lower limit is less than 0 there will be no lower limit.

Table 14.1: Number of Orders with Errors Out of 100 Orders Audited

X	27	19	18	16	16	12	15	13	16	16	9	17	21	15	39	21	14	23	19	29	30

The supervisor of a telephone order service center audits 100 orders each day. Each order is characterized by whether or not it contains an error. The numbers of orders found to have one or more errors in the daily audits for 21 working days are shown in Table 14.1. These counts were also shown on the *XmR* Chart in Figure 13.3.

Do the data of Table 14.1 satisfy the binomial conditions? They are counts of items (orders with errors), and if it makes sense to assume that each of the 100 orders has the same chance of containing an error, then we might put these counts on an *np*-chart. If different operators have different skill levels however, then the assumption of a constant value for **p** throughout any one day's audit is incorrect and the use of an *np*-chart is inappropriate.

Assuming that an *np*-chart is appropriate, we proceed as follows. The total number of errors found in these 21 samples was 404. The total number of orders examined was 21 times 100 = 2100. Thus,

$$\bar{p} = \frac{404}{2100} = 0.1924$$

so that the central line will be:

$$CL_{np} = \mathbf{n}\bar{p} = (100)(0.1924) = 19.24$$

and the estimated three-sigma distance will be:

$$3\sqrt{\mathbf{n}\bar{p}(1-\bar{p})} = 3\sqrt{19.24(0.8076)} = 11.8$$

so that the limits will be:

$$UL_{np} = \mathbf{n}\bar{p} + 3\sqrt{\mathbf{n}\bar{p}(1-\bar{p})} = 19.2 + 11.8 = 31.0$$

$$LL_{np} = \mathbf{n}\bar{p} - 3\sqrt{\mathbf{n}\bar{p}(1-\bar{p})} = 19.2 - 11.8 = 7.4$$

Figure 14.1: *np*-Chart for Number of Orders with Errors

If you compare the *np*-chart in Figure 14.1 with the X Chart in Figure 13.3 you will see that there is no practical difference. Even though the limits are slightly different (31.8 and 6.6 instead of 31.0 and 7.4) the two charts tell the same story.

Note also that the *np*-chart is a chart for individual values. The points plotted are the individual counts for each sample. This is why there is such a strong degree of similarity between the *np*-chart and the X Chart. They both use the same plot, and they both have the same central line. They only differ in the way they compute the three-sigma distance.

14.2 Charts for Binomial Proportions: the *p*-Chart

The *p*-chart is appropriate when you have *rates* based on counts which satisfy the two binomial conditions in the preceding section. The *p*-chart is a chart for binomial proportions.

If a set of counts satisfies the two binomial conditions given in the preceding section, and if the smallest of their areas of opportunity is greater than 80% of the average size of their areas of opportunity and the largest of their areas of opportunity is less than 120% of the average size of their areas of opportunity, then it is acceptable to consider the *counts* to be roughly comparable. Such counts may be charted directly using either an *XmR* Chart or an *np*-chart, or they may be converted into *rates* and placed on a *p*-chart.

If a set of counts satisfy the two binomial conditions given in the preceding section, and if their areas of opportunity vary by *more* than ± 20 percent from the average size of the areas, then we need to convert the counts into rates prior to placing them on any chart. As noted earlier, counts are converted into rates by dividing each count by its own area of opportunity.

When working with counts that satisfy the two binomial conditions we will denote the area of opportunity for the ith count X_i by the symbol:

$$\mathbf{n}_i$$

The ratio of the ith count X_i to its area of opportunity $\mathbf{n}_i$ will be a *proportion*, and will be denoted by:

$$p_i = \frac{X_i}{\mathbf{n}_i}$$

- The *p*-chart will be based upon a plot of the p_i values. The central line will be defined by the average proportion of items having the attribute, $\bar{p}$.

$$\bar{p} = \frac{\text{total number of items in baseline samples with attribute}}{\text{total number of items examined in baseline samples}}$$

- For the ith sample the three-sigma distance will be estimated by:

$$\text{Estimated three-sigma distance for binomial proportions} = 3\sqrt{\frac{\bar{p}\,(1-\bar{p})}{\mathbf{n}_i}}$$

- So the limits for a *p*-chart will be computed to be:

$$\bar{p} \pm 3\sqrt{\frac{\bar{p}\,(1-\bar{p})}{\mathbf{n}_i}}$$

- If the computed value for the upper limit exceeds 1.0, then there is no upper limit. If the computed value for the lower limit falls below 0.0, then there is no lower limit. It should also be noted that these formulas apply to *proportions*. They are not appropriate when the *proportions* have been converted into *percentages*.

Table 14.2: The Proportion of Orders Shipped by Premium Freight

Date	X	n	p	Date	X	n	p	Date	X	n	p	Date	X	n	p
1	27	102	.265	8	28	99	.283	15	19	101	.188	22	21	94	.223
2	31	146	.212	9	37	143	.259	16	33	140	.236	23	32	139	.230
3	70	280	.250	10	47	235	.200	17	68	292	.233	24	65	229	.284
4	54	207	.261	11	46	185	.249	18	44	207	.213	25	46	170	.271
5	69	322	.214	12	70	271	.258	19	74	257	.288	26	75	290	.259
6	101	410	.246	13	105	469	.224	20	124	511	.243	27	117	407	.287

The data of Table 13.2 are repeated in Table 14.2. The counts satisfy the two binomial conditions and the areas of opportunity vary considerably, so the proportions, p, will be placed on a p-chart. The total number of orders shipped by premium freight during this period was 1403. The total number of orders was 5706. Thus, the average proportion of orders shipped by premium freight is:

$$\bar{p} = \frac{1403}{5706} = 0.246$$

The estimated three-sigma distance for a p-chart depends upon the value of **n**. This means that the limits for the p-chart for Table 14.2 have to be computed for each point—a total of 24 times in all. The result is shown in Figure 14.2.

Figure 14.2: *p*-Chart for Proportion of Orders Shipped by Premium Freight

Just as in Figure 13.4, these data reveal a predictable process. Unlike Figure 13.4, this chart was a lot of work to create. With a *p*-chart you effectively have to compute your limits every time you plot a point. Because of this complexity, people have been using simplified versions of the *p*-chart for years.

One traditional modification consists of using an average value of **n** in the computations. For the data of Table 14.2, this average value of **n** is 238. Using this value for **n** yields limits of 0.330 and 0.162. These are the narrower of the two sets of limits shown in Figure 14.3. The wider set of limits are those from the *X* Chart in Figure 13.4. (The offset in the two central lines occurs because the *X* Chart uses a simple average of the proportions while the *p*-chart uses a weighted average.)

Figure 14.3: Limits for *X* Chart and Limits for *p*-Chart Based on Average Value for n

The *p*-chart is a chart for individual values. This is why it tells essentially the same story as the *X* Chart. So what is the difference between the *XmR* Chart and either the *np*-chart or the *p*-chart? The main difference is in the way these charts estimate the three-sigma distance.

The *XmR* Chart measures the variation present in the data empirically (using the moving ranges). Thus the *XmR* Chart uses *empirical* limits.

Both the *np*-chart and the *p*-chart assume that a binomial probability model is appropriate for the count data. Since the binomial model requires the *variation* to be a function of the *location* (as well as the area of opportunity), the *p*- and *np*-charts compute a theoretical value for the three-sigma distance (based on the central line) and use *theoretical* limits.

If the theory is right, then the theoretical limits will be right, and the empirical limits will mimic the theoretical limits. But if the theory is wrong, then the theoretical limits will be wrong, yet the empirical limits will still be correct. Think it over....

14.3 Charts for Poisson Counts: the *c*-Chart

The *c*-chart is a chart for individual counts which satisfy two special conditions:

Poisson Condition 1: The count is a count of events.

Poisson Condition 2: The events occur independently of each other, and the likelihood of an event is *proportional* to the size of the area of opportunity. (This means that the likelihood of an event is not affected by *which* portion of the continuum of space or time or product is selected as the area of opportunity—there is a uniform likelihood of an event throughout each sample.)

There are many counts that satisfy the first of these conditions but fail to satisfy the second condition. Such data cannot be said to follow the Poisson probability model.

Counts which satisfy the two conditions above, and which have areas of opportunity that are approximately constant, can be placed on an *c*-chart.

- The plot for the *c*-chart will be the time-series of count values.

- The central line for the *c*-chart will be the average count, which can be denoted as either:

$$\bar{X} \quad \text{or} \quad \bar{c}$$

where the average count of events is defined by:

$$\bar{c} = \frac{\text{total number of events observed in baseline samples}}{\text{total number of baseline samples}}$$

- Since the Poisson model establishes a relationship between location and dispersion we do not compute moving ranges for a *c*-chart. Instead we use $\bar{c}$ to compute our three-sigma distance according to the formula:

$$\text{Estimated Three-Sigma Distance for Poisson Counts} = 3\sqrt{\bar{c}}$$

- So the limits for the *c*-chart will be:

$$\bar{c} \pm 3\sqrt{\bar{c}}$$

- When the value computed for the lower limit is negative there will be no lower limit.

The Poisson probability model has been the standard model for accident data since Ladislaus von Bortkiewicz demonstrated its effectiveness in characterizing the number of Prussian officers killed by horse kicks between 1875 and 1894!

The data in Figure 14.4 are the number of lost-time accidents for one plant. There were 49 accidents in the past 31 months, giving an average count of 1.58 accidents per month. Since the areas of opportunity for these counts (the number of man-hours worked each month) are approximately the same we can consider these counts to be comparable and place them on a c-chart. With an average count of 1.58 accidents per month, the upper limit will be:

$$UL_c = 1.58 + 3\sqrt{1.58} = 5.35$$

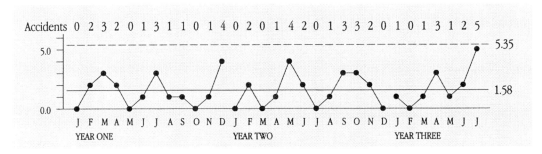

Figure 14.4: *c*-**Chart for Lost Time Accidents**

14.4 Charts for Poisson Rates: the *u*-Chart

The *u*-chart is appropriate when you have *rates* based on counts which satisfy the two Poisson conditions in the preceding section. The *u*-chart is a chart for individual rates.

If a set of counts satisfy the two Poisson conditions given in the preceding section, and if their areas of opportunity vary by *less* than ± 20 percent, then it is acceptable to consider the counts to be roughly comparable. Such counts may be charted directly using either an *XmR* Chart or a c-chart.

If a set of counts satisfy the two Poisson conditions given in the preceding section, and if their areas of opportunity vary by *more* than ± 20 percent, then we shall convert the counts into rates prior to placing them on a chart. As noted earlier, counts are converted into rates by dividing the each count by its own area of opportunity.

When working with counts that satisfy the two Poisson conditions we will denote the area of opportunity for the ith count X_i by the symbol:

$$a_i$$

The ratio of the ith count to its area of opportunity will be a rate, and will be denoted by:

$$u_i = \frac{X_i}{a_i}$$

- The u-chart will be based upon a plot of the u_i values. The central line will be defined by the average rate $\bar{u}$.

$$\bar{u} = \frac{\text{total number of events observed in baseline period}}{\text{sum of the areas of opportunity in baseline period}}$$

- For the ith sample the three-sigma distance will be estimated by:

$$\text{Estimated Three Sigma Distance for Poisson Rates} = 3\sqrt{\frac{\bar{u}}{a_i}}$$

- So the limits for a u-chart will be computed to be:

$$\bar{u} \pm 3\sqrt{\frac{\bar{u}}{a_i}}$$

- If the value computed for a lower limit falls below 0.0, then there is no lower limit for that sample.

As an example of the use of rates based upon Poisson counts we will use the data for the number of hospital days per month for a small health-care plan. The data are given in Table 14.4. Each month the total number of days which members of the health plan spent in the hospital is reported. Since the number of members is changing from month to month, the area of opportunity for this count is taken to be the membership on the first day of the month times the number of days in that month. When the counts are divided by the number of member days a very small ratio is obtained. To turn these small numbers into numbers that are easy to use they are multiplied by 1,000,000. The resulting rate is the hospitalization days per million member days (hosp. days/mmd).

For this two-year period, the total number of hospital days was 17,690 while the total number of member days was 85,392,513. This gives an average rate of 0.0002072 which, when multiplied by one million is:

$$\bar{u} = \frac{\text{total number of hospital days in baseline period}}{\text{total number of million member days in baseline period}} = \frac{17\ 690}{85.392\ 513} = 207.2$$

As with the p-chart, the u-chart requires that the limits be computed for each point. This results in stair-step limits and considerable complexity when the limits are done by hand.

The u-chart for Table 14.3 is shown in Figure 14.5. At the beginning of this chart there is one point above the upper limit and a run of four points near the upper limit. At the end of this two-year period there is a run of ten successive values below the central line. Of course the health plan administrators were happy to see this evidence of a downward trend.

Table 14.3: Hospital Days Per Million Member Days

Month	No. of Hosp. Days	No. of Member Days	Hosp. Rate/ mmd	Month	No. of Hosp. Days	No. of Member Days	Hosp. Rate/ mmd
Jan.	656	2,864,648	229.0	Jan.	762	3,589,304	212.3
Feb.	620	2,725,604	227.5	Feb.	735	3,371,676	218.0
Mar.	681	2,972,063	229.1	Mar.	780	3,833,863	203.5
Apr.	681	3,000,390	227.0	Apr.	737	3,667,800	200.9
May	660	3,102,449	212.7	May	770	3,917,966	196.5
Jun.	731	3,125,700	233.9	Jun.	727	3,773,580	192.7
Jul.	694	3,366,972	206.1	Jul.	784	4,006,316	195.7
Aug.	695	3,381,294	205.5	Aug.	839	4,121,853	203.5
Sept.	683	3,362,310	203.1	Sept.	779	3,978,360	195.8
Oct.	729	3,406,373	214.0	Oct.	853	4,182,985	203.9
Nov.	715	3,480,510	205.4	Nov.	804	4,137,480	194.3
Dec.	743	3,657,287	203.2	Dec.	832	4,365,730	190.6

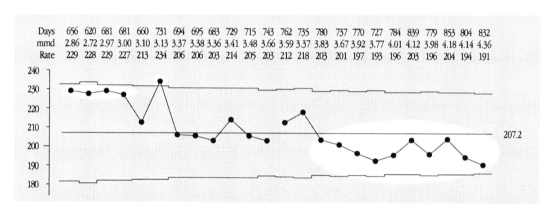

Figure 14.5: *u*-Chart for Hospital Days per Million Member Days

Of course there is little difference between the *u*-chart and the *X* Chart for the same data, which is shown in Figure 14.6.

Figure 14.6: *X* Chart for Hospital Days per Million Member Days

For the X Chart the average of the rates is 208.5, and the average moving range is 7.54, giving Natural Process Limits of 228.6 and 188.5. Both the *u*-chart and the X Chart tell the same story. These rates show a definite downward trend over this two-year period.

14.5 So How Should You Chart Count Data?

The *XmR* Chart gives limits that are *empirical*—they are based upon the variation that is present in the data (as measured by the moving ranges). The *np*-chart, the *p*-chart, the *c*-chart, and the *u*-chart all use a specific probability model to construct *theoretical* limits. These theoretical limits all use an estimate of the three-sigma distance that is based upon the value for the central line.

- If the theoretical model correctly describes the data, then the theoretical limits will be appropriate.

- If the theoretical model correctly describes the data, then the empirical limits will mimic the theoretical limits, and will also be appropriate.

- If the theoretical model does not correctly describe the data, then the theoretical limits will be incorrect, while the empirical limits will still be appropriate.

So if you are sophisticated enough to judge when the different probability models apply, by all means use the theoretical approach and the Flowchart in Figure 14.8. But if you are not sure about when to use a particular probability model, then you may still use the empirical approach of the *XmR* Chart. Remember, the objective is to take the right action, rather than to find the "right" number.

Data Characterized by Binomial Model		Data Characterized by Poisson Model		Other Data Based On Counts	
Area of Opportunity = **n**		Area of Opportunity = ***a***		Area of Opportunity	
constant **n**	variable **n**	constant ***a***	variable ***a***	constant	variable
np-chart or *XmR* for Counts	*p*-chart or *XmR* for Rates	*c*-chart or *XmR* for Counts	*u*-chart or *XmR* for Rates	*XmR* for Counts	*XmR* for Rates

Figure 14.7: Charts for Count Data

The only instance of count data which cannot be reasonably placed on an *XmR* Chart is that of very rare items or very rare events: data for which the average count per sample falls below 1.0. The problem with trying to put such data on an *XmR* Chart is the problem of chunky data, which was described in Chapter Eleven.

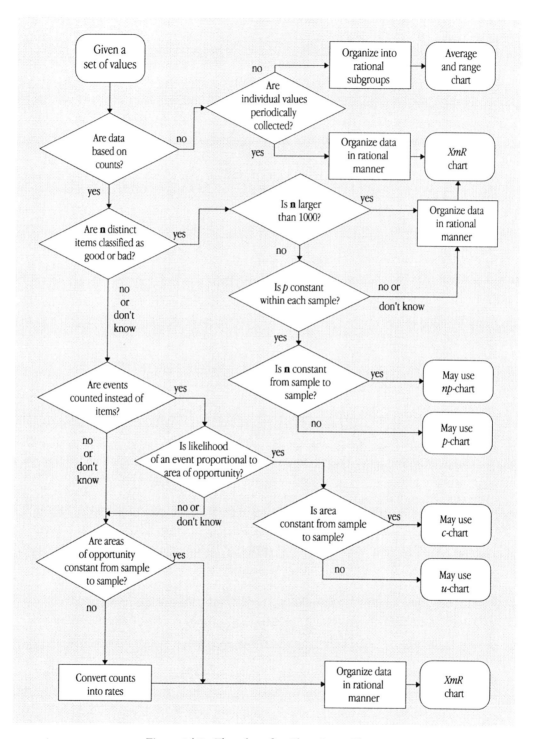

Figure 14.8: Flowchart for Choosing a Chart

14.6 *XmR* Charts for Chunky Ratios

The *p*-chart allows for the discreteness that is inherent in chunky ratios. Some who have gotten used to the complexity of the *p*-chart are not satisfied with using the constant-width limits of the ordinary *XmR* Chart when the data consists of chunky ratios. They fear that they will miss signals and get an excessive number of false alarms when using an *XmR* Chart for chunky ratios.

Both experience and research have shown that the ordinary *XmR* Chart will still have an acceptable false alarm rate of 1 percent or less even when used with chunky ratios. However, if you wish, you may adjust the limits on the X Chart to allow for the different sized areas of opportunity of the chunky ratios. The following modification of the standard *XmR* Chart is appropriate when:

- you are working with counts of items,

- the areas of opportunity, n_i, vary by more than $\pm 20\%$ from the average, $\bar{n}$, and

- some of the areas of opportunity are less than 20.

When these three conditions exist you will be working with chunky ratios, and you might wish to adjust the limits on the X Chart to allow for this chunkiness.

To adjust the limits for chunky ratios you begin by computing the average size for the areas of opportunity in the baseline samples:

$$\bar{n} \;=\; \text{average size of the areas of opportunity for baseline ratios}$$

Next you compute the chunkiness scaling factor w_i for the ith ratio:

$$w_i \;=\; \sqrt{\frac{\bar{n}}{n_i}}$$

where n_i is the area of opportunity for the ith ratio. The limits for the ith ratio on the X Chart are calculated according to the formula:

$$\bar{X} \pm 2.660 \; w_i \; \overline{mR} \qquad or \qquad \bar{X} \pm 3.145 \; w_i \; \widetilde{mR}$$

The data of Table 14.2 are repeated in Table 14.4. The average area of opportunity is:

$$\bar{n} = 238.$$

The smallest area of opportunity is 94, which is 39% of 238. The maximum area of opportunity is 511, which is 215% of 238. So the areas of opportunity vary –61% and +115% from the average size of 238.

Table 14.4: The Proportion of Orders Shipped by Premium Freight

Date	X	n	p	mR	w	Date	X	n	p	mR	w
1	27	102	.265		1.53	15	19	101	.188	.036	1.54
2	31	146	.212	.053	1.28	16	33	140	.236	.048	1.30
3	70	280	.250	.038	0.92	17	68	292	.233	.003	0.90
4	54	207	.261	.011	1.07	18	44	207	.213	.020	1.07
5	69	322	.214	.047	0.86	19	74	257	.288	.075	0.96
6	101	410	.246	.032	0.76	20	124	511	.243	.045	0.68
8	28	99	.283	.037	1.55	22	21	94	.223	.020	1.59
9	37	143	.259	.024	1.29	23	32	139	.230	.007	1.31
10	47	235	.200	.059	1.01	24	65	229	.284	.054	1.02
11	46	185	.249	.049	1.13	25	46	170	.271	.013	1.18
12	70	271	.258	.009	0.94	26	75	290	.259	.012	0.91
13	105	469	.224	.034	0.71	27	117	407	.287	.028	0.76

Thus the counts of Table 14.4 are (1) counts of items where (2) the areas of opportunity vary by more than ± 20 percent. Since none of the values for **n** are less than 20, these data do not satisfy the third condition for chunky ratios. However, since the computations are the same regardless of the size of the n_i values, I will use the data of Table 14.4 to illustrate the computation of variable width limits for the *X* Chart portion of an *XmR* Chart.

To place the proportions of Table 14.4 on an *XmR* Chart with variable limits we will need to compute the moving ranges using the proportions. We will also have to compute the chunkiness scaling factors, w_i, for each sample. These values are shown in Table 14.4. The average of these proportions is 0.245, and the average moving range is 0.033. The limits are computed for each point according to the formulas given earlier in this section, and are plotted as shown in Figure 14.9.

Figure 14.9: *XmR* Chart with Variable Width Limits for Proportions Premium Freight

The straight limits in Figure 14.9 are those from the ordinary *XmR* Chart given in Figure 13.4. Points that would be outside the variable width limits would also be close to, or outside, the straight limits. On the other hand, some points that would be outside the straight limits could still be within the variable width limits. This means that using the straight line limits with chunky ratios would result in slightly more false alarms, but relatively few missed signals.

Figure 14.10 compares the variable width limits on the *X* Chart with those of the *p*-chart. The *p*-chart limits are shown stair-step style. While the two sets of limits are not identical, they are sufficiently close that there will be no practical difference in using one over the other. However, as noted earlier, the *p*-chart limits are based on a theoretical model and are appropriate only when the data satisfy the binomial conditions. The *X* Chart limits are empirical, and will work without reference to any particular probability model.

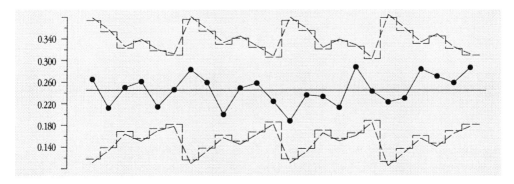

Figure 14.10: Variable Width Limits for *X* Chart Compared to *p*-Chart Limits (Premium Freight Data)

Table 14.5: Hospital Days Per Million Member Days

Month	No. of Hosp. Days	No. of Member Days	Hosp. Rate/ mmd	*mR*	*w*	Month	No. of Hosp. Days	No. of Member Days	Hosp. Rate/ mmd	*mR*	*w*
Jan.	656	2,864,648	229.0		1.11	Jan.	762	3,589,304	212.3	9.1	1.00
Feb.	620	2,725,604	227.5	1.5	1.14	Feb.	735	3,371,676	218.0	5.7	1.03
Mar.	681	2,972,063	229.1	1.6	1.09	Mar.	780	3,833,863	203.5	14.5	0.96
Apr.	681	3,000,390	227.0	2.1	1.09	Apr.	737	3,667,800	200.9	2.6	0.98
May	660	3,102,449	212.7	14.3	1.07	May	770	3,917,966	196.5	4.4	0.95
June	731	3,125,700	233.9	21.2	1.07	June	727	3,773,580	192.7	3.8	0.97
July	694	3,366,972	206.1	27.8	1.03	July	784	4,006,316	195.7	3.0	0.94
Aug.	695	3,381,294	205.5	0.6	1.03	Aug.	839	4,121,853	203.5	7.8	0.93
Sept.	683	3,362,310	203.1	2.4	1.03	Sept.	779	3,978,360	195.8	7.7	0.95
Oct.	729	3,406,373	214.0	10.9	1.02	Oct.	853	4,182,985	203.9	8.1	0.92
Nov.	715	3,480,510	205.4	8.6	1.01	Nov.	804	4,137,480	194.3	9.6	0.93
Dec.	743	3,657,287	203.2	2.2	0.99	Dec.	832	4,365,730	190.6	3.7	0.90

The variable limit *XmR* Chart may also be used with ratios based on counts of events. The chunkiness scaling factor would be defined as the square root of the ratio of the average area of opportunity to the area of opportunity for a particular period. The data of Table 14.3 are repeated in Table 14.5, along with the moving ranges for the hospitalization rates and the chunkiness weighting factors, w_i. The average is 207.6, the average moving range is 7.53, and the average number of member days is 3.558 million.

The variable limit *XmR* Chart for these data is shown in Figure 14.11. The *u*-chart limits are shown stair-step style on the same graph. In this instance the *u*-chart limits fall outside the variable width limits for the X Chart. As before, there is no practical difference between these two charting techniques.

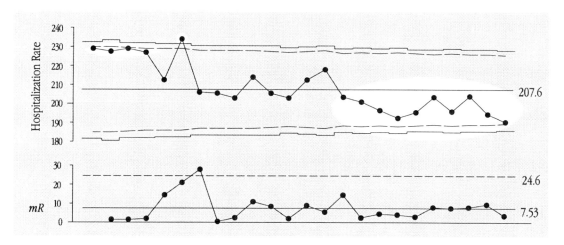

Figure 14.11: Variable Limit *XmR* Chart Compared to *u*-Chart Limits

So, for those who are sophisticated enough to judge when a particular probability model should apply to a given set of count data, there are the traditional, model-specific, charts—the *np*-chart, the *p*-chart, the *c*-chart, and the *u*-chart. These charts use a probability model to justify the computation of the three-sigma distance based upon the value for the central line— that is, they use a measure of location to also characterize dispersion. When the probability model does approximate the behavior of the counts this practice is sound. If the probability model does not approximate the behavior of the counts then the formulas for the traditional, model-specific, charts will be incorrect.

If you do not feel sophisticated enough to judge the appropriateness of various probability models, you may place your count-based data on an *XmR* Chart. The empirical limits of the *XmR* Chart will always be appropriate.

14.7 Process Behavior Charts for Rare Events

There is a limitation on the use of the *XmR* Chart with count data. Just as with measurement data, the process behavior chart limits will be corrupted when the measurement increment becomes too large to properly reflect the variation of the data. When the round-off obscures the process variation the process behavior limits will be artificially constricted, and the chart becomes unreliable (see Section 11.7). This also can happen with count data.

Typically, count data can be said to be chunky when the average count falls below 1.0 per sample. When this happens the only charts available are the *np*-, *p*-, *c*-, and *u*-charts. However, since these charts become very insensitive when the average count falls below 1.0 per sample, there is very little to be gained by charting the counts of rare events. The following example illustrates this problem and outlines a solution.

Chemical plants are required to track spills. While spills are not desirable, and while everything possible is done to prevent them, they do occasionally happen. Over the past few years one plant has averaged one spill every eight months. Of course, if the plant averages one spill every eight months, then in those months in which they have a spill their spill rate is 700 percent above average. When dealing with very small numbers, such as the counts of rare events, a one unit change can result in a huge percentage difference. The usual process behavior chart for these data would be the *c*-chart, and the basic statistic for a *c*-chart is the average count. During the first four years there were a total of six spills. Six spills in 48 months gives an average of:

$$\bar{c} \ = \ \frac{6 \text{ spills}}{48 \text{ months}} \ = \ 0.125 \text{ spills per month}$$

This average will be the central line for the *c*-chart, and the upper limit will be computed to be:

$$UL_c \ = \ \bar{c} \ + 3 \sqrt{\bar{c}} \ = \ 0.125 + 3 \sqrt{0.125} \ = \ 1.186$$

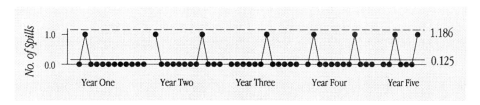

Figure 14.12: *c*-Chart for Spills

The *c*-chart is shown in Figure 14.12. In spite of the fact that a single spill is 700 percent above the average, the *c*-chart does not show any points outside the limits. It would take two spills in a single month to make this chart signal a change. This is not a problem with the charts, but rather a problem with the data themselves. (When you are averaging one spill every eight months, a month with two spills will be a remarkable event whether or not you are using a process behavior chart!)

CAUTION: The sequences of zeroes in Figure 14.12 do not constitute runs below the central line. In the first place you have to make allowance for the chunkiness of the values. Zero is as close to the central line as these values can be, and therefore should not be interpreted as being either above or below the central line. Secondly, when working with counts, a count of zero means that nothing was found, which is a negative type of information, rather than a positive signal of anything.

Counts of rare events are inherently insensitive and weak. No matter how these *counts* are analyzed there is nothing to discover on this chart. Yet there are other ways to characterize rare events. Instead of *counting* the number of spills each year (counting events), you could instead *measure* the number of days between the spills (measure the area of opportunity). For the first four years the time intervals between the spills are computed as follows.

Table 14.6: Dates of Spills

Date of Spill	2/23/01	1/11/02	9/15/02	7/6/03	2/19/04	9/29/04	3/20/05	7/13/05
Day of Year	54	11	258	188	50	272	79	194
Days Between Spills		322	247	295	227	222	172	115

One spill in 322 days converts into a spill rate of:

$$\frac{1\ \text{spill}}{322\ \text{days}} = 0.0031\ \text{spills per day}$$

Multiplying the daily spill rate by 365 gives a yearly spill rate.

(0.0031 spills per day) x (365 days per year) = 1.13 spills per year.

Table 14.7: Instantaneous Spill Rates

Days Between Spills		322	247	295	227	222
Spills per Day		0.0031	0.0040	0.0034	0.0044	0.0045
Spills per Year	X	1.13	1.48	1.24	1.61	1.64
Moving Ranges	mR		0.35	0.24	0.37	0.03

Thus, the interval between the first and second spills is equivalent to having 1.13 spills per year. Continuing in this manner, the intervals between the first six spills are converted into five instantaneous spill rates (in spills per year). These five spill rates and the accompanying moving ranges are shown in Table 14.7.

The average spill rate during the first four years is 1.42 spills per year. The average moving range is 0.2475. Using these values we obtain the *XmR* Chart shown in Figure 14.13.

Figure 14.13: *XmR* Chart for Spill Rates

The two spills in the current year had intervals of 172 days and 115 days respectively. These intervals convert into spill rates of 2.12 spills per year and 3.17 spills per year. When these values are added to the *XmR* Chart the result is Figure 14.14.

Figure 14.14: Complete *XmR* Chart for Spill Rates

Since the limits shown in Figures 14.13 and 14.14 are based on four moving ranges they must be interpreted as being very soft. (The greater the number of moving ranges used the more solid the limits become—they are constrained to be closer to the theoretical values. The limits are said to be soft when fewer than 17 moving ranges are used.) While the first spill in the current year is outside the limit, it is barely outside. Given the softness of limits based on four moving ranges, it is difficult to say if the first spill in the current year is a definite signal or not. However, the second spill is far enough outside the limits to be safely interpreted as a definite signal—there has been an increase in the spill rate during the current year.

You should also note that while the chart in Figure 14.14 has both upper and lower limits, it is possible that rare events will result in XmR charts which only have an upper limit. In such a case, both the times between events and the instantaneous rates are likely to have a highly skewed distribution like the one on the bottom of Figure 11.2. When this happens, and you want to detect a deterioration in the process, the instantaneous rates will be the values to plot on an XmR Chart (a point above the upper limit on this chart would be equivalent to an increased rate of occurrence). On the other hand, if you are trying to detect improvement, such as in the question of whether or not a prevention program has been effective in reducing lost-time accidents, then the *times between events* will be the values to plot on an XmR Chart (here a large value corresponds to a long time between events).

In general, *counts are weaker than measurements.* Counts of rare events are no exception. When possible, it will always be more satisfactory to *measure the activity* than to merely *count events*.

CAUTION: The use of the time between events, as outlined in this section, makes sense only as long as the events themselves come from a single system of causes. Measuring the time between events when one event comes from one cause system and the other event comes from another cause system does not make sense. For example, a single plant may have an environmental permit that requires notification for any one of a dozen different types of events. If every notification event is tracked, and if the time between notifications is used as suggested in this section, then just what does it mean when a point goes above the upper limit on the X-Chart? Generally, such a point will denote the *concurrency* of events from separate and independent systems. This will not produce any insight into how to improve the process. Moreover, a chart which combines events coming from separate cause systems will not even be useful as a report card since points above the upper limit will indicate concurrency rather than a change in the system. Such a chart will not allow one to learn from an analysis of the past.

14.8 Summary

When dealing with count data you may choose to use a theoretical approach or an empirical one. With the theoretical approach you will, of necessity, have to be concerned with the appropriateness of the assumptions required by the theory. When you have a strong belief in the appropriateness of the assumptions, the use of the theoretical approach will allow you to detect departures from the theoretical model. David S. Chambers' famous example of personnel reporting fictitious data which is given in *Out of the Crisis*, page 265, and in *Understanding Statistical Process Control, Second Edition*, page 283, will serve to illustrate this point. There the failure of the data to behave as they ought to behave, given the conditions under which they were supposed to have been collected, was a clear indication that the data were artificially restricted in range. They were never allowed to get too high, nor were they allowed to get too low. The *XmR* Chart for these data does not show this problem as clearly as the *p*-chart. So there are occasional instances where the theoretical model provides additional insight beyond what can be obtained from the *XmR* Chart. Yet, for most who have to use process behavior charts, the verification of the assumptions required for the use of the theoretical model is the greatest hurdle in the charting of count data. Experts may tread here; others need to be very careful.

Another bonus of the theoretical approach is the elegance of the equations—only one statistic is needed and no scaling factors are required—yet this elegance can be accessed only after the assumptions have been verified. The complexity of the latter will generally more than offset the advantage of simple computations.

Finally, when there is a serious discrepancy between the theoretical limits and the empirical limits of an *XmR* Chart, priority should be given to the empirical limits since such a discrepancy will most likely be due to a breakdown in the theory.

- When a theoretical model is appropriate both the theoretical approach and the empirical approach will yield limits that are quite similar.

- When the theoretical model used is inappropriate the theoretical approach will yield incorrect limits, while the empirical approach will still yield appropriate limits.

- Which is why you can't go far wrong using an *XmR* Chart with count data.

14.9 Exercises

EXERCISE 14.1: In Exercise 13.1 a total of 685 cases were examined and 95 were found to have excessive costs. Use the form on the next page to create a *p*-chart for these data

Provider	104	140	147	376	378	411	564	643	664	668	698	703
No. Cases	30	40	37	34	20	30	40	21	21	24	30	29
No. Excessive	8	7	5	7	2	5	4	3	5	3	2	8
Proportion	0.27	0.18	0.14	0.21	0.10	0.17	0.10	0.14	0.24	0.13	0.07	0.28

Provider	704	706	708	714	719	725	740	741	747	776	977	1021
No. Cases	22	29	37	22	23	32	34	24	20	29	20	37
No. Excessive	4	4	4	4	2	5	3	1	1	3	1	4
Proportion	0.18	0.14	0.11	0.18	0.09	0.16	0.09	0.04	0.05	0.10	0.05	0.11

Provider	n_i	X_i	p_i	$3\sqrt{\bar{p}(1-\bar{p})/n_i}$	LL_p	UL_p
104	30	8	.27			
140	40	7	.18			
147	37	5	.14			
376	34	7	.21			
378	20	2	.10			
411	30	5	.17			
564	40	4	.10			
643	21	3	.14			
664	21	5	.24			
668	24	3	.13			
698	30	2	.07			
703	29	8	.28			
704	22	4	.18			
706	29	4	.14			
708	37	4	.11			
714	22	4	.18			
719	23	2	.09			
725	32	5	.16			
740	34	3	.09			
741	24	1	.04			
747	20	1	.05			
776	29	3	.10			
977	20	1	.05			
1021	37	4	.11			

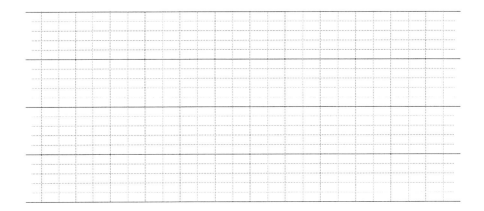

Does this chart reveal anything different from what you saw on the X Chart in Exercise 13.1?

Chapter Fifteen

Using Count Data Effectively

The preceding chapters have outlined the different ways to place count data on a process behavior chart. Regardless of which approach is appropriate for a particular set of data, the ultimate effectiveness of any chart for count data will depend more upon the structure of the data than whether you use an *XmR* Chart or an *np-, p-, c-,* or *u-* chart.

15.1 Three Characteristics of Count Data

Three characteristics are common to all types of count data. Understanding these characteristics is the first step toward using count data effectively.

First, the inherent frustration in count data must be recognized. The better the process, the greater the area of opportunity must be in order to have sensitive process behavior charts. As was noted in Section 14.7, if the average count per sample is not at least 1.0, the charts will be insensitive.

Second, count data are no substitute for measurements. Inspection may well result in a count of how many transactions or items failed to be acceptable, but it will always be preferable to measure some characteristic rather than to count failures.

In manufacturing a simple device known as a go-no-go gauge has been in use for 140 years. This device results in efficient 100 percent inspection, but it does *not* yield satisfactory data for use with a process behavior chart. Moreover, any time that a go-no-go

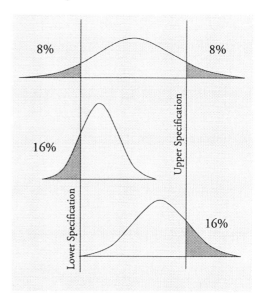

Figure 15.1: Three Distributions
With 16 Percent Nonconforming

gauge can be used, a measurement is possible. Measurements of a few items are much more revealing than the proportion nonconforming in a large sample. The reason for this can be seen in Figure 15.1. While the three distributions shown are considerably different, they would all show a total of 16% nonconforming on a *p*-chart.

The third common characteristic of count data is that variation coming from separate sources is difficult to identify. This characteristic is due to the inherent structure of the data—when we are counting unacceptable outcomes, the tendency is to lump all types of unacceptable outcomes together. As a result we will not know exactly what a given count represents. In addition we will also have to deal with the ambiguity between the effects of the data collection process and the behavior of the production process.

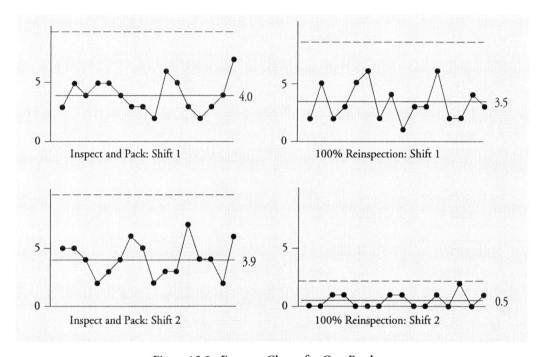

Figure 15.2: **Four *np*-Charts for One Product**

Consider the four *np*-charts shown in Figure 15.2. All parts coming off the line were inspected by an inspect-and-pack operator. Twice each shift, a data clerk monitored the disposition of 40 consecutive parts. The charts on the left of Figure 15.2 show the results of these samples from the inspect-and-pack station. The counts on these charts reflect the initial fraction nonconforming in this process. The similarity of the averages of these two charts (4.0 and 3.9) suggests that a comparable number of nonconforming parts are being produced and found on each of the two shifts.

Due to customer complaints, the particular part represented in these charts was also subjected to an additional 100% re-inspection. Since the parts were packaged in baskets of 40 pieces, the area of opportunity is the same for both sets of *np*-charts. The *np*-charts for the 100% re-inspection are shown on the right side of Figure 15.2. These charts show a substantial difference between the two shifts. The first shift reinspector averages 3.5 nonconforming per 40 piece basket, while the second shift reinspector averages 0.5 nonconforming per 40 piece basket. How do you explain this difference? Remember these counts reflect the number nonconforming found *after* the inspect-and-pack operator has supposedly removed all nonconforming product!

One explanation for the differences on reinspection could be that the first shift inspect-and-pack operator is doing a sloppy job. However, since the two shifts have the same average number rejected at inspect-and-pack, this is unlikely. A simpler explanation is that there is a difference in the way the two reinspectors are doing their job—they have different definitions of what is nonconforming. While these charts do not provide a definite answer to what the problem is here, they do raise some important questions that would never be considered in the normal course of events.

This confusion between variation due to the way the data were collected and variation due to the production process is part of the difficulty in using count data effectively. This is especially true when dealing with data from 100 percent inspection at the end of the line. As soon as the results of 100 percent inspection are charted, problems similar to those in the preceding example arise. With several inspectors, how can consistency be guaranteed? With only one inspector, on the other hand, how can the contributing factor of fatigue be ruled out?

For these reasons, the results of 100 percent inspection are rarely the best data for a process behavior chart. The purpose of the 100 percent inspection is to sort the "good" outcomes from the "bad" outcomes. The process behavior chart, on the other hand, is intended to be used to improve the process to the point where there will be little or no need for 100 percent inspection. Simply putting the result of the inspection operation on the charts is better than nothing, but it is not the best way to use the charts. In general, a smaller amount of data, collected consistently, is much more useful than a greater amount of data collected in an inconsistent manner.

15.2 The Problems of Aggregation

Another way that variation from separate sources gets confused on charts for count data is when different types of problems are combined on one chart. This is illustrated by the following example.

The data on the next page consist of the total number of parts rejected for any reason at the inspect-and-pack station. The area of opportunity for each of these counts is 60 consecutive parts coming down the line. Two 60-piece samples are observed and recorded each day. There were seven specific categories of nonconformity in addition to a catch-all category. The breakdown of these total counts is shown in Table 15.1, and the *np*-chart for the total count is reproduced in Figure 15.3.

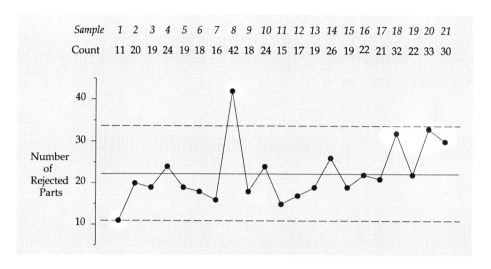

Figure 15.3: *np*-Chart for the Total Number of Rejected Parts per Basket

Table 15.1: **Breakdown of Number of Rejected Parts per Basket**

Sample	1	2	3	4	5	6	7	8	9	10	11	12	13	14	15	16	17	18	19	20	21
Total Nonconforming	**11**	**20**	**19**	**24**	**19**	**18**	**16**	**42**	**18**	**24**	**15**	**17**	**19**	**26**	**19**	**22**	**21**	**32**	**22**	**33**	**30**
Foreign Material	3	5	4	4	4	3	3	30	4	11	2	3	3	5	3	7	4	5	5	15	2
Damaged Edge		2	4	5	3	5	1	3	3	4	2	3	7	3	3	3	1	10	6	2	14
Sinks	1		1		1	1	1											2	1		
Damaged Mount			1	14	2							1	5	2	7	6	5	1	2		1
Stress Marks		1	5	1	7	1	1	2		1	9	3	1	11	1		2	4	3		
Bubbles		3			1	2	6	3	2			1		2	1	2	1		7	2	
Bad Trim	5	1	1		1			4	6	6	1			5	1	1	3	2	2	2	
Other	2	8	3			6	4		3	2	1	7	2		2	4	4	7	3	7	11

Each of these categories could have its own *np*-chart. These are shown in Figure 15.4. The limits given are the revised limits calculated after deleting those values that fell outside the original limits. When the information on these eight charts is combined, fourteen out of twenty-one samples show at least one point above the upper limit. Yet the chart for the total counts, shown in Figure 15.3, does not look like two-thirds of the values are signals of exceptional variation.

The problem with Figure 15.3 is the problem of charting aggregate counts. The more sources of nonconformity that are combined on one chart, the greater the likelihood that the chart will appear to be predictable. Charts, such as that in Figure 15.3, may provide a useful record of what is happening, but they are not very useful in improving the process. They are simply fancy running records, good for telling how bad things have been, but of little use in identifying the actual assignable causes of excessive variation.

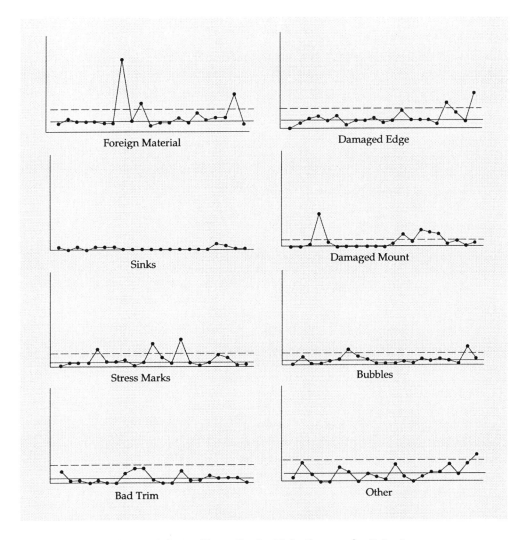

Figure 15.4: *np*-Charts for the Eight Reasons for Rejection

This is another reason that 100 percent inspection data are ineffective for use on an process behavior chart. They rarely discriminate between the different sources of nonconformity, and the counts are generally too aggregated to be useful.

These characteristics of count data create pitfalls for the unwary. The decreasing sensitivity of the charts as the process gets better, the all-or-nothing nature of the attributes, and the possibilities for aggregating the data until they are useless, combine to make count data difficult to use effectively. However, once the nature of these problems is understood, steps can be taken to avoid them.

15.3 The Difference Between Aggregations and Summaries

When a measure is obtained for different locations, or different categories, and the values for this measure are combined across locations or categories, the result is said to be an aggregated measure. Aggregated measures are common in all types of business. When such measures are placed on charts they will commonly have fairly wide limits. In spite of this it is possible to learn useful things from charts for aggregated measures.

Another example of aggregated data comes from Dr. Neil R. West of Millennium Medicine, who tells about a management meeting at a Health Maintenance Organization. Since the HMO has to pay whenever a member is referred to an outside physician the chief financial officer carefully tracks these expenses each month. When the costs of these outside referrals goes down he is happy, and when it goes up he is unhappy. The plot of these values for the past twelve months is shown in Figure 15.5.

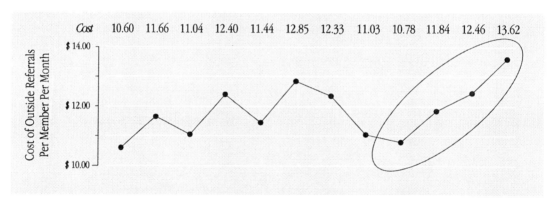

Figure 15.5: Running Record for Costs of Outside Referrals for an HMO

In this meeting the chief financial officer got out his red pencil, circled the last four points, and said, "Over the past four months the cost of outside referrals has gone from $10.78 per member per month to $13.62 per member per month." He continued, "This amounts to $1.42 million per month in extra expenses." And then he looked at the chief medical officer and added, "What are you going to do about this?"

The Chief Medical Officer, who had already looked at these data on an *XmR* Chart, responded, "What would you like for me to do? Run around the block naked? That might be as helpful as anything. This is routine variation, and that is just the way it is!"

The Chief Medical Officer's *X* Chart is shown in Figure 15.6. He was right. So what can the HMO do? The limits in Figure 15.6 are very wide, and represent a huge difference in costs. How can they live with this much uncertainty?

The answer is that they are already living with this amount of uncertainty, whether they like it or not. Routine, month-to-month variation can cause the outside referral costs to vary between a low of $9.34 to a high of $14.33. Values in this range are not exceptional, no matter who takes exception to them. All the X Chart does is make the uncertainty visible, instead of leaving everyone in the dark.

The question is not "how can we live with such wide limits?" The question is whether you know the difference between routine variation and exceptional variation. The fact is that their process has averaged about $12.00 per member per month for outside referrals, and unless the system is changed in some fundamental way, it can be expected to continue at this level in the near future. If the HMO fees do not have at least $12.00 per member per month budgeted for this expense, they will be losing money on these referrals. Even better would be $15.00 per member per month, which would cover the expected expenses with a little left over for profit. Good management requires planning, not reacting.

Figure 15.6: *X* Chart for Costs of Outside Referrals for an HMO

You may think your limits are far too wide to be of any practical use, but the limits only reflect the routine variation of your process. Some measures, and some processes, are full of noise. Crying about the noise does not do anything to change it.

Wide limits can occur when the measure on the chart is highly aggregated. As measures are combined from different categories the noise associated with each value is also aggregated, so that the totals end up displaying a large amount of routine variation.

Table 15.2: Revenues by Category and Time Periods

	Period 1	Period 2	Period 3	Period 4	Period 5	Period 6	Period 7
Category A	X_1	X_2	X_3	X_4	X_5	X_6	X_7
Category B	Y_1	Y_2	Y_3	Y_4	Y_5	Y_6	Y_7
Category C	Z_1	Z_2	Z_3	Z_4	Z_5	Z_6	Z_7

When you combine values across categories, across departments, or across regions, you are essentially combining different variables even though they all measure the same thing.

When you summarize a measure across time you are combining multiple observations on a single variable.

Thus there are two major dimensions present in service and administrative data—time and categories. We could, for example, measure revenues for a single category at different time periods. We could also measure revenues for different categories at the same time period.

When you combine revenues across categories you will obtain an *aggregated* measure of the form:

$$X + Y + Z$$

When you combine revenues across time periods you will obtain a *summary* measure of the form:

$$X_1 + X_2 + X_3$$

As you combine measures in either manner you will also accumulate the noise that is associated with every measure. When a summary measure is converted into an average, which is commonly done, the accumulated noise is deflated by the act of averaging. However, aggregated measures are most often used as totals, and when this happens the accumulated noise has its full effect. This is why aggregated measures will sometimes end up having wide limits on an X Chart. The more highly aggregated a value, the greater the amount of noise that has been accumulated and the more likely it becomes that the values will fall within the computed limits.

So when a highly aggregated measure shows evidence of an assignable cause, you can be confident that there really is an assignable cause. But when a highly aggregated measure behaves predictably, that does not mean that all of the components of that measure are predictable. See Section 12.4 for an example of this. So while highly aggregated measures may give you nice "report-card" charts, you may well need to disaggregate your measures to identify the opportunities for improvement.

Then why would we ever put highly aggregated measures on an *XmR* Chart? In order to know the answer to the question "Has a change occurred?" When highly aggregated measures are predictable, it does not mean that you cannot improve the process. It just means that you will need to look at your data in a less highly aggregated manner in order to detect signals of exceptional variation.

15.4 The Power of Disaggregation

The problems identified in the preceding sections suggest that it may be more difficult to use count data than it is to use measurements. Count data have to be made useful. You will have to choose which type of chart to use, define the categories of nonconformity, and choose an area of opportunity that is adequate. Then, you will need to disaggregate the sources of nonconformity.

A major difficulty in defining, or disaggregating, the types of nonconformities is the problem of operational definitions. Since it rarely makes sense to use count data when measurements can be obtained, the use of count data is generally restricted to those situations in which unacceptable outcomes are being counted. It is the definition of an unacceptable outcome that usually presents the greatest difficulty. Of course, a full-blown operational definition for each type of nonconformity will take some time to develop. This evolutionary process is often best accomplished by a real-time analysis of the charts. For it is only by interpreting the chart as it is filled out that you can gain insights into the nature of the different sources of nonconformity. Such insights are the basis for both improved operational definitions and process improvements.

In Table 15.1 the sources of nonconformity were divided into eight categories. Six months later, these eight categories had been refined into sixteen different categories. The new categories are shown in Table 15.3.

Table 15.3: Number of Rejected Parts Per Basket
(Six Months After Table 15.1)

Sample	1	2	3	4	5	6	7	8	9	10	11	12	13	14	15	16	17	18	19	20	21	22	23	24	25	26	27	28
Foreign Material	8		3	3	8		6	4	2	1	5	1	4	4	2		4	2			1	1	1	1	2	3		
Damaged Edge			1	2	2	1	1	1	4	6	1	3	5		1			5	1									
Stress Marks	2	2	2	1	3	1			1		2	1	1	2	3	1		1				1	1	1	5	10		
Flash On Edge							2										1											
Lint	1	16		2	1			2		10	5	1	1		1	1	2		1									
Flo-Line (outer)				1																								
Flo-Line (center)																												
Chatter on Edge				10	8	16																	1	3				
Sink in Center						1												1										
Sink on Edge																1												
Bad Insert Trim	3	3					1							7	2	3	1										38	30
Bubbles	1	1	1				1	4	1			1	1					1										
Vapor Drip	1	1					1	2												1								
Flash on Center																												
Bad Trim on Edge	4						3	1	1			1					2											
Other	1	8		6	1		1	1						12	2	2	1		1	2								
Total Count	21	31	7	24	26	18	9	14	15	10	16	12	13	25	9	9	10	10	6	4	1	2	3	5	7	13	38	30

With these new groupings, many categories became specific to single assignable causes. As such, they became effective indicators of the presence of those assignable causes, making identification and removal much more likely. The *np*-chart for the total number of rejected parts is shown in Figure 15.7.

Figure 15.7: *np*-Chart for Total Number of Rejected Parts

Among the categories of Table 15.3 there is one for "Lint." Rejects for lint were formerly counted as foreign material rejects, along with those due to vapor drip and other types of contamination. Since everyone in the department wore cotton gloves, lint seemed to be inevitable. But when lint was listed as a separate category, the data immediately challenged this commonly held notion.

Figure 15.8: Running Record for Parts Rejected for Lint

The rejections for lint came in clusters, as can be seen in Figure 15.8. Once the data for lint were separated from other counts, it was only a short time until the quality control technician noticed that rejections for lint correlated with the amount of rework coming to the inspect-and-pack station. Since the rework operation consisted of wiping the plastic part with an acetone-soaked cheesecloth, it was an obvious source of contamination. When further investigation confirmed this suspicion, the cheesecloth was changed to organdy at the rework station. This change took place just before sample 19. As the data show, this simple change in the system solved the lint problem.

By getting the categories specific to individual assignable causes, the counts become very effective monitors. But when the counts are aggregated, they are much less useful.

The total counts still track the overall performance, but the individual categories target the problems. Looking at the overall counts in Table 15.3, it can be seen that this process was much improved over the six month period. This improvement was primarily due to the solution of simple problems, like the one described above, and these solutions resulted from the use of the specific breakdown of the total count.

The focused nature of the breakdown of the total count is shown in the last two samples in Table 15.3. It can be seen that the sudden increase in rejections was entirely due to Bad Trim on Insert. This problem occurred whenever the trim operators were using dull trim blades. However, in an effort to control non-product inventory, the operators were only issued one blade at a time, and could not leave their station to obtain a new blade during their shift. Therefore, they remained at their station, turning out nonconforming product. This process behavior chart opened the eyes of management to the inherent problem in this system. By simply issuing two blades to each trim operator at the start of each shift, they always had a replacement set, and thus this problem was eliminated.

15.5 Disaggregation Across Workers

This process of getting count data focused and specific is the heart of using count data effectively. The actual way to do this varies with the situation, but the principle is the same across all applications. Until count data are made specific, nothing will happen. The following example shows how to do this when the process is highly operator dependent.

A medium-sized hosiery mill, employing about 1500 workers, had the reputation of being a "quality" mill. This was based on careful 100 percent inspection that graded the output of the plant into four categories: Firsts, Irregulars, Seconds, and Rags.

In spite of this reputation the mill faced a real problem. Since workers were paid by the piece, each had to process a certain number of pieces per week in order to earn the minimum wage. If a worker's output did not meet the minimum wage amount the company had to make up the difference. Facing an increase in the minimum wage rate, the managers realized that it would be nearly impossible to operate with the current equipment and technology without making substantial "make-up" payments each week. Some way had to be found to increase income in spite of a soft market and stiff competition.

The obvious solution was to change the mix of Firsts, Irregulars, Seconds, and Rags. By making more Firsts, and less of the other grades, revenues could be increased without increased costs. Operators would also benefit since a penalty system for bad work was in effect (each worker was docked two good pieces for each bad piece found at final inspection).

After consultation with David Chambers, the company president decided to send about 20 of his supervisors to an SPC class. Incidentally, this was the first time many of these supervisors had ever had a chance to talk with each other. After this class, David sat down with the supervisors and helped to plan how to use SPC in the plant. Due to the nature of the work, and the enthusiasm of the foreman, they decided to begin in the Looping Department.

The looping operation closed the toe of a knitted stocking. It was a tedious operation, requiring the operator to thread the toe of the stocking onto a comb-like device called the looper dial. Exactly one thread, from each side of the stocking, had to go into each gap between the teeth. A missed gap would create a hole in the finished stocking, and placing two threads from the same side in one gap would create a pucker. After the stocking was threaded onto the dial, the end was trimmed. If it was trimmed too long the seam would be bulky which would result in a downgraded stocking. If it was trimmed too short, the stocking would fall off the dial and the operator would have to start all over again. Since they were paid by the piece, the loopers considered this to be "bad form." After being trimmed, the toe of the stocking was stitched by the looping machine, and the finished stocking was automatically ejected into the looper's production box.

To collect some data an inspector was brought into the looping department from the boxing department. This inspector would inspect four consecutively looped stockings, four times each day, from each operator. In this manner, sixteen pieces were obtained from each operator during the course of each day. The inspector was taught how to randomize the order in which she visited the different operators in order to prevent the operators from "loading" the output box. The inspector recorded the type and number of defects found, by operator, and records were kept on a historical basis during the months of June and July. (Since these data were considered to be personnel records, a secretary in the personnel department actually maintained these process behavior charts.)

During that time no conscious effort was made to improve the process. The objective was merely to measure the quality of the looping work. Individual records were combined into a departmental record for each day of the two-month period. The departmental average amount of defective work was 4.8 percent for those two months. The *p*-chart for the department is shown in Figure 15.9. The limits shown are based on the average area of opportunity.

Figure 15.9: *p*-Chart for Looping Department during June and July

The chart in Figure 15.9 shows a fair degree of stability with only two points outside the limits. The first point was expected, since there had never before been an inspector located in the department. The presence of a person taking work from a machine, and inspecting it on the spot, was very upsetting to the operators. On the second day of the inspection the operators were so upset that it showed on the chart. In fact, on that day the employees were in such an uproar that it was necessary to tell the operators that the company was cooperating with a professor in gathering some "real" data for class use and their jobs were not threatened. This explanation seemed to reassure them.

The second out-of-limits point had a different cause. It was the custom in the hosiery industry to shut down for a week-long holiday around the 4th of July. The second point outside the limits occurred on the Monday following this mid-summer holiday.

The chart in Figure 15.9 was explained to the vice president for manufacturing in the following manner. The conditions in the looping department were described as being relatively stable. Assuming that no changes were made, about five percent defective product would be produced weekly.

Upon hearing this the vice president swore that the company could not continue to operate with 5 percent defective products in looping—the company would be closed within six months under these conditions!

Of course, he had not previously known what the defect level was in the looping department, nor in any other particular department. The only record ever kept had been at the final pairing and boxing operation. No one had ever known just how bad things really were in the various departments even though the company had been in operation for 65 years.

Since the vice president was dissatisfied with five percent defectives in the looping operation, he was asked what a "good" level would be. After reflection, he replied that a good operation would produce "no more than two percent defectives." Of course, statements of this sort tend to become targets or goals, and this proved to be no exception. However, since goals do not provide the means to improve the system they can easily lead to the distortion of both the data and the system itself. Fortunately, in this case, they already had an action plan for process improvement.

A meeting was called for all employees involved in the looping operation. The consensus was that the optimum method of improvement was to work individually with each operator who needed help. Accordingly, the previously-collected data were used to create an *np*-chart for each worker during the June-July period. Based on the departmental average of 4.8% defective and the audit size of 16 pieces per day per operator, the central line was placed at 0.8 units (16 times 0.048 = 0.77) and the corresponding Upper Limit for these *np*-charts was computed to be 3.4.

Beginning in August, the supervisor sat down with each operator and showed her her own chart. The operators were told that one, two, or three defectives out of sixteen was average performance. Consistently producing zero defectives out of sixteen was better than average, and four or more defectives out of sixteen was worse than average. (Although employees were not shown the charts of others, everyone seemed to know how everyone else was doing within 10 minutes of their review. The news traveled at the speed of sound!) Since these charts revealed who could be classified as good, average, or poor, they were reviewed by the departmental supervisor to see who needed help as part of the improvement effort.

Some of the case histories follow. The supervisor decided to begin by learning what he could from those who were performing consistently "better than average."

OPERATOR 75

Based on her chart, Operator 75 was an excellent operator. When the supervisor went out to watch her work he noticed that she was using a different technique than they were teaching in the training room. Upon investigation it turned out that her technique was superior to the standard technique and could be used by the other operators. So he got Operator 75 to start teaching her technique to others.

Figure 15.10: *np*-Chart for Operator 75

OPERATOR 22

Operator 22 was much worse than average in July. After observing her at work, the supervisor referred her to the personnel department for a possible eye examination. Upon examination, the doctor found that she was blind in the left eye, and only had 6/20 vision in the right eye. Her right eye was correctable to 20/20, and with new glasses, her work immediately improved.

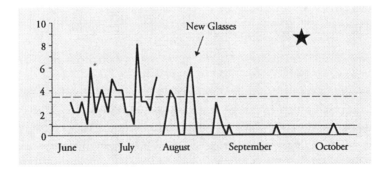

Figure 15.11: *np*-Chart for Operator 22

This experience caused the company to reconsider its lack of policy regarding eye exams. It finally mandated periodic vision examinations for all operators. The initial group of examinations revealed additional operators who had real difficulties in seeing well enough to do their work.

New glasses helped Operator 22 increase her hourly earnings by over 15 percent. At the same time, she increased her quality sufficiently to become a "Gold Star" looper. (The basic requirement to become a "Gold Star" looper was to produce no more than three mendable defectives per month. Being a "Gold Star" looper was a considerable honor, and those who lost this rating worked hard to regain it the next month.)

OPERATOR 27

Operator 27 seemed to be the least capable operator during the analysis period. When the supervisor discussed her chart with her, and explained the quality improvement program, her response was: "Why, I've been here for five years, and this is the first time anybody has told me they were interested in good quality. I can do a much better job, if it makes any difference." Her record in August, and thereafter, attests to the accuracy of her statement.

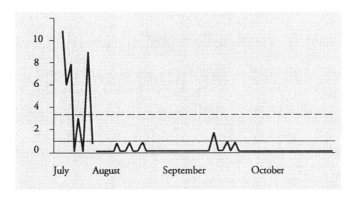

Figure 15.12: *np*-Chart For Operator 27

OPERATOR 106

The record of Operator 106 deteriorated between June and July. Examination of her personnel record revealed that she had been moved from the training classes to the production line in June. Beginning in July she was pressured to improve her production in order to minimize the make-up pay. In response to this pressure she had increased production, as well as the proportion of defective stockings!

As the supervisor searched for an explanation for her poor performance, he found that

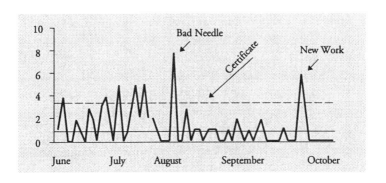

Figure 15.13: *np*-Chart For Operator 106

her personnel record noted an impairment in her right arm. This impairment made it difficult for her to load the stockings on the looping machine, thus slowing her down. By obtaining a Handicapped Worker's Certificate from the Dept. of Labor the supervisor could exempt her from the minimum wage. This removed the pressure to produce more, and allowed her to produce a higher percentage of good pieces. Following this exemption her only bad day occurred when she had to adjust to a new type of knitting.

OPERATOR 73

In spite of these successes, it was the case of Operator 73 that ended resistance to SPC in the plant. Operator 73 had ten years experience and was in her early sixties. During June and July her production had either been up or down, with nothing in between. The supervisor worked with her during August and noted some improvement. In September she decided that new glasses might help, but the chart shows no evidence of improvement.

By October it was apparent that she had improved as much as possible. When compared to other operators during the same time period, her work was indeed poor. Although the supervisor did not think that she could do any other job at the plant, he was reluctant to terminate a ten-year employee. He decided to give her more time.

In November her record was no better. By that time every operator in the Looping Department knew that all employees, except Operator 73, had made vast improvements. The other loopers began to resent the effort they had made to improve when nothing seemed to be done about the poor work of Operator 73. During November she contributed 20 percent of the defectives for the whole department!

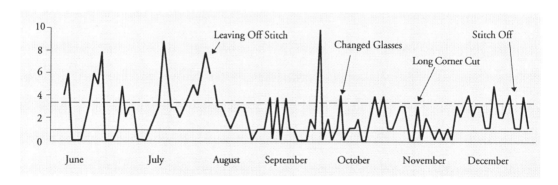

Figure 15.14: *np*-Chart for Operator 73

The operators began to question the supervisor about what he intended to do about Operator 73. Group pressure continued to build until the supervisor finally advised the personnel department that something had to be done. "Old 73" was disrupting progress, and requiring more and more of his time. The managers reluctantly, and with real fear of the consequences, agreed to let her go at the end of December.

At the company Christmas party it turned out that "Old 73" won the first prize—an expensive electric range—in a "random" drawing. Near the end of the year, she was informed that the company could no longer use her, and that arrangements for a suitable pension had been made. When told of this action "Old 73" was neither surprised, nor dismayed. She said, in fact, that she had known for 10 years that she could not loop well, and could not learn how. She was ten years ahead of the management! She left with a good attitude, realizing that the supervisor had done everything possible to help her improve her performance.

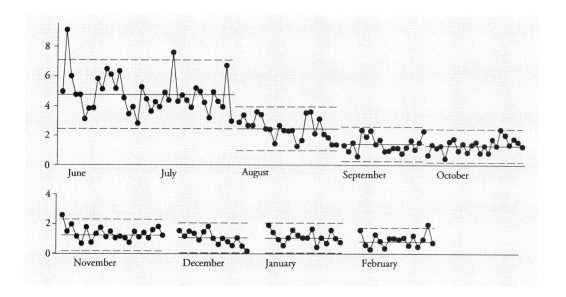

Figure 15.15: *np*-Chart for Looping Department

Figure 15.15 shows the steady and continual improvement experienced in the Looping Department. In the first month, the percentage of defective pieces dropped from 4.8 percent to 2.4 percent. In the following months, it rarely rose above two percent. By February, it was down to an average of 0.8 percent. This amounted to an 83 percent reduction in the number of defective pieces produced, and this reduction was accomplished in a period of seven months.

15.6 Disaggregation Across Problems

When the quality of the product is highly operator-dependent, count data will generally need to be made operator-specific. When operators do not have a direct influence on the product, then other factors must be used to make count data useful.

An automotive supplier was attempting to use six robots to install pal-nuts on a door trim panel. Two door trim panels would ride on a cart down a track past the robots. While the cart was stopped at each station a robot would attempt to install four pal-nuts. Each trim panel was designed to have 12 pal-nuts in all.

Of course these robots had a vision system to identify the parts and locate the position of the studs for the pal-nuts. With the constant attention of twelve skilled tradesmen, these six robots were consistently installing about 70 percent of the nuts. The other 30 percent simply slid down the face of the trim panel and fell off. In fact, so many nuts were falling off that these six robots had been specially modified—they had diapers! Large sheets of vinyl were attached to each robot to catch the dropped nuts and funnel them into collection boxes.

Figure 15.16: A Pal-Nut

Finally, in a cramped space beside the robot station two men had the inevitable job of installing pal-nuts on mangled plastic studs. Needless to say, they were the bottleneck for this operation.

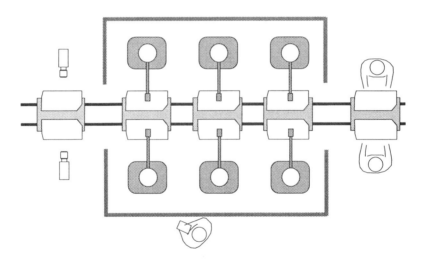

Figure 15.17: The Pal-Nut Robots

Knowing that this operation was in trouble, the engineering and production staff had spent five months collecting information about their purchased parts. The "capability studies" which they had performed filled a two inch binder, yet these data were all worthless. None of these capability studies had considered the production processes. None of the data had been rationally subgrouped. No one knew how many sources they had for a single item, and no one knew if their suppliers production processes were operated predictably or not. In short, they had spent five months collecting data, yet they had absolutely no way to extrapolate from these data to make reasonable predictions for the future.

During this same time they had also tried to collect some data from the assembly operation. These data were collected in the following manner. Several times during the day shift one of the six robots would be randomly selected. The number of missed nuts would then be recorded, either for a certain period of time, or until a change in the part number occurred. At the end of the day, these data would be entered into a computerized data base. By the next day, the engineers would have tables of percentages to examine.

This approach was problematic in that there were nine different parts going down each assembly line, giving a total of 54 different robot-part combinations. While each "subgroup" represented only one of these combinations, successive "subgroups" did not represent the same combinations. In fact, it could be several days before the same robot-part combination reappeared in the data. This made interpretation of the data very difficult. Although the data were selected from across all combinations, the record was incoherent and fragmentary.

It was at this point that I began to work with the group. At my suggestion, the group began with a cause-and-effect diagram. Here, their broad, but unfocused, data base was useful, especially in forming a Pareto diagram to show where in the process their problems occurred. Following this, they began to collect data for just one robot-part combination. The robot selected was the one which appeared to have the worst record, and the part selected was one of the high-volume parts. The intent was to observe Robot 7L continuously while Trim Panel A was being assembled in order to have a coherent record of what was happening in this process.

Two weeks later, one of the engineers excitedly gave me a description of a problem with the stopping mechanism for the assembly-line carts. He was sure that this was the reason for the missed installations, and was trying to think of ways to measure the stop position for each cart. When asked what data confirmed that this was indeed the problem, he said that he had none. He had slipped back into the old way of problem solving—trying to leap from the statement of the problem to the solution, without any intervening steps. I then suggested that since the assembly operation was a very dynamic process, the only way to gain the necessary insight would be to use a dynamic monitor, such as a process behavior chart. If the carts were suspect, then the methods of data collection should be changed in order to preserve the information about the carts. Beginning at this point a new data collection worksheet was used. In addition, a second high-volume part was added to the data base. Now Robot 7L was observed whenever either one of these two high-volume parts was being assembled. A facsimile of the data sheet is shown in Figure 15.18.

There were seven different reasons for a missed installation that could be observed from outside the robot cage. With this new data collection sheet the context for each missed installation is preserved. One can tell which robot, which trim panel, which cart, which position, and which failure mode for each and every missed installation. It would take about ten minutes for a full round of carts to pass the robots. With each round a new sheet of paper was used. Each check mark in the "attempted" column represented four attempted installations. The sum of these check marks, times four, defined the Area of Opportunity for the total number of missed installations. Thus, the data collection sheet organized the data for easy collection and the preservation of the context for each event.

Cart No.	Attempted	Position 1							Position 2							Position 3							Position 4							Totals
		1	2	3	4	5	6	7	1	2	3	4	5	6	7	1	2	3	4	5	6	7	1	2	3	4	5	6	7	
1	X							X																						1
2	X																													
3	X								X							X														2
4	X			X							X							X								X				4
5																														
6	X			X							X							X								X				4
7	X			X																										1
8	X																													
9	X																													
10	X																													
11																														
12																														

Robot No. *7L*
Part No. *Panel A*
Time and Date *1:15 pm 4/1*

Figure 15.18: Data Collection Sheet for Trim Line Pal-Nut Robots

With this in-depth data on specific robot-part combinations, the skilled tradesmen began to look over the shoulder of the data collector. They found that they could identify problems quickly and easily by looking at this data collection sheet. For example, one discovery was that the filter for the vacuum system needed to be cleaned every three days rather than once a week. Of course, such discoveries were applied to all six robots.

A new data collection sheet was started each time the carts made a complete cycle of the assembly line or whenever the part number changed. The structure imposed by this data collection sheet allowed many different questions to be answered from the same data. If one location was consistently missed, then the programming would be suspect. If one cart consistently had misses, then the cart would be suspect. Other combinations of failure mode and location would be suggestive of other problems. The running records for the two robot-part combinations are shown in Figures 15.19 and 15.20.

Both of these running records show 4/3 and 4/12 to have been very good days. However, the erratic performance on other days suggested that many assignable causes were still present. It seemed that the equipment was capable of doing the job, but the personnel had not yet learned how to maintain it properly. In fact, on the chart for Panel B, the data for 4/2 show just how fast the process could deteriorate. Each sample point represents a ten-minute interval, and most of these were sequential. From the third sample to the eighth, within an hour's time, the process went from 6 percent missed to 34 percent missed. This suggested that until the robots were maintained more consistently, they would have to be monitored almost constantly.

Figure 15.19: **Running Record of Missed Installations for Panel A**

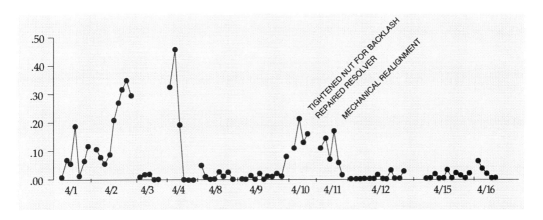

Figure 15.20: **Running Record of Missed Installations for Panel B**

While many were pleased that the overall installation rate had climbed from 70 percent to 92 percent during this period when the data were used effectively, these results were nowhere near what could have been done. The robots appear to be capable of 100 percent installation if and when they are maintained and operated predictably.

15.7 Ratios of Aggregated Measures

Another of the perils of aggregation is illustrated by the data for the number of Hospital Days per Million Member Days introduced in Chapter Fourteen. Over a two-year period the X Chart for these values showed a favorable downward trend. This chart is reproduced in Figure 15.21.

Figure 15.21: **Hospital Days per Million Member Days Over a Two-Year Period**

The healthcare plan represented by these values was sponsored by two hospitals located in two cities in one state. The members of this healthcare plan were primarily residents of these two cities. In Table 15.4 the membership, number of hospital days, and the hospitalization rate per million member days are shown for each city.

Figure 15.22: **Hospital Days per Million Member Days for City A**

Figure 15.22 shows the X Chart for the Hospitalization Rate per Million Member Days for City A. The average is 240. The average moving range is 8.8. The Natural Process Limits for this hospitalization rate are 217 to 264. Over this two-year period all of the observed rates fall within these limits, although the last 8 values do fall below the central line, suggesting a weak but sustained drop in the hospitalization rate in City A.

Comparison of Figures 15.21 and 15.22 leads to the conclusion that the drop in the hospitalization rate cannot be fully explained by what happened in City A.

Figure 15.23 shows the X Chart for the Hospitalization Rate per Million Member Days for City B. The Average is 160. The Average Moving Range is 15. The Natural Process Limits for this hospitalization rate are 121 to 200. Over this two-year period there is one run of two points beyond the upper two-sigma line at the start, but otherwise there is no clear change in the hospitalization rate in City B.

Figure 15.23: Hospital Days per Million Member Days for City B

So where did the drop shown in Figure 15.21 come from? City A shows a slight drop, but nothing as dramatic as seen in Figure 15.21, while City B shows hardly any change at all. So what caused the overall hospitalization rate, shown in Figure 15.21, to decline over this two-year period?

To understand what is happening here we have to consider the different ratios plotted in Figures 15.21, 15.22, and 15.23. The measure plotted in Figure 15.22 is a simple ratio of the form:

$$\frac{\text{Hosp Days City A}}{\text{mmd City A}}$$

The measure plotted in Figure 15.23 is a simple ratio of the form:

$$\frac{\text{Hosp Days City B}}{\text{mmd City B}}$$

Table 15.4: Hospital Days Per Million Member Days

Month	Total No. of Hosp. Days	Total No. of Member Days	Total Hosp. Rate/ mmd	CityA No. of members	CityA No. of Hosp. Days	CityA Hosp. Rate/ mmd	CityB No. of members	CityB No. of Hosp. Days	CityB Hosp. Rate/ mmd
Jan.	656	2,864,648	229.0	69,306	556	258.7	23,102	100	139.6
Feb.	620	2,725,604	227.5	71,347	483	241.7	25,996	137	188.2
Mar.	681	2,972,063	229.1	67,038	511	245.8	28,835	170	190.1
Apr.	681	3,000,390	227.0	70,434	521	246.5	29,579	160	180.3
May	660	3,102,449	212.7	67,633	483	230.3	32,446	177	175.9
Jun.	731	3,125,700	233.9	68,897	529	255.9	35,293	202	190.7
Jul.	694	3,366,972	206.1	70,281	525	240.9	38,331	169	142.2
Aug.	695	3,381,294	205.5	68,205	509	240.7	40,869	186	146.8
Sept.	683	3,362,310	203.1	70,637	507	239.2	41,440	176	141.5
Oct.	729	3,406,373	214.0	66,480	491	238.2	43,403	238	176.8
Nov.	715	3,480,510	205.4	70,263	516	244.7	45,754	199	144.9
Dec.	743	3,657,287	203.2	70,236	531	243.8	47,741	212	143.2
Jan.	762	3,589,304	212.3	67,024	502	241.6	48,760	260	172.0
Feb.	735	3,371,676	218.0	69,396	509	261.9	51,021	226	158.1
Mar.	780	3,833,863	203.5	70,327	532	244.0	53,346	248	149.9
Apr.	737	3,667,800	200.9	67,471	496	245.0	54,789	241	146.6
May	770	3,917,966	196.5	70,314	515	236.2	56,072	255	146.7
Jun.	727	3,773,580	192.7	67,906	484	237.5	57,880	243	139.9
Jul.	784	4,006,316	195.7	68,926	476	222.7	60,310	308	164.7
Aug.	839	4,121,853	203.5	70,074	508	233.8	62,889	331	169.7
Sept.	779	3,978,360	195.8	68,311	464	226.4	64,301	315	163.2
Oct.	853	4,182,985	203.9	68,832	502	235.2	66,103	351	171.2
Nov.	804	4,137,480	194.3	69,016	495	239.0	68,900	309	149.4
Dec.	832	4,365,730	190.6	69,833	480	221.7	70,997	352	159.9

But the measure plotted in Figure 15.21 is a ratio of aggregated values having the form:

$$\frac{\text{Hosp Days City A} + \text{Hosp Days City B}}{\text{mmd City A} + \text{mmd City B}}$$

When you have a simple ratio, you can get a signal on a process behavior chart from either a change in the numerator or a change in the denominator. When you have a complex ratio of aggregated values the number of ways in which changes can occur increase dramatically, making interpretation more complicated. In this case, the signals seen in Figure 15.21 are due to the enrollments. Inspection of Table 15.4 shows that the enrollments in City B were increasing during this two years while those in City A were fairly steady. Since City B had a lower average hospitalization rate than City A, this shift in enrollment caused an overall drop in the combined hospitalization rate. As this growth in City B tapers off, the "improvement" seen in Figure 15.21 will evaporate.

Ratios of aggregated measures can be hard to interpret. When aggregated measures are placed on an *XmR* Chart, and a signal is found, it is best to look at the disaggregated measures separately in order to determine what is happening.

15.8 The Cumulative Effect of Reducing Variation

While disaggregation is the key for the use of count data, it also plays a role with measurement data as well—as may be seen in the following example.

A company that produced motor mounts had a continuing problem with adhesion failures. Out of each batch of mounts, a certain number were tested to the point of failure. The value recorded for this test was the tension at which the failure occurred. Quarter by quarter, the test showed that at least 4 percent of the mounts failed at performance load levels. This poor showing was even worse in the spring and summer quarters. This high failure rate had persisted for years, in spite of many attempts by the engineers to make things better. The actual percentages of mounts that failed under performance loads are shown in Figure 15.24.

Figure 15.24: Percentage Failing Under Performance Loads 1976-1981

The motor-mount area began to implement the techniques given in this book in late winter of 1982. In the spring of that same year only 3 percent of the tested mounts failed under performance loads. In the summer quarter, this value was down to 2.5 percent. This unparalleled improvement caught everyone's attention. When the plant manager asked what had been done to make this improvement, the engineers and supervisors could not identify any one particular thing that was different. The only identifiable difference was the use of process behavior charts at each step of the operation. These charts showed that there had been a slight reduction in the variation for each step of the process. The lower rate of failure was due to the cumulative effect of these reductions of variation. Moreover, these improvements continued in the following quarters, as can be seen in Figure 15.25.

Figure 15.25: Percentage Failing Under Performance Loads 1976-1984

Making slight improvements in the consistency of each step in the production process pays off in a compound manner. As the variation is reduced at one step, subsequent steps are made easier. The material coming to each step is more uniform. This makes it possible to spend less time coaxing the process to work, and more time on ways to improve the process. By continuing this cycle throughout the process, the final product can be dramatically improved.

The running records in Figures 15.24 and 15.25 are report cards. They do not actually identify the changes that need to be made. They do, however, record the cumulative effect of the improvements that were made by *using process behavior charts at each of the 14 process steps.* The information in Figures 15.24 and 15.25 is far too cumulative to pin-point specific problems. Finally, note that there was no one "magic bullet" fix for this process. There was no one thing that needed to be changed in order to improve their performance. Instead, it was a matter of doing the same things they had always done, but doing them with less variation. And the key to doing this was the effective use of the process behavior charts at each step of the process.

15.9 Summary

The key feature of the data collection described in the previous example is the preservation of the ordering of each count in space and time so that this information could be used to assist in interpreting the counts. When people think of count data in terms of simple tallies, they usually fail to impose a useful structure on their data. This failure is a major cause of disappointing results in the use of count data.

This is why you must work to make the count data specific. With measurements, this is not a major problem because the act of obtaining the measurement usually makes the values specific enough. But with count data, the act of counting allows a certain vagueness to creep in: What is being counted? Are successive counts obtained the same way?

Moreover, once the count has been made specific, the structure of the data must be preserved by the way the counts are recorded. Measurements of different characteristics are not usually combined, but counts are routinely combined, and every time this happens some of the structure in the data is lost. This loss of information can only be avoided by positive action on the part of the investigator.

There are two guidelines for this positive action. First, are the categories of nonconformity sufficiently focused so that there is likely to be only one assignable cause per category? Secondly, does the data collection system allow backtracking to identify exactly what happened and where it happened? As long as the answer to either of these questions is minimally negative, there is room for improvement in the quality of the count data.

Good count data are not obtained by chance. They occur when people think about, and carefully plan, the collection of the data for the charts. While this is important with measurements, it is absolutely essential when dealing with counts.

By What Method?

What Do You Want to Accomplish?

How Will You Know?

Chapter Sixteen

Average and Range Charts

The previous nine chapters have discussed the Individual Value and Moving Range Chart (*XmR* Chart). In this chapter I introduce another type of chart: the Average and Range Chart (also known as the *X*-bar and *R* Chart). While Average and Range Charts are somewhat more specialized than *XmR* Charts, they do have certain advantages which make them particularly well suited for specific applications. At the same time, their greater specialization imposes certain restrictions upon their use. The advantages, restrictions, and issues surrounding Average and Range Charts are the topics of this chapter.

Administrative applications of the Average and Range Chart will be discussed and illustrated in this chapter and also in Chapter Eighteen. However, in the introduction of this technique, I will use a simple production example.

16.1 Creating an Average and Range Chart

In Shewhart's book, *Economic Control of Quality of Manufactured Product*, the basic chart is the Average and Range Chart. The reason for this is seen in the title above—Shewhart was focused on manufacturing problems, which was natural since he worked with Western Electric and Bell Laboratories.

When you are making widgets you usually have the option of collecting multiple measurements within a short period of time. When this happens it is logical to arrange these data—which are collected under essentially the same conditions—together into a group. Since there will be many of these small groups it is customary to call them *subgroups*, and the act of arranging the data into these subgroups is called *subgrouping*.

When you have data arranged in subgroups you can characterize the location of the process using the subgroup averages, and you can characterize the dispersion of the process using the subgroup ranges.

Imagine that you operate a small winery and that your bottling operation consists of a simple, single-head filler. You can fill about 300 bottles per hour, and you wish to monitor the filling operation by actually checking the fill weights of five bottles each hour. A timer is used to select one bottle every twelve minutes, and the five bottles from each hour are arranged together in a single subgroup. The fill weights are measured in milliliters (ml), and the label fill weight is 750 ml. The fill weights for the first hour are:

$$751 \text{ ml, } 754 \text{ ml, } 756 \text{ ml, } 754 \text{ ml, and } 753 \text{ ml}$$

- These five values comprise the first subgroup.

- The subgroup average is 753.6 ml.

- The subgroup range is 5 ml, which is the difference between the maximum value of 756 ml and the minimum value of 751 ml.

- These five measurements, along with their average and range, are placed on the Average and Range Chart, and the subgroup average and subgroup range are plotted as shown in Figure 16.1:

Figure 16.1: The First Subgroup on the Average and Range Chart for Fill Weights

The second hour you again measure the fill weights for five bottles. You get values of:

757 ml, 755 ml, 756 ml, 754 ml, and 756 ml

These five values are written on the Average and Range Chart, and the subgroup average and subgroup range are computed, entered, and plotted as shown in Figure 16.2.

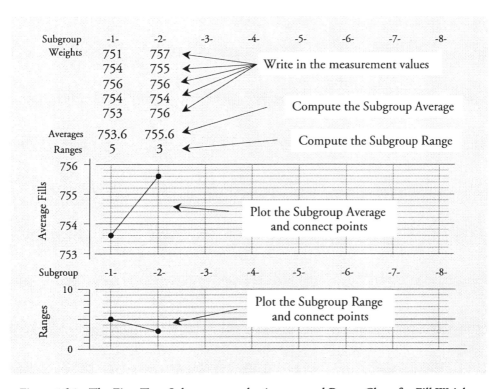

Figure 16.2: The First Two Subgroups on the Average and Range Chart for Fill Weights

Continuing in this manner, the measurements, subgroup averages, and subgroup ranges for one eight-hour shift are shown in Figure 16.3. With the addition of limits this figure will become an Average and Range Chart.

Subgroup	-1-	-2-	-3-	-4-	-5-	-6-	-7-	-8-
Weights	751	757	755	755	758	754	754	752
	754	755	757	751	753	755	758	757
	756	756	756	756	756	755	756	755
	754	754	752	757	754	754	757	754
	753	756	755	753	758	752	759	756
Averages	753.6	755.6	755.0	754.4	755.8	754.0	756.8	754.8
Ranges	5	3	5	6	5	3	5	5

Figure 16.3: The Fill Weight Data for Shift One

The two summary statistics used to compute limits for Average and Range Charts are the grand average and the average range.

- The *grand average* is the average of the subgroup averages, and is commonly denoted by the symbol:

$$\bar{\bar{X}}$$

- The *average range* is the average of the subgroup ranges and is commonly denoted by the symbol:

$$\bar{R}$$

For the data in Figure 16.3 the grand average is the average of the 8 subgroup averages, which is 755.0 milliliters.

For the data in Figure 16.3 the average range is the average of the 8 subgroup ranges, which is 4.625 milliliters.

To convert these two summary statistics into the appropriate limits we again make use of certain scaling factors. There are three scaling factors needed for Average and Range Charts:

A_2 is the scaling factor used to compute limits for the subgroup averages.

D_3 is the scaling factor used to compute the Lower Range Limit.

D_4 is the scaling factor used to compute the Upper Range Limit.

The values for these scaling factors will depend upon the subgroup size, n. Some values for these scaling factors are given in Table 16.1 and also in Tables 4 and 5 in the Appendix.

Table 16.1: Scaling Factors for Average and Range Charts

n	A_2	D_3	D_4
2	1.880	—	3.268
3	1.023	—	2.574
4	0.729	—	2.282
5	0.577	—	2.114
6	0.483	—	2.004
7	0.419	0.076	1.924
8	0.373	0.136	1.864
9	0.337	0.184	1.816
10	0.308	0.223	1.777
11	0.285	0.256	1.744
12	0.266	0.283	1.717
13	0.249	0.307	1.693
14	0.235	0.328	1.672
15	0.223	0.347	1.653

When n is 6 or less there will be no Lower Range Limit, and so no value for D_3 is given until n exceeds 6. Since Figure 16.3 has a subgroup size of $n = 5$ we will use the scaling factors of $A_2 = 0.577$ and $D_4 = 2.114$.

- The limits for the subgroup averages are commonly called "control limits." A more descriptive label is "limits for averages." To compute these limits for the subgroup averages you begin by multiplying the average range by the appropriate value of A_2.

$$A_2 \bar{R} = 0.577 \times 4.625 \text{ ml} = 2.67 \text{ ml}$$

- The Upper Average Limit will be found by adding this value to the grand average:

$$UAL = \bar{\bar{X}} + A_2 \bar{R} = 755.0 + 2.67 = 757.67 \text{ ml}$$

- In a similar manner, the Lower Average Limit will be found by subtracting the value of 2.67 milliliters from the grand average:

$$LAL = \bar{\bar{X}} - A_2 \bar{R} = 755.0 - 2.67 = 752.33 \text{ ml}$$

- To compute limits for subgroup ranges you multiply the average range by the appropriate values of D_3 and D_4. The Upper Range Limit for the data of Figure 16.3 is:

$$URL = D_4 \bar{R} = 2.114 \times 4.625 \text{ ml} = 9.78 \text{ ml}$$

and there is no Lower Range Limit in this case because $n = 5$.

When these limits are added to Figure 16.3 we get the Average and Range Chart shown in Figure 16.4.

Figure 16.4: **Average and Range Chart for Fill Weight Data for Shift One**

The Average and Range Chart in Figure 16.4 shows a predictable process. With a grand average of 755.0 this process can be said to be averaging about 5 milliliters above the label value of 750 milliliters.

The limits on the Average Chart define the routine variation for the average fill weights of five bottles. In this case, as long as the *process* average remains close to 755, the *subgroup averages* may vary in the region of 752.3 to 757.7. Whenever a subgroup average falls outside this region it should be taken to be a signal that the process average has changed.

The limit on the Range Chart defines the routine amount of variation for the subgroup ranges. In this case, as long as the *process* variation does not change the subgroup ranges should fall in the region of 0 to 10.

16.2 What Average Charts Do Best

Figure 16.5 shows the Average Charts for the fill weights from Shifts One and Two. While the two charts are not identical, they do tell the same story. This consistency from time period to time period is characteristic of a predictable process. Since the process is uniform and unchanging, the different segments reveal the same basic story. While the details change, the big picture remains the same.

Figure 16.5: Average Charts for Fill Weights from Shifts One and Two

So what is the advantage of using subgroup averages rather than individual values? When it makes sense to arrange the data into subgroups you will gain sensitivity by doing so. This increased sensitivity may be seen in the comparison shown in Figure 16.6, where the 16 Hourly Average Fill Weights are shown next to the 80 Individual Fill Weights.

The Average Chart and the X Chart have the same central lines, but the Average Chart has considerably narrower limits. With these narrower limits the Average Chart will be more sensitive to a process shift. Thus, the advantage of using subgrouped data is the advantage of increased sensitivity to process changes. With an Average and Range Chart you will be able to detect smaller process changes than you could detect with an *XmR* Chart. However, in order to achieve this greater sensitivity, it is imperative that the subgrouping used is a rational subgrouping.

Figure 16.6: Average Chart and Individual Values Chart for the Fill Weight Data

16.3 When Does It Make Sense To Use Subgroups?

When you place two or more values together in a subgroup you are making a *judgment* that you consider these values to have been collected under essentially the same conditions. This means that the differences between the values within a subgroup will represent nothing more, and nothing less, than routine, background variation.

> *Thus, the first requirement for rational subgrouping is that of*
> *internal homogeneity for the subgroups.*

One way to satisfy this requirement of internal homogeneity is to collect multiple measurements within a reasonably short time. While this is easy to do when making widgets, it becomes less feasible with continuous processes and administrative systems. In the example above we had one subgroup per hour and five pieces per subgroup. When we placed the five values from each hour together in one subgroup we were making a judgment that within each hour the five pieces could be considered to be essentially uniform.

This requirement of internal consistency means that you are willing to consider the variation within the subgroups as "background noise." The assumption that the values were collected under essentially the same conditions means that you are not concerned with the differences between the values. Thus these differences must be thought of as the background level of noise which is present in your system. And, as you may see from the computations, it is this background noise within the subgroups (as characterized by the average range) that is used to determine the limits for the Average and Range Chart.

> ***Thus, the second requirement for rational subgrouping is that***
> ***the variation within the subgroups must truly represent***
> ***the reasonable and proper amount of background variation for the process.***

In the previous example, when we computed the limits for the Average and Range Chart, we were using the average variation within the subgroups to set limits on how much variation we should expect to see from subgroup to subgroup. We used the average variation among the five bottles collected each hour to determine how much variation should occur from hour to hour. And the only way to *judge* if this is appropriate is to know both the process and the way the measurements are made.

In other words, there has always been an element of judgment involved in subgrouping. Subgrouping cannot be automated. It is the conclusion of a *thought* process that combines the context for the data with the purpose of the process behavior chart and then organizes the data in such a way that the chart will answer the questions of interest.

16.4 Daily Department Store Sales

There are many situations where people will tend to collect administrative data into subgroups. Some typical examples follow.

Table 16.2 shows the daily sales figures for a department store over a three month period. These values are given to the nearest hundred dollars. Each week's worth of sales have been made into a subgroup and the weekly averages and ranges are included at the bottom of Table 16.2.

Table 16.2: Daily Department Store Sales

Day	Week 1	Week 2	Week 3	Week 4	Week 5	Week 6	Week 7	Week 8	Week 9	Week 10	Week 11	Week 12	Week 13
Sun.	66	67	69	71	77	122	67	76	108	76	87	126	82
Mon.	44	46	56	86	67	76	65	85	77	60	64	55	68
Tues.	54	54	44	53	45	64	64	76	65	85	54	47	44
Wed.	108	107	100	92	112	100	89	87	98	71	107	103	121
Thurs.	78	109	88	70	90	70	89	103	100	100	99	113	100
Fri.	107	86	127	111	65	85	109	88	74	111	114	75	100
Sat.	150	142	149	160	189	139	163	151	158	171	159	180	180
Averages	86.7	87.3	90.4	91.9	92.1	93.7	92.3	95.1	97.1	96.3	97.7	99.9	99.3
Ranges	106	96	105	107	144	75	99	75	93	111	105	133	136

The grand average is 93.84, and the average range is 106.5.

The scaling factors for subgroups of size $n = 7$ are: $A_2 = 0.419$, $D_3 = 0.076$, and $D_4 = 1.924$.

The limits for the Average Chart are thus:

$$\bar{\bar{X}} \pm A_2 \bar{R} \ = \ 93.84 \pm (0.419 \times 106.5) = 49.21 \text{ to } 138.46$$

while the Range Chart limits are:

$$D_3 \bar{R} = 0.076 \times 106.5 = 8.1 \quad \text{and} \quad D_4 \bar{R} = 1.924 \times 106.5 = 204.9$$

These limits are shown in Figure 16.7.

Figure 16.7: Average and Range Chart for Daily Department Store Sales

Does the subgrouping of the Daily Department Store Sales shown in Table 16.2 satisfy the two requirements of rational subgrouping? Are the subgroups internally homogeneous? Does the variation within the subgroups provide the proper yardstick for measuring the variation from subgroup to subgroup?

Even a cursory reading of the data in Table 16.2 shows that there are substantial differences in the sales volumes of different days of the week, with Mondays and Tuesdays being low and Saturdays being highest. Therefore, when the seven days of one week are subgrouped together we have a collection of unlike things. This represents a violation of the first requirement of rational subgrouping.

In addition, the variation within the subgroups is the day-to-day variation, while the variation between the subgroups is the week-to-week variation. Since the day-to-day variation is a completely different type of variation than the week-to-week differences, it is unreasonable to expect that the variation within the subgroups will provide an appropriate yardstick for setting the limits on the Average Chart.

Therefore, the weekly subgroups shown in Table 16.2 violate both requirements of rational subgrouping. While it is possible to perform the computations and to create a chart using the "subgrouping" of Table 16.2, the failure to organize the data into *rational* subgroups will result in a chart that is useless.

Well, if we cannot subgroup these data by weeks, could we subgroup them by days? Table 16.3 shows the data of Table 16.2 rearranged into seven subgroups of size $n = 13$. Each of these subgroups represent a day of the week. The seven subgroup averages and subgroup ranges are shown on the right side of the table.

Table 16.3: Daily Department Store Sales

Day	Week 1	Week 2	Week 3	Week 4	Week 5	Week 6	Week 7	Week 8	Week 9	Week 10	Week 11	Week 12	Week 13	Average	Range
Sun.	66	67	69	71	77	122	67	76	108	76	87	126	82	84.1	60
Mon.	44	46	56	86	67	76	65	85	77	60	64	55	68	65.3	42
Tues.	54	54	44	53	45	64	64	76	65	85	54	47	44	57.6	41
Wed.	108	107	100	92	112	100	89	87	98	71	107	103	121	99.6	50
Thurs.	78	109	88	70	90	70	89	103	100	100	99	113	100	93.0	43
Fri.	107	86	127	111	65	85	109	88	74	111	114	75	100	96.3	62
Sat.	150	142	149	160	189	139	163	151	158	171	159	180	180	160.8	50

The grand average is still 93.84. The average range is 49.7.

With subgroups of size 13 the scaling factors are: $A_2 = 0.249$, $D_3 = 0.307$, and $D_4 = 1.693$.

The limits for the Average Chart are thus:

$$\bar{\bar{X}} \pm A_2 \bar{R} = 93.84 \pm (0.249 \times 49.7) = 81.46 \text{ to } 106.22$$

while the Range Chart limits are:

$$D_3 \bar{R} = 0.307 \times 49.7 = 15.3 \quad \text{and} \quad D_4 \bar{R} = 1.693 \times 49.7 = 84.1$$

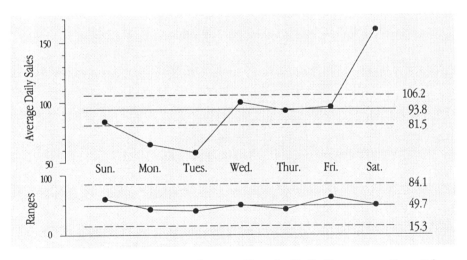

Figure 16.8: Another Average and Range Chart for Daily Department Store Sales

But do the subgroups of Table 16.3 satisfy the requirements of rational subgrouping? Is each subgroup internally homogeneous? Is it logical to assume that the sales volumes on a given day of the week are essentially the same from week to week? If there were substantial week-to-week differences, then would not these differences inflate the variation within each subgroup and thereby affect the limits computed?

While the subgrouping in Table 16.3 is not as severely flawed as that of Table 16.2, there are still potential problems with this second arrangement of these data. For example, while this subgrouping does allow you to distinguish the weekly sales pattern, it does not allow you to track your process over time.

How then can we track these sales over time? Could we plot these 91 values in a running record of Daily Sales? Yes. Should we turn this running record of 91 Daily Sales values into an *XmR* Chart? Probably not.

Figure 16.9: Running Record for Daily Department Store Sales

If we placed the 91 values from Table 16.2 on an *XmR* Chart, the strong daily cycle of sales would inflate the moving ranges, which would in turn inflate the limits. The principles of rational subgrouping require successive values on an *XmR* Chart to be collected under conditions that are, at least most of the time, reasonably similar. When your data display a recurring pattern this requirement is not satisfied. The name given to recurring patterns like the one in Figure 16.9 is seasonality. The next chapters will discuss ways of working with data that display such seasonal patterns.

Could we plot the weekly totals on an *XmR* Chart? Yes. This will probably be the most satisfying way of tracking these data over time.

16.5 Regional Sales by Quarter

Table 16.4 shows the quarterly sales for each of six regions for the past five years. These values have been arranged into 20 subgroups of size 6 so that each quarter is a subgroup. What type of variation occurs *within* the subgroups in Table 16.4? What type of variation occurs *between* subgroups in Table 16.4?

Table 16.4: Quarterly Sales for Five Years

Quarter	Region A	Region B	Region C	Region D	Region E	Region F	Averages	Ranges
1	924	1,412	1,056	539	397	431	793.2	1015
2	928	1,280	1,048	558	391	470	779.2	889
3	956	1,129	1,129	591	414	439	776.3	715
4	1,222	1,181	1,073	556	407	431	811.7	815
5	748	1,149	1,157	540	415	471	746.7	742
6	962	1,248	1,146	590	442	496	814.0	806
7	983	1,103	1,064	606	384	506	774.3	719
8	1,024	1,021	1,213	643	448	573	820.3	765
9	991	1,085	1,088	657	441	403	777.5	685
10	978	1,125	1,322	602	366	440	805.5	956
11	1,040	910	1,256	596	470	371	773.8	885
12	1,295	999	1,132	640	426	405	816.2	890
13	765	883	1,352	691	445	466	767.0	907
14	1,008	851	1,353	723	455	536	821.0	898
15	1,038	997	1,466	701	363	551	852.7	1103
16	952	878	1,196	802	462	670	826.7	734
17	1,041	939	1,330	749	420	588	844.5	910
18	1,020	834	1,003	762	454	699	795.3	566
19	976	688	1,197	807	447	743	809.7	750
20	1,148	806	1,337	781	359	702	855.5	978

The grand average for the subgroups of Table 16.4 is 803. The average range is 836. The Average and Range Chart for these 20 subgroups is shown in Figure 16.10.

Figure 16.10: Average and Range Chart for Quarterly Sales in Table 16.4

What is the problem with the subgrouping in Table 16.4? Are the subgroups internally homogeneous? It is the region-to-region variation that occurs within the subgroups in Table 16.4, while the quarter-to-quarter variation shows up between the subgroups. Is the region-to-region variation the proper yardstick for characterizing the variation from quarter to quarter? Would it not make more sense to acknowledge that the six regions are different, and then (as was done in Chapter Twelve) to track each region separately on an *XmR* Chart?

16.6 More on Peak Flow Rates

In Chapter Nine some peak flow rates were used to illustrate a clinical use of the *XmR* Chart. As was mentioned there, the patient was asked to obtain a peak flow rate four times each day: (1) in the morning before taking any medication, (2) in the morning fifteen minutes after taking medication, (3) in the evening prior to taking any medication, and (4) in the evening fifteen minutes after taking medication. Table 16.5 shows a set of peak flow rate data for one patient for a two-week period.

Table 16.5: Two Weeks of Peak Flow Rates

Day	1	2	3	4	5	6	7	8	9	10	11	12	13	14
morning pre-med	282	264	276	252	356	310	326	322	290	371	376	330	351	376
morning post-med	412	376	381	351	406	391	444	432	406	438	432	426	456	444
evening pre-med	322	386	314	302	421	432	396	396	314	456	371	391	438	391
evening post-med	411	396	416	361	421	432	426	450	342	486	468	468	429	432

One article, published in a medical journal, in an attempt to describe the clinical use of process behavior charts, arranged data like these into daily subgroups of size four—that is, each column in Table 16.5 was made into a subgroup. Each subgroup combined the a.m. pre-med value, the a.m. post-med value, the p.m. pre-med value, and the p.m. post-med value for a single day. This subgrouping fails both requirements for rational subgrouping. These subgroups are not internally homogeneous. Neither would the variation within these subgroups be the proper yardstick for evaluating the day-to-day variation (since these ranges would characterize the differences in pre-med vs. post-med and a.m. vs. p.m. rather than day-to-day differences).

Since the 56 values in Table 16.5 constitute a time series (as shown in Figure 16.11) another person suggested that these values should be placed on an *XmR* Chart. This approach would also be incorrect because the *XmR* Chart requires that successive values be logically comparable (see Section 10.1).

So how could you chart these data? You could take any *one* row of Table 16.5 and place the values on their own *XmR* Chart (see Section 9.3). Anything else amounts to nothing less than garbage in-garbage out.

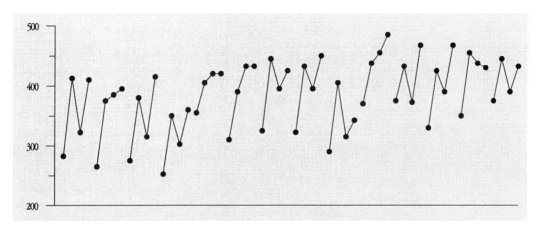

Figure 16.11: Four Peak Flow Rates Obtained Each Day

16.7 Administrative Average and Range Charts

When unlike things are subgrouped together the subgroups are said to be stratified. The problem of stratification will be apparent on the Average and Range Chart because it will result in limits that look too wide for the graph. This phenomenon may be seen in Figures 16.7 and 16.10. When the computations for an Average and Range Chart result in limits that look far too wide for the graph, check to see if unlike things have been grouped together. To understand this problem, return to the examples for Figures 16.7 and 16.10 and see how unlike things were subgrouped together in these two cases.

The Average and Range Chart, for all of its power and sensitivity, requires data which contain multiple measurements collected under essentially the same conditions. This requirement is rarely satisfied in service and administrative applications, where data tend to come along one value at a time. This means that it will be difficult to find ways of using Average and Range Charts to directly monitor service and administrative data. As outlined above, there are many ways to arrange data into what look like subgroups, but not all of these will result in charts that are appropriate, useful, or meaningful. If the subgrouping is not rational, then the chart will not work correctly, and you will be in danger of misleading yourself and others.

While it is difficult to use an Average and Range Chart to directly track administrative data over time, there are indirect ways of using the Average and Range Chart to gain insight into this kind of data. One way is to evaluate and estimate seasonal effects which might be present in your data. This use of the Average and Range Chart will be illustrated in Chapter Eighteen.

16.8 Exercises

EXERCISE 16.1:

The fill weights for Shift Two are given below:

Hour	Weights					Average	Range
9	755	754	753	754	755	754.2	2
10	757	758	755	753	754	755.4	5
11	757	755	756	753	752	754.6	5
12	759	758	755	756	753	756.2	6
13	756	754	756	755	755	755.2	2
14	755	750	755	757	755	754.4	7
15	757	754	756	754	754		
16	750	756	752	755	754		

(a) Compute the missing subgroup averages and subgroup ranges.
(b) Compute the grand average (the average of the averages).
(c) Compute the average range for the 8 subgroups of size 5.
(d) Plot the subgroup averages and subgroup ranges on the next page.
(e) Compute and plot the appropriate limits for the Average and Range Chart.
(f) Compare your Average Chart with the right-hand portion of Figure 16.5.

Computation Worksheet:

Grand Average = _____   Average Range = _____

Subgroup Size = n = ____   Number of Subgroups = k = ____

Multiply Average Range by A_2 = _____

UAL = Grand Average + A_2 times Average Range = _____

LAL = Grand Average − A_2 times Average Range = _____

URL = D_4 times Average Range = _____

(Exercise 16.1 Continued)

EXERCISE 16.2:

In Chapter 18 the Average and Range Chart will be used to evaluate seasonal relatives. A seasonal relative is computed by dividing the sales for a given month by the average monthly sales value. These seasonal relatives can be analyzed to determine whether the sales show definite seasonal effects.

The data from one of the examples in Chapter 18 are given below. The entry for January of Year One is 0.316, which means that the sales for January of Year One were 31.6% of the average monthly sales for Year One.

Since the seasonal relatives are given for two years worth of data, they have been organized by months into $k = 12$ subgroups of size $n = 2$.

Seasonal Relatives for Boutique Sales

Month	Year One	Year Two	Average	Range
January	0.316	0.355	0.3355	0.039
February	0.490	0.311	0.4005	0.179
March	0.749	0.422	0.5855	0.327
April	0.736	0.793	0.7645	0.057
May	1.075	1.276	1.1755	0.201
June	1.067	1.044	1.0555	0.023
July	0.959	0.857	0.908	0.102
August	1.094	1.179	1.1365	0.085
September	0.985	0.747	0.866	0.238
October	1.014	1.064	1.039	0.050
November	1.483	1.456	1.4695	0.027
December	2.032	2.495	2.2635	0.463

(a) Compute the grand average for these data.
(b) Compute the average range for the 12 subgroups of size 2.
(c) Finish plotting the subgroup averages and subgroup ranges on the next page.
(d) Compute and plot the appropriate limits for this Average and Range Chart.
(e) Compare your Average and Range Chart with that shown in Figure 18.10.

Computation Worksheet:

Grand Average = _____   Average Range = _____

Subgroup Size = n = ____   Number of Subgroups = k = ____

Multiply Average Range by A_2 = _____

UAL = Grand Average + A_2 times Average Range = _____

LAL = Grand Average – A_2 times Average Range = _____

URL = D_4 times Average Range = _____

(Exercise 16.2 Continued)

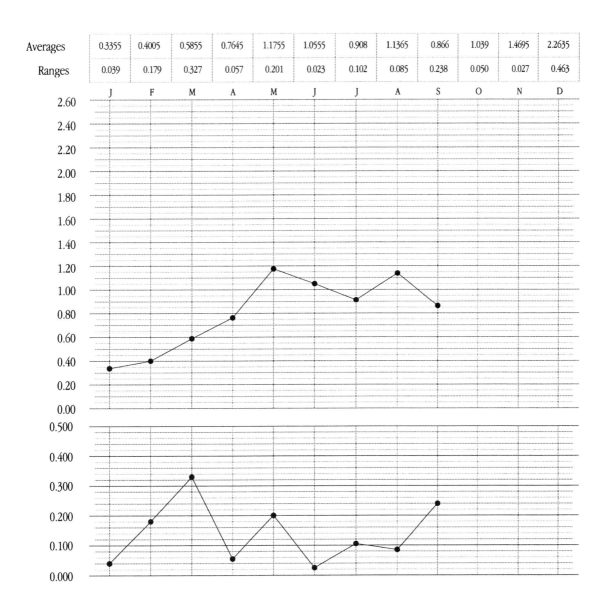

Averages	0.3355	0.4005	0.5855	0.7645	1.1755	1.0555	0.908	1.1365	0.866	1.039	1.4695	2.2635
Ranges	0.039	0.179	0.327	0.057	0.201	0.023	0.102	0.085	0.238	0.050	0.027	0.463
	J	F	M	A	M	J	J	A	S	O	N	D

EXERCISE 16.3

The total sales for each week from Table 16.2 are, respectively:

607, 611, 633, 643, 645, 656, 646, 666, 680, 674, 684, 699, and 695.

Find and plot the limits for the *XmR* Chart for these 13 weekly totals.

XmR Chart for Weekly Total Sales

Sales	607	611	633	643	645	656	646	666	680	674	684	699	695
mR		4	22	10	2	11	10	20	14	6	10	15	4

EXERCISE 16.4

The total sales for the 13 weeks from Table 16.2 are, respectively:

607, 611, 633, 643, 645, 656, 646, 666, 680, 674, 684, 699, and 695.

Place the data above on an X Chart with trended limits:

(a) Use the first six weeks values and the last six weeks values to construct a trend line.
(b) Estimate the amount by which this trend increases each week.
(c) Plot the Weekly Total Sales values, the trend line, and the trended limits on the graph.
(d) Estimate the total sales for week 14.
(e) How low would the sales for week 14 need to be to signal lower sales growth?
(f) How high would the sales for week 14 need to be to signal increased sales growth?

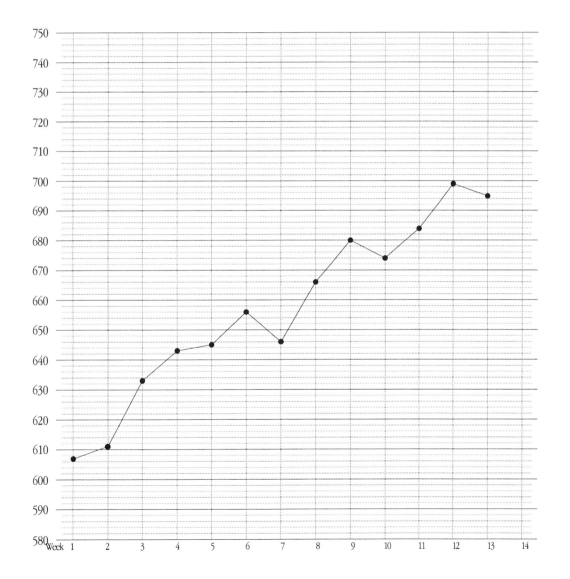

EXERCISE 16.5

For the subgrouping of Table 16.4 the grand average is 803; the average range is 836.

(a) Verify the limits shown in Figure 16.10.

(b) The median range is 850. Use the scaling factors from Table 5 in the Appendix to compute limits for Figure 16.10.

—◆—

No matter how you compute limits, the subgrouping in Table 16.4 is still stratified, and therefore not a rational subgrouping. Computations cannot correct the defects of bad subgrouping.

Chapter Seventeen

Smoothing Out Seasonal Data

Many time series display regular seasonal patterns and trends. These patterns and trends can be useful in your analysis and understanding of the data, but they also may obscure signals of changes which you would like to detect. Therefore, in order to get the most out of your data, you may need to be able to work with seasonal patterns and trends. Chapter Twelve showed how to construct simple trend lines and trended limits for a time-series plot. In this chapter and the next I will outline some ways of working with data which display seasonal patterns.

Of course, the use of the term "seasonal" does not restrict us to working with quarterly data. Seasonality is a label for any regularly recurring pattern in a time series.

17.1 Moving Averages

Perhaps the simplest way to handle seasonal patterns is to average or smooth them out, and one way to do this is to plot the totals or averages for each complete seasonal cycle. For example, Figure 16.9 shows data with a pattern that repeats itself every week. In Exercise 16.3 the weekly totals for these data were plotted on an *XmR* Chart, revealing the underlying trend without the clutter of the weekly pattern. But this method has the disadvantage of requiring that you wait until the end of the week to plot a point. While this may not represent too great an inconvenience with weekly data, it can become a problem with annual patterns—we do not want to wait until the end of the year to see how we are doing.

A second way of removing a seasonal pattern is to use a year-long *moving average*. With quarterly data, a four-period moving average will always contain four quarters worth of data, and therefore will average out the seasonal effects to reveal the underlying average. (With monthly values a year-long moving average would become a twelve-point moving average.)

To illustrate a moving average I will begin with the quarterly sales values from Region C, shown in Table 17.1. To compute a four-period moving average you obtain the sum of each successive group of four periods. The sum of the sales for the first four periods is 4306. The sum for Periods 2, 3, 4 and 5 is 4407. The sum for Periods 3, 4, 5, and 6 is 4505, etc.

Table 17.1: Quarterly Sales for Region C

Year	Quarter	Period	Region C Sales	4-Period Sum	4-Period Moving Average
One	I	1	1056	—	—
	II	2	1048	—	—
	III	3	1129	—	—
	IV	4	1073	4306	1076.50
Two	I	5	1157	4407	1101.75
	II	6	1146	4505	1126.25
	III	7	1064	4440	1110.00
	IV	8	1213	4580	1145.00
Three	I	9	1088	4511	1127.75
	II	10	1322	4687	1171.75
	III	11	1256	4879	1219.75
	IV	12	1132	4798	1199.50
Four	I	13	1352	5062	1265.50
	II	14	1353	5093	1273.25
	III	15	1466	5303	1325.75
	IV	16	1196	5367	1341.75
Five	I	17	1330	5345	1336.25
	II	18	1003	4995	1248.75
	III	19	1197	4726	1181.50
	IV	20	1337	4867	1216.75

Next you divide each of the four-period sums by 4 to obtain the four-period moving averages shown in the last column of Table 17.1. While a moving average is not hard to compute, the computations can become tedious, which is where modern spreadsheet programs become useful. Figure 17.1 combines the individual values with the four-period moving average for Region C.

Figure 17.1: Sales for Region C and Four-Period Moving Average

The plot shown in Figure 17.1 is a very powerful summary. The individual values show the levels for each month, allowing you to look for seasonal patterns and abnormal events. At the same time the four-period moving average removes any seasonality that might be present. It also removes the month-to-month noise that complicates the interpretation of the individual values. The four-period moving average reveals the long-term trends in a way that is simple and easy to interpret. This estimate of the trend is automatically updated every time you compute the moving average. And the latest value of the moving average provides you with an instantaneous estimate of current sales levels, after making allowance for recent trends and removing seasonal influences. Finally, the four-period moving average provides a balanced view of the sales levels without being unduly influenced by the euphoria of a good quarter or the depression of a bad quarter.

For report card measures (i.e. highly aggregated values) the simple plot of Figure 17.1 may be all that is needed in the way of analysis. By the time you have plotted both the latest value and the moving average you will know virtually everything that the report card measure can tell you.

The moving average is sometimes said to lag behind the time-series. This is because any moving average is constructed using historical values. We computed the first value of the four-period moving average at Time Period 4, and this is where we plotted it in Figure 17.1. In truth, the first value for the four-period moving average is the average for Time Periods 1, 2, 3, and 4, and might more properly be plotted at the mid-point of these four time periods (at Time Period 2.5). When this is done for the values shown in Figure 17.1, it has the effect of shifting the moving average curve back 1.5 time periods. This shifted curve is shown in Figure 17.2, along with the trended limits found (back in Chapter Twelve) using the first four years of values. Notice how closely the shifted four-period moving average matches the trend line during Years One to Four.

Figure 17.2: Sales for Region C and Four-Period Moving Average

To illustrate a 12-period moving average I will use the data from Table 17.2.

Table 17.2: Monthly Boutique Sales

Year	J	F	M	A	M	J	J	A	S	O	N	D
One	15.0	23.3	35.6	35.0	51.1	50.7	45.6	52.0	46.8	48.2	70.5	96.6
Two	20.1	17.6	23.9	44.9	72.2	59.1	48.5	66.7	42.3	60.2	82.4	141.2
Three	19.0	28.8	35.6	48.1	63.8	49.3	45.6	52.2	46.1	72.9	98.4	122.1

Table 17.3: 12-Period Moving Average for Boutique Sales

Time Period	Values Used (12-period moving subgroups)												Moving Average
12	15.0	23.3	35.6	35.0	51.1	50.7	45.6	52.0	46.8	48.2	70.5	**96.6**	**47.53**
13	23.3	35.6	35.0	51.1	50.7	45.6	52.0	46.8	48.2	70.5	**96.6**	20.1	47.96
14	35.6	35.0	51.1	50.7	45.6	52.0	46.8	48.2	70.5	**96.6**	20.1	17.6	47.48
15	35.0	51.1	50.7	45.6	52.0	46.8	48.2	70.5	**96.6**	20.1	17.6	23.9	46.51
16	51.1	50.7	45.6	52.0	46.8	48.2	70.5	**96.6**	20.1	17.6	23.9	44.9	47.33
17	50.7	45.6	52.0	46.8	48.2	70.5	**96.6**	20.1	17.6	23.9	44.9	72.2	49.09
18	45.6	52.0	46.8	48.2	70.5	**96.6**	20.1	17.6	23.9	44.9	72.2	59.1	49.79
19	52.0	46.8	48.2	70.5	**96.6**	20.1	17.6	23.9	44.9	72.2	59.1	48.5	50.03
20	46.8	48.2	70.5	**96.6**	20.1	17.6	23.9	44.9	72.2	59.1	48.5	66.7	51.26
21	48.2	70.5	**96.6**	20.1	17.6	23.9	44.9	72.2	59.1	48.5	66.7	42.3	50.88
22	70.5	**96.6**	20.1	17.6	23.9	44.9	72.2	59.1	48.5	66.7	42.3	60.2	51.88
23	**96.6**	20.1	17.6	23.9	44.9	72.2	59.1	48.5	66.7	42.3	60.2	82.4	52.88
24	20.1	17.6	23.9	44.9	72.2	59.1	48.5	66.7	42.3	60.2	82.4	**141.2**	**56.59**
25	17.6	23.9	44.9	72.2	59.1	48.5	66.7	42.3	60.2	82.4	**141.2**	19.0	56.50
26	23.9	44.9	72.2	59.1	48.5	66.7	42.3	60.2	82.4	**141.2**	19.0	28.8	57.43
27	44.9	72.2	59.1	48.5	66.7	42.3	60.2	82.4	**141.2**	19.0	28.8	35.6	58.41
28	72.2	59.1	48.5	66.7	42.3	60.2	82.4	**141.2**	19.0	28.8	35.6	48.1	58.68
29	59.1	48.5	66.7	42.3	60.2	82.4	**141.2**	19.0	28.8	35.6	48.1	63.8	57.98
30	48.5	66.7	42.3	60.2	82.4	**141.2**	19.0	28.8	35.6	48.1	63.8	49.3	57.16
31	66.7	42.3	60.2	82.4	**141.2**	19.0	28.8	35.6	48.1	63.8	49.3	45.6	56.92
32	42.3	60.2	82.4	**141.2**	19.0	28.8	35.6	48.1	63.8	49.3	45.6	52.2	55.71
33	60.2	82.4	**141.2**	19.0	28.8	35.6	48.1	63.8	49.3	45.6	52.2	46.1	56.03
34	82.4	**141.2**	19.0	28.8	35.6	48.1	63.8	49.3	45.6	52.2	46.1	72.9	57.08
35	**141.2**	19.0	28.8	35.6	48.1	63.8	49.3	45.6	52.2	46.1	72.9	98.4	58.42
36	19.0	28.8	35.6	48.1	63.8	49.3	45.6	52.2	46.1	72.9	98.4	**122.1**	**56.83**

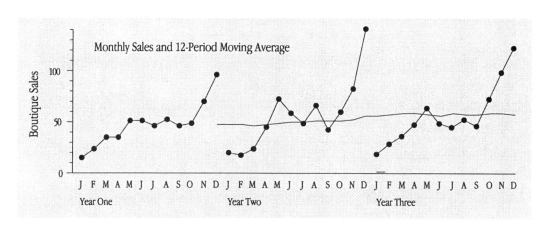

Figure 17.3: Boutique Sales and 12-Period Moving Average

The 12-period moving average is found by computing the average for each successive group of 12 values, as shown in Table 17.3. Since it will take 12 values to get started, the first value is computed at the 12th time period. Thus we get 25 moving averages from the 36 monthly values above. Figure 17.3 shows the monthly sales and the moving averages.

While the monthly values show the pronounced seasonality of the Boutique sales, the moving averages in Figure 17.3 remove these seasonal effects and show a gradual upward trend in sales. The current value of the moving average can always be converted into an annual sales amount by multiplying by 12. For example, the last value of 56.83 in Table 17.3 converts into total sales for the past 12 months of approximately 682 thousand dollars.

The advantages of combining a year-long moving average with the time-series plot of the individual values are simplicity, accessibility, and interpretability. The information contained in the data is conveyed to your readers with a minimum of fuss, with a minimum of effort, and without distracting details. For report card measures, this simple graph will often be sufficient.

As an additional example, Figure 17.4 shows the Daily Department Store Sales values from Table 16.3 with a 7-point moving average superimposed. The breaks in the running record provide anchor points for your eye so that you can see each week's values and the pattern within each week. The 7-point moving average removes this weekly pattern and provides a floating central line which serves to show the overall trend in these sales values. While the daily sales vary from 4,000 to 19,000, the average can be seen to have edged up slightly from just below 9,000 to just below 10,000 during this 13 week period.

Figure 17.4: Daily Department Store Sales and a 7-Period Moving Average

The one drawback to a *n*-period moving average is its tendency to show *n*-period cycles. This phenomenon can be seen in Figure 17.4. The excessively high sales on the last day of Week 5 and the first day of Week 6 each affect the next seven moving averages, creating the upswing in the moving average seen in Week 6. In the same way, the lower sales on the following weekend (the end of Week 6 and the beginning of Week 7) create the "recession" seen in Week 7. Exceptionally large or exceptionally small values will always influence the moving average for the next *n*-periods, and will give rise to these spurious cycles. The user should therefore refrain from interpreting an *n*-period cycle as a change in the underlying system until after checking to see if it is due to one or two extreme values.

17.2 Year-to-Date Plots

The problems of noise in the data and of seasonal effects have been appreciated for a long time. What has been lacking is an appreciation of the effective ways of handling these problems in an understandable and straightforward manner. The year-long moving average superimposed on a plot of the individual values, as described in the previous section, is an effective way of dealing with both noise and seasonal effects. Moreover, it is far superior to the more common practice of plotting the year-to-date values.

Table 17.4: Appliance Store Sales

Monthly Sales

Year	J	F	M	A	M	J	J	A	S	O	N	D
One	86.9	78.3	97.2	77.3	113.5	99.5	75.0	81.8	113.4	122.3	74.4	80.4
Two	72.3	78.1	91.5	91.7	141.5	113.2	107.0	96.7	99.1	71.8	78.4	46.5

Twelve-Period Moving Averages

Year	J	F	M	A	M	J	J	A	S	O	N	D
One												91.7
Two	90.5	90.4	90.0	91.1	93.5	94.6	97.3	98.5	97.4	93.1	93.5	90.7

Year-to-Date Values

Year	J	F	M	A	M	J	J	A	S	O	N	D
One	87	165	262	340	453	553	628	710	823	945	1020	1100
Two	72	150	242	334	475	588	695	792	891	963	1041	1088

The first problem with year-to-date values is the naive comparisons which they encourage. For example, consider the year-to-date values for Year Two above. In January it is reported that sales are lagging behind last year's sales (72 is less than 87). They are behind in February. They are behind in March. They are still behind in April. What a disaster! But wait, in May they pull ahead of last year's sales level and the gloom is dispelled. They are ahead in June. They are ahead in July. They are ahead in August. What a great year! They are ahead in September. They are ahead in October. They are ahead in November. And yet they finish the year behind last year—so kiss the bonus good-bye. And that is how year-to-date values are one of the major causes of man-made chaos. Whether we look at the year-to-date plot or the year-to-date values in the table we end up making the same naive comparisons because that is all these values will allow.

The second problem with year-to-date values is the way they are inappropriately plotted as a bar graph. The bars create visual clutter that distracts the eye from the comparison that is to be made while encouraging the naive comparisons described above.

Figure 17.5 Two Year-to-Date Plots for the Appliance Store Sales

Removing the bars and connecting the points will improve the graph as shown in the right panel in Figure 17.5. But while this improved year-to-date plot overcomes the second problem, it does not provide a remedy for the following problems.

The third problem with year-to-date values is that they do not provide a simple and direct way of estimating the overall monthly sales level. In contrast to this, consider Figure 17.6, which shows the monthly sales and the 12-period moving average for the appliance store sales. There the overall monthly sales level is represented by the moving average and is instantly comprehended by the reader.

The fourth problem with year-to-date values is that they do not easily provide an estimate of the annual sales. In contrast to this the total sales for the past 12 months is easily obtained at any point in time from Figure 17.6 by multiplying the moving average times 12.

The fifth problem with the year-to-date plots is that the improved version replaces the "levels" of Figure 17.6 with "slopes." Since slopes are much more subjective to interpret, and since the lines are seldom straight, this shift is one that introduces more complexity than clarity (a return to graphical purgatory). Furthermore, the bar chart version effectively hides the slopes that represent sales levels and makes them much harder to see.

The sixth problem with year-to-date plots is that they require an extremely compressed scale. This happens because the vertical scale has to allow for the annual total. As a consequence, even big swings in monthly values will result in small changes in angle. For example, the spike in sales in May of Year Two is easy to see in Figure 17.6, but hard to find in Figure 17.5. And the dramatic drop in sales in December of Year Two is only a slight change in angle on the year-to-date plots. While it is good to smooth out noise, the compressed scale of the year-to-date plot tends to obliterate more than just the noise.

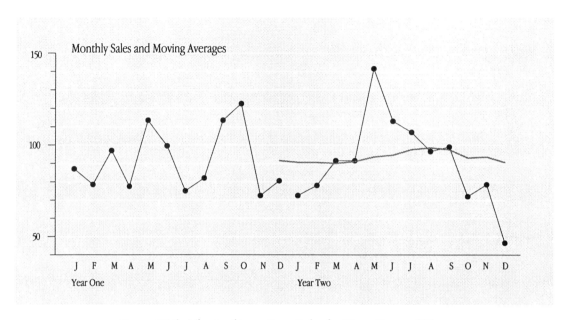

Figure 17.6: The Appliance Store Sales for Years One and Two

So year-to-date values will tell you that "when you're up you're up, and when you're down you're down, but when you're only half-way up you're neither up nor down." A plot that combines the running record with a year-long moving average will provide more useful information, in a more accessible format, than will a year-to-date plot in any form.

17.3 Summary

Moving averages allow you to smooth out the noise in the data and to average out recurring patterns, so that you can visualize the underlying trends and levels in those data. They provide a floating central line for the monthly individual values, and when combined with those values, as in Figure 17.6, they provide a powerful descriptive graph for your data.

While techniques exist for computing limits for Moving Average Charts, the issues of rational subgrouping undermine the use of these techniques with most types of administrative and service sector data (see Section 16.7). For this reason, the techniques for creating Moving Average and Moving Range Charts were not included in this book. In this chapter we are using a moving average to characterize the underlying trend rather than using it to look for signals. Methods for detecting signals in spite of seasonal effects will be described in the next chapter.

17.4 Exercises

EXERCISE 17.1 Compute a four-period moving average for the sales data below:

	Year	Qtr	Sales	Sums	Averages
-1-	One	I	46		
-2-		II	39		
-3-		III	35		
-4-		IV	40	_____	_____
-5-	Two	I	50	_____	_____
-6-		II	41	_____	_____
-7-		III	39	_____	_____
-8-		IV	42	_____	_____
-9-	Three	I	53	_____	_____
-10-		II	43	_____	_____
-11-		III	41	_____	_____
-12-		IV	45	_____	_____
-13-	Four	I	54	_____	_____
-14-		II	46	_____	_____
-15-		III	46	_____	_____
-16-		IV	50	_____	_____
-17-	Five	I	60	_____	_____
-18-		II	50	_____	_____
-19-		III	47	_____	_____
-20-		IV	53	_____	_____

Plot both the sales values and the moving averages below.

EXERCISE 17.2 Compute a four-period moving average for the quarterly sales data:

	Year	Qtr	Sales	Sums	Averages
-1-	One	I	141.8		
-2-		II	148.3		
-3-		III	137.1		
-4-		IV	142.6	_____	_____
-5-	Two	I	141.7	_____	_____
-6-		II	150.2	_____	_____
-7-		III	139.2	_____	_____
-8-		IV	142.7	_____	_____
-9-	Three	I	141.3	_____	_____
-10-		II	151.9	_____	_____
-11-		III	139.5	_____	_____
-12-		IV	143.1	_____	_____
-13-	Four	I	140.8	_____	_____
-14-		II	148.4	_____	_____
-15-		III	139.8	_____	_____
-16-		IV	144.0	_____	_____
-17-	Five	I	143.1	_____	_____
-18-		II	153.9	_____	_____
-19-		III	140.6	_____	_____
-20-		IV	146.4	_____	_____

Plot both the sales values and the moving averages below.

Chapter Eighteen

Deseasonalizing Data

While the previous chapter described the simplest way to deal with seasonality in your data, there are times when a more sophisticated approach is required. The techniques described in this chapter will allow you to analyze data containing strong seasonal components in a manner that is consistent with the approach described in earlier chapters.

18.1 The Problem of Seasonal Effects

The year-long moving average hides seasonal effects by averaging them out. Another way of working with seasonal effects is to explicitly adjust the data to allow for seasonality.

To illustrate data that have a strong seasonal pattern which is recurring from year to year we shall look at the monthly sales figures for a single store in a chain of department stores. The monthly sales, in thousands of dollars, are shown in Table 18.1, and the time series plot for these data is shown in Figure 18.1.

Table 18.1: Monthly Department Store Sales

	J	F	M	A	M	J	J	A	S	O	N	D
Year One	242.5	295.1	377.9	330.6	425.0	395.3	384.3	415.8	380.8	447.9	525.0	566.6
Year Two	241.0	287.2	365.0	322.1	418.8	400.2	403.7	410.9	382.8	449.8	520.7	549.1
Year Three	252.4	309.5	405.1									

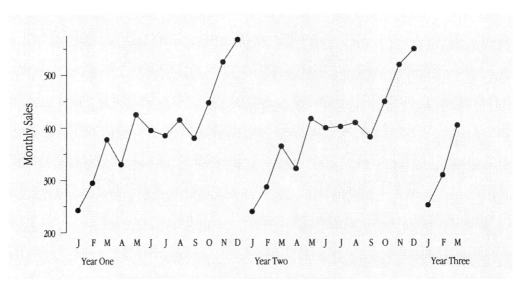

Figure 18.1: Monthly Department Store Sales

Clearly the dominant feature of the running record in Figure 18.1 is an annual pattern. This annual pattern effectively undermines simple comparisons between successive months—January cannot be compared with either December or February. So while we can use these data to compare January with January, and February with February, etc., we cannot compare months within a year.

If we should attempt to place these data on an *XmR* Chart we would get something like Figure 18.2, which only reveals what we already knew—there is a detectable difference in sales volume from month to month throughout the year.

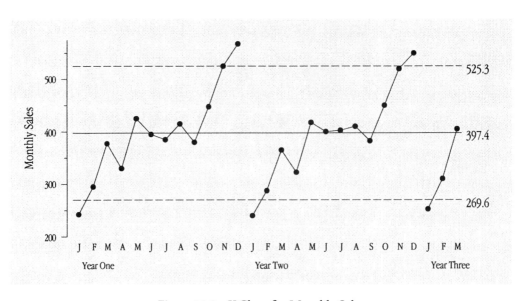

Figure 18.2: *X* Chart for Monthly Sales

Now just how can the manager of this store interpret the sales for the First Quarter of Year Three? He has made changes in the store's advertising, and he wants to know if it has had an impact. Can he use Figure 18.2 to tell if sales have changed? With the strong monthly pattern, and the large amount of month-to-month variation, it is difficult to make a reliable judgment using either Figure 18.1 or 18.2. We ought to be able to exploit the annual pattern to make our analysis more sensitive. And this is where *deseasonalized* data are helpful.

18.2 Deseasonalized Values

A value is deseasonalized when we remove the average seasonal effect. (Thus we will have to have previously determined the average seasonal effect. A way of doing this is outlined in the next section.) Deseasonalized monthly sales are obtained by dividing each monthly sales value by the corresponding seasonal factor.

$$\text{Deseasonalized January Sales} \ = \ \frac{\text{January Sales}}{\text{Seasonal Factor for January}}$$

For the Department Store Sales, the actual sales for January of Year One are 242.5 thousand. As we will find in the next section, the sales in January are typically about 61% as big as the average monthly sales for the year:

$$(\text{Average Monthly Sales for Year}) \ \times \ (0.61) \ = \ \text{Average January Sales Value}$$

So if we divide our current January Sales figure of 242.5 thousand by the January Seasonal Factor of 0.61 we will obtain an estimate of our average monthly sales for this year:

$$\frac{242.5 \text{ thousand}}{0.61} \ = \ 397.5 \text{ thousand}$$

Sales of 242.5 thousand in January are equivalent to an average monthly sales level of 397.5 thousand per month, or an annual sales level of:

$$12 \ \times \ 397.5 \text{ thousand} \ = \ \$ 4,770,000$$

The actual sales for February of Year One were 295.1 thousand. In the past, the sales in February have been about 73% of the average monthly sales for the year. Therefore, sales of 295.1 thousand in February are equivalent to an average monthly sales level of:

$$\frac{295.1 \text{ thousand}}{0.73} \ = \ 404.2 \text{ thousand}$$

Notice how the different sales values for January and February (242.5 and 295.1 differ by 18%) become quite similar when adjusted for seasonal effects (397.5 and 404.2 differ by 1.7%).

Thus, a deseasonalized value (also known as a seasonally adjusted value) is one that has been converted into an estimated average value.

When you deseasonalize a set of values you are dividing those numbers that tend to be large by a large seasonal factor, and you are dividing those numbers that tend to be small by a small seasonal factor, with the result that "things even out" and the adjusted values may reasonably be compared. You can see this happening in Table 18.2 which contains: (1) the monthly sales, (2) the seasonal factors, and (3) the deseasonalized monthly sales for the Department Store Sales for Years One and Two.

Figure 18.3 shows the deseasonalized monthly sales superimposed upon the monthly sales. Clearly when you deseasonalize a time series you remove the average annual pattern. This allows you to look for other interesting signals which may be contained in the data. The vertical scale of Figure 18.3 is such that about all we can tell from the deseasonalized data is that they approximate the annual average for each year. To learn more from the deseasonalized data we will eventually place them on an *XmR* Chart.

Table 18.2: Deseasonalized Monthly Department Store Sales

	J	F	M	A	M	J	J	A	S	O	N	D
Yr One Monthly Sales	242.5	295.1	377.9	330.6	425.0	395.3	384.3	415.8	380.8	447.9	525.0	566.6
Seasonal Factors	*0.61*	*0.73*	*0.93*	*0.82*	*1.06*	*1.00*	*1.00*	*1.04*	*0.96*	*1.13*	*1.32*	*1.40*
Yr I Deseasonalized	397.5	404.2	406.3	403.2	400.9	395.3	384.3	399.8	396.7	396.3	397.7	404.7
Yr Two Monthly Sales	241.0	287.2	365.0	322.1	418.8	400.2	403.7	410.9	382.8	449.8	520.7	549.1
Seasonal Factors	*0.61*	*0.73*	*0.93*	*0.82*	*1.06*	*1.00*	*1.00*	*1.04*	*0.96*	*1.13*	*1.32*	*1.40*
Yr II Deseasonalized	395.1	393.4	392.5	392.8	395.1	400.2	403.7	395.1	398.8	398.1	394.5	392.2

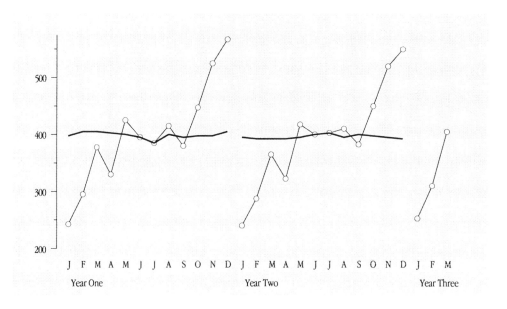

Figure 18.3: Monthly Sales and Deseasonalized Monthly Sales

18.3 Finding Seasonal Factors

In computing seasonal factors you will need at least two years worth of data. Three or more years may be used, but since we are not interested in ancient history we will rarely need more than four or five years worth of data. I will illustrate this procedure using the department store sales for Years One and Two.

The first step in constructing seasonal factors is to compute the seasonal relatives for each season or month. This is done by dividing each month's value by the average value for that year—the value for January of Year One would be divided by the average monthly value for Year One, etc. In Year One the department store had sales of 4,786.8 thousand. This corresponds to a monthly average of 398.9 thousand. The January sales were 242.5 thousand. The seasonal relative for January of Year One is thus:

$$\text{Seasonal Relative} = \frac{\text{this month's value}}{\text{average monthly value}} = \frac{242.5 \text{ thousand}}{398.9 \text{ thousand}} = 0.608$$

Since we are only concerned with the approximate relationship between the monthly values and the annual average, it is unnecessary to record the seasonal relatives to more than three decimal places. The seasonal relatives for Years One and Two are shown in Table 18.3.

Table 18.3: Seasonal Relatives for the Department Store Sales

	J	F	M	A	M	J	J	A	S	O	N	D
Year One Sales	242.5	295.1	377.9	330.6	425.0	395.3	384.3	415.8	380.8	447.9	525.0	566.6
Average for Year 1	398.9	398.9	398.9	398.9	398.9	398.9	398.9	398.9	398.9	398.9	398.9	398.9
Seasonal Relatives	.608	.740	.947	.829	1.065	.991	.963	1.042	.955	1.123	1.316	1.420
Year Two Sales	241.0	287.2	365.0	322.1	418.8	400.2	403.7	410.9	382.8	449.8	520.7	549.1
Average for Year 2	395.9	395.9	395.9	395.9	395.9	395.9	395.9	395.9	395.9	395.9	395.9	395.9
Seasonal Relatives	.609	.725	.922	.814	1.058	1.011	1.020	1.038	.967	1.136	1.315	1.387

Having computed these seasonal relatives, the next question is whether or not they represent real, detectable seasonal effects. To answer this question we place the seasonal relatives on an Average and Range Chart. All of the seasonal relatives for January are placed in one subgroup, and all of the seasonal relatives for February are placed in a second subgroup, and so on until you have 12 subgroups of two seasonal relatives each. (If you use three years of data then you would have 12 subgroups of size three.) The limits for this Average and Range Chart are computed in the usual manner, and averages that fall outside the limits are interpreted to be *detectable seasonal effects*.

The grand average for the 12 subgroups in Figure 18.4 is 1.0000. (While the grand average for the seasonal relatives will often be close to 1.0, there is no guarantee that it must be exactly 1.0.) The average range for these 12 subgroups is 0.0169. Since we are using two years worth of data here, our subgroups are of size two. From Table 4 in the Appendix, the scaling factors for subgroups of size $n = 2$ are $A_2 = 1.880$, and $D_4 = 3.268$. Thus, we compute limits to be:

$$Upper\ Average\ Limit\ =\ \bar{\bar{X}}\ +\ A_2\ \bar{R}\ =\ 1.0000\ +\ (1.880\ \times\ 0.0169)\ =\ 1.032$$
$$Lower\ Average\ Limit\ =\ \bar{\bar{X}}\ -\ A_2\ \bar{R}\ =\ 1.0000\ -\ (1.880\ \times\ 0.0169)\ =\ 0.968$$
$$Upper\ Range\ Limit\ =\ D_4\ \bar{R}\ =\ 3.268\ \times\ 0.0169\ =\ 0.055$$

These limits are shown in Figure 18.4. With ten averages outside the limits, and with some of these falling far outside the limits, the chart indicates strong seasonality in these data.

The strength of the seasonal pattern present in the data is shown by the relationship between the running record and the limits on the Average Chart. If there are only two or three averages outside the limits, and if they are only slightly outside the limits, then you will not gain much by deseasonalizing the data. When there are many averages outside the limits, and when some of those averages are far outside the limits, there is strong seasonality present, and you will gain sensitivity in your analysis by deseasonalizing the data.

Average and Range Chart for Seasonal Relatives

	Jan	Feb	Mar	Apr	May	Jun	Jul	Aug	Sept	Oct	Nov	Dec
Year One	0.608	0.740	0.947	0.829	1.065	0.991	0.963	1.042	0.955	1.123	1.316	1.420
Year Two	0.609	0.725	0.922	0.814	1.058	1.011	1.020	1.038	0.967	1.136	1.315	1.387
Averges	0.6085	0.7325	0.9345	0.8215	1.0615	1.001	0.9915	1.040	0.961	1.1295	1.3155	1.4035
Ranges	0.001	0.015	0.025	0.015	0.007	0.020	0.057	0.004	0.012	0.013	0.001	0.033

Figure 18.4: Average and Range Chart for Seasonal Relatives for Department Store Sales

The Range Chart checks for consistency within the subgroups. Any range values that fall above the upper limit indicate that the seasonal pattern for that month may be changing from year to year, or else that a special event changed the seasonal pattern for one of the years used. Here the month of July shows excessive variation from Year One to Year Two. In general, an explanation for any discrepancy between seasonal relatives should be sought. In this case, since the average seasonal relative for July is so close to 1.00, any inconsistency in our estimate of the seasonality for July will be small compared to the seasonalities for the other months. This means that any uncertainty in the estimated seasonal factor for July will not have any real impact on our seasonal adjustments, so that here we can safely ignore the inconsistency in the seasonal relatives for July.

Seasonal factors do not need to be known to high degrees of precision. Generally two or three decimal places will be sufficient. We are going to use the seasonal factors to characterize the relative inflation or deflation that is expected for each month. Rarely do we need to know this type of adjustment to more than the nearest percent. So if the Average Chart shows evidence of sufficient seasonality to make it worthwhile to deseasonalize the data, we will convert the average seasonal relatives into seasonal factors by rounding them off to two (or three) decimal places.

As a check on everything having been done right, the seasonal factors should always add up to be equal to the number of seasons. For monthly data, the sum of the 12 seasonal factors should add up to 12.00, and for quarterly data the four seasonal factors should sum up to 4.00. Since the rounded values in Table 18.4 sum to 11.99 a slight adjustment is needed. In this case I arbitrarily added 0.01 to the July seasonal factor, making it 1.00 and making the sum of all the seasonal factors equal to 12.00.

Table 18.4: **Average Seasonal Relatives Converted into Seasonal Factors**

	J	F	M	A	M	J	J	A	S	O	N	D
Averages	.6085	.7325	.9345	.8215	1.0615	1.001	.9915	1.040	.961	1.1295	1.3155	1.4035
Rounded	.61	.73	.93	.82	1.06	1.00	0.99	1.04	.96	1.13	1.32	1.40
Adjusted	.61	.73	.93	.82	1.06	1.00	1.00	1.04	.96	1.13	1.32	1.40

For this department store we estimate that January sales are typically 61% of the average monthly sales for the year, February sales are typically 73% of the average, March sales are typically 93% of the average, etc. These seasonal factors may be used to seasonalize forecast sales values or to deseasonalize actual sales values.

18.4 Deseasonalizing the Sales Values

When we deseasonalize our data we need to make a distinction between "baseline" values and "future" values. Baseline values will be those data that were used to compute the seasonal factors. Subsequent values will be those data that were not used in the computation of the seasonal factors. In general, the purpose of finding seasonal factors is to use them to better understand the future values, and the means by which we do this is deseasonalization. However, in addition to deseasonalizing the future values, we will also want to know whether or not the future values are consistent with the baseline values. And to do this we will need an *XmR* Chart.

Therefore, the first step in analyzing the deseasonalized values will consist of placing the deseasonalized baseline values on an *XmR* Chart in the usual way. Table 18.5 contains the these baseline values for our department store for Years One and Two. The *XmR* Chart for these data is shown in Figure 18.5. The average value is 397.4 and the median moving range is 3.1.

The impact of removing the annual pattern from these data can be seen by comparing the width of the limits in Figure 18.2 (255.6 units) with the width of the limits on the *X* Chart of Figure 18.5 (19.5 units). By deseasonalizing these data we have removed over 90% of the month-to-month variation, resulting in a much more sensitive analysis.

Table 18.5: Deseasonalized Monthly Department Store Sales

	J	F	M	A	M	J	J	A	S	O	N	D
Yr One Monthly Sales	242.5	295.1	377.9	330.6	425.0	395.3	384.3	415.8	380.8	447.9	525.0	566.6
Seasonal Factors	*0.61*	*0.73*	*0.93*	*0.82*	*1.06*	*1.00*	*1.00*	*1.04*	*0.96*	*1.13*	*1.32*	*1.40*
Yr I Deseasonalized	397.5	404.2	406.3	403.2	400.9	395.3	384.3	399.8	396.7	396.3	397.7	404.7
mR	–	*6.7*	*2.1*	*3.1*	*2.3*	*5.6*	*11.0*	*15.5*	*3.1*	*0.4*	*1.4*	*7.0*
Yr Two Monthly Sales	241.0	287.2	365.0	322.1	418.8	400.2	403.7	410.9	382.8	449.8	520.7	549.1
Seasonal Factors	*0.61*	*0.73*	*0.93*	*0.82*	*1.06*	*1.00*	*1.00*	*1.04*	*0.96*	*1.13*	*1.32*	*1.40*
Yr II Deseasonalized	395.1	393.4	392.5	392.8	395.1	400.2	403.7	395.1	398.8	398.1	394.5	392.2
mR	*9.6*	*1.7*	*0.9*	*0.3*	*2.3*	*5.1*	*3.5*	*8.6*	*3.7*	*0.7*	*3.6*	*2.3*

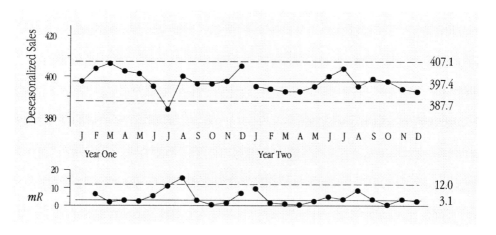

Figure 18.5: *XmR* Chart for Deseasonalized Baseline Monthly Sales

The only signal seen in Figure 18.5 is the value for July of Year One. (This signal corresponds to the range point outside the limits in Figure 18.4.) The sales for this month were exceptionally low for some reason. Since this is a historical point, it may not be possible to identify the assignable cause of this signal. However, if it is possible, we might well learn something that can be advantageous in the future.

The main reason to construct the *XmR* Chart for the deseasonalized baseline values is to obtain values that can be used to construct limits for use with the deseasonalized future values. In and of itself, the chart in Figure 18.5 will not be of very great interest. The reason for this lies in an anomaly that will always be present in the deseasonalized baseline values.

When the seasonal factors are based on two years of data the pattern shown by one year will also be seen repeated, upside-down, in the other year. Figure 18.6 shows the pattern for Year One with the pattern for Year Two flipped vertically about the Grand Average of 397.4. Except for the rounding and adjusting of the seasonal factors, these two patterns would be exactly the same.

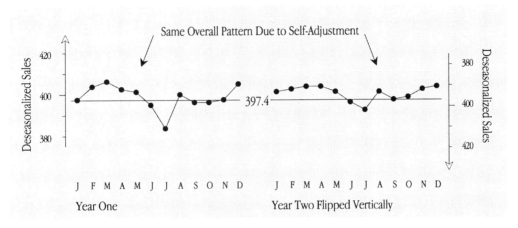

Figure 18.6: Deseasonalized Baseline Values Show the Same Pattern of Variation

This flipped pattern between Years One and Two is due to the self-adjustment that occurs when we deseasonalize the baseline values.

The reason for this flipped pattern can be seen when we realize that we are dividing each of the January sales values by their average seasonal relative, therefore one of the values will be above the their average and the other value will be a equal distance below their average. The rounding and adjusting of the average seasonal relatives will disturb this equilibrium to some extent, but the overall patterns will be strikingly similar (as seen in Figure 18.6).

When three or more years are used to find the seasonal factors a more complex version of this symmetry between the baseline years will be present. In every case, this symmetry between the baseline years will make the interpretation of the *XmR* Chart for the deseasonalized baseline values questionable. Since these patterns are consequences of the arithmetic of deseasonalizing the baseline data, rather than a characteristic of the underlying process, they should not be interpreted as having any meaning.

So why did we construct the *XmR* Chart in Figure 18.5? We construct a chart using the baseline values in order to obtain limits to use with deseasonalized future values. However, we cannot simply use the limits from Figure 18.5. The self-adjustment that created the patterns noted above also reduces the variation of the deseasonalized baseline values. Therefore, before we can compute limits for future deseasonalized values we will have to make allowance for this reduced variation in the baseline values.

Table 18.6: **Factors for Computing Limits for Deseasonalized Future Values Based on the Deseasonalized Baseline Values**

m	E_7	D_7	$\sqrt{\dfrac{m+1}{m-1}}$	E_8	D_8
2	4.607	5.660	1.732	5.447	6.694
3	3.762	4.622	1.414	4.448	5.466
4	3.434	4.219	1.291	4.060	4.990
5	3.258	4.002	1.225	3.852	4.734
6	3.147	3.867	1.183	3.721	4.573
7	3.072	3.774	1.155	3.632	4.463
8	3.016	3.706	1.134	3.566	4.382
9	2.974	3.654	1.118	3.516	4.321
10	2.941	3.613	1.106	3.477	4.273

Given an **Average** and an **Average Moving Range** computed from the m years of *deseasonalized baseline values*, compute limits for the *deseasonalized future values* according to:

$$UNPL = \bar{X} + 2.660 \sqrt{\frac{m+1}{m-1}}\, \bar{R} = \bar{X} + E_7\, \bar{R}$$

$$CL = \bar{X}$$

$$LNPL = \bar{X} - 2.660 \sqrt{\frac{m+1}{m-1}}\, \bar{R} = \bar{X} - E_7\, \bar{R}$$

$$URL = 3.268 \sqrt{\frac{m+1}{m-1}}\, \bar{R} = D_7\, \bar{R}$$

$$CL_R = \sqrt{\frac{m+1}{m-1}}\, \bar{R}$$

Given an **Average** and a **Median Moving Range** computed from the m years of *deseasonalized baseline values*, compute limits for the *deseasonalized future values* according to:

$$UNPL = \bar{X} + 3.145 \sqrt{\frac{m+1}{m-1}}\, \tilde{R} = \bar{X} + E_8\, \tilde{R}$$

$$CL = \bar{X}$$

$$LNPL = \bar{X} - 3.145 \sqrt{\frac{m+1}{m-1}}\, \tilde{R} = \bar{X} + E_8\, \tilde{R}$$

$$URL = 3.865 \sqrt{\frac{m+1}{m-1}}\, \tilde{R} = D_8\, \tilde{R}$$

$$CL_R = \sqrt{\frac{m+1}{m-1}}\, \tilde{R}$$

The deseasonalized future values will always show greater variation than the deseasonalized baseline values. In fact, when the seasonal factors are based on m years worth of data, the variation in the deseasonalized future values will be greater than the variation of the deseasonalized baseline values by a factor of:

$$\sqrt{\frac{m+1}{m-1}}$$

This inflation will change the formulas in the manner shown in Table 18.6. For the department store sales the seasonal factors were based on $m = 2$ years of data, the deseasonalized baseline values had an average of 397.4 and a median moving range of 3.1. Using these values the limits for the deseasonalized future values, shown in Figure 18.7, are:

$$UNPL = 414.3, \; LNPL = 380.5,$$

$$URL = 20.75 \; \text{and} \; CLR = 5.37$$

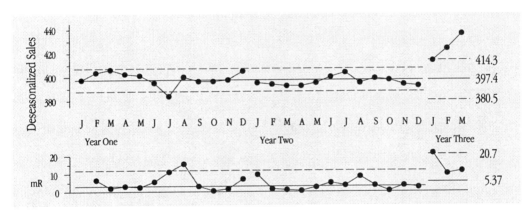

Figure 18.7: Has a Change Occurred in Year Three of Deseasonalized Monthly Sales?

What can we say about the new advertising campaign in Year Three? Did it have any impact upon sales? Should the manager continue this new approach or drop it to save money? The deseasonalized values for the first quarter of Year Three show a detectable improvement in sales. Thus, it would seem that the change in advertising strategy was worthwhile. It is instructive to note how Figure 18.7 makes this change clear while Figures 18.1, 18.2, and 18.3 tend to obscure it.

Given that we now have evidence that Year Three is different from Years One and Two, we might want to shift our central line to reflect this change. The average of the first three deseasonalized values from Year Three is 424.5 thousand. With a central line of 424.5 thousand, and the spread of ± 16.9 thousand used in Figure 18.7, we get the limits of 407.6 thousand to 441.4 thousand shown in Figure 18.8. Thus, when seasonally adjusted, the sales for the first three months of Year Three are equivalent to an average sales level of 424.5 thousand per month. Furthermore, if this new sales level is maintained, the remaining months should have seasonally adjusted sales in the region of 408 thousand to 441 thousand.

Table 18.7: Monthly Department Store Sales

	J	F	M	A	M	J	J	A	S	O	N	D
Year One	242.5	295.1	377.9	330.6	425.0	395.3	384.3	415.8	380.8	447.9	525.0	566.6
Year Two	241.0	287.2	365.0	322.1	418.8	400.2	403.7	410.9	382.8	449.8	520.7	549.1
Year Three	252.4	309.5	405.1	345.3	477.5	417.5	423.1	462.3	414.0	480.0	556.2	591.5

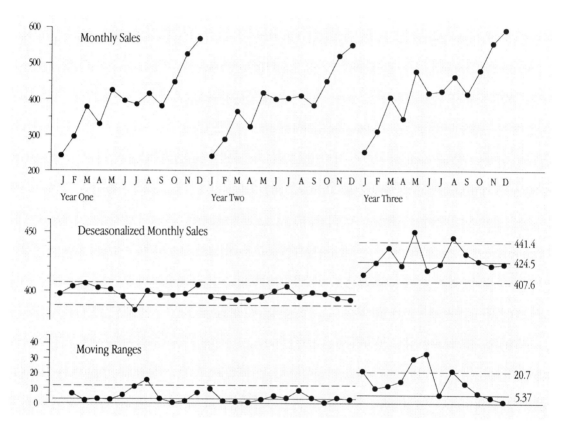

Figure 18.8: Department Store Sales for Years One, Two and Three

Perhaps the best way to present data having a strong seasonal component is a combination graph like that shown in Figure 18.8. There we combine the time-series plot of the original data with the *XmR* Chart for the deseasonalized values. The time-series plot of the raw data shows both the seasonality and the actual levels of the measure, while the deseasonalized data on the *XmR* Chart allows your readers to spot interesting features in the data and prompts them to ask the right questions.

In addition to the increased sales level in Year Three, both the X Chart and the *mR* Chart show an increased level of volatility for those sales. We could obtain limits to use with Year Four from the deseasonalized values for Year Three by using the regular formulas given in Table 2 of the Appendix.

18.5 Not All Data Show Strong Seasonality

The Department Store Sales Data in the previous section displayed strong seasonality. But not all sales data have such a consistent pattern from year to year. Here I shall return to the data shown in Table 17.2. The first two years of sales for a retail boutique, in thousands of dollars, are shown in Figure 18.9. While each year shows a general trend of increasing sales throughout the year, these values do not show the same degree of parallelism from year to year that we saw in Figure 18.1.

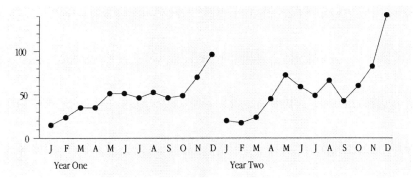

Figure 18.9: Monthly Sales for Boutique

Average and Range Chart for Seasonal Relatives

	Jan	Feb	Mar	Apr	May	Jun	Jul	Aug	Sept	Oct	Nov	Dec
Year One	0.316	0.490	0.749	0.736	1.075	1.067	0.959	1.094	0.985	1.014	1.483	2.032
Year Two	0.355	0.311	0.422	0.793	1.276	1.044	0.857	1.179	0.747	1.064	1.456	2.495
Averages	0.3355	0.4005	0.5855	0.7645	1.1755	1.0555	0.908	1.1365	0.866	1.039	1.4695	2.2635
Ranges	0.039	0.179	0.327	0.057	0.201	0.023	0.102	0.085	0.238	0.050	0.027	0.463

Figure 18.10: Average and Range Chart for Boutique Seasonal Relatives

The average monthly sales for Year One (in thousands of dollars) was 47.533; for Year Two it was 56.592. Dividing the monthly sales by these averages, we obtain the seasonal relatives shown in Figure 18.10. Even though these seasonal relatives are generally further from 100% than those in Figure 18.4, only five months show detectable seasonal effects (January, February, March, November, and December). The large amount of variation between the seasonal relatives from year to year makes it hard to detect seasonal effects here. The limits in Figure 18.10 suggest that effects smaller than 28% of the average sales level are indistinguishable from routine variation. Using three years worth of data does not substantially change things. The Boutique Sales Data contain both seasonal effects and substantial amounts of noise.

The average seasonal relatives shown in Figure 18.10 are listed as the first row of Table 18.8. Since the rounded values add up to 12.02, the May and June values were adjusted down 0.01 each to give the seasonal factors shown in the third row of Table 18.8. (While only five months show a detectable seasonal effect, we will need to estimate a seasonal effect for each month and to adjust every month's values in order to use the scaling factors for computing limits given in Table 18.6.)

Table 18.8: Average Seasonal Relatives Converted into Seasonal Factors

	J	F	M	A	M	J	J	A	S	O	N	D
Averages	.3355	.4005	.5855	0.7645	1.1755	1.0555	.908	1.1365	.866	1.039	1.4695	2.2635
Rounded	.34	.40	.59	.76	1.18	1.06	.91	1.14	.87	1.04	1.47	2.26
Adjusted	.34	.40	.59	.76	1.17	1.05	.91	1.14	.87	1.04	1.47	2.26

Table 18.9: Monthly Boutique Sales and Deseasonalized Baseline Sales

	J	F	M	A	M	J	J	A	S	O	N	D
Yr I Monthly Sales	15.0	23.3	35.6	35.0	51.1	50.7	45.6	52.0	46.8	48.2	70.5	96.6
Seasonal Factors	0.34	0.40	0.59	0.76	1.17	1.05	0.91	1.14	0.87	1.04	1.47	2.26
Yr I Deseasonalized	44.1	58.3	60.3	46.1	43.7	48.3	50.1	45.6	53.8	46.3	48.0	42.7
mR		14.1	2.1	14.3	2.4	4.6	1.8	4.5	8.2	7.4	1.6	5.2
Yr II Monthly Sales	20.1	17.6	23.9	44.9	72.2	59.1	48.5	66.7	42.3	60.2	82.4	141.2
Seasonal Factors	0.34	0.40	0.59	0.76	1.17	1.05	0.91	1.14	0.87	1.04	1.47	2.26
Yr II Deseasonalized	59.1	44.0	40.5	59.1	61.7	56.3	53.3	58.5	48.6	57.9	56.1	62.5
mR	16.4	15.1	3.5	18.6	2.6	5.4	3.0	5.2	9.9	9.3	1.8	6.4

Table 18.9 gives (1) the Monthly Boutique Sales for Years One and Two, (2) the seasonal factors for these data, (3) the Deseasonalized Boutique Sales for Years One and Two, and (4) the moving ranges for these deseasonalized baseline values. The *XmR* Chart for these Deseasonalized Boutique Sales for Years One and Two is included as part of Figure 18.11. The average deseasonalized baseline value is 51.87, and the median moving range is 5.2.

Once again, the self-adjustment inherent in deseasonalizing the baseline values creates the flipped pattern on the X Chart and a repeated pattern on the *mR* Chart. While these patterns make the interpretation of the *XmR* Chart for the deseasonalized baseline values uninteresting, they do not interfere with our use of these values to obtain limits we can use with deseasonalized future values. To compute limits for the deseasonalized future values we return to Table 18.6: When the number of years in the baseline period is $m = 2$, we find $E_8 = 5.447$ and $D_8 = 6.694$, which result in the limits shown in Figure 18.11.

Table 18.10 contains both the Boutique Sales and the deseasonalized values for Year Three, while Figure 18.11 combines the actual sales with the *XmR* Chart for the deseasonalized values for Years One, Two and Three.

The seasonal effects make it difficult to use the actual values to compare Year Three with the preceding years. However, with nine of the deseasonalized values for Year Three above the central line the increase in Year Three is easy to see. Although the deseasonalized data have wide limits, they still provide useful insights into the process.

Table 18.10: Monthly Boutique Sales and Deseasonalized Future Sales for Year Three

	J	F	M	A	M	J	J	A	S	O	N	D
Yr III Monthly Sales	19.0	28.8	35.6	48.1	63.8	49.3	45.6	52.2	46.1	72.9	98.4	122.1
Seasonal Factors	*0.34*	*0.40*	*0.59*	*0.76*	*1.17*	*1.05*	*0.91*	*1.14*	*0.87*	*1.04*	*1.47*	*2.26*
Yr III Deseasonalized	55.9	72.0	60.3	63.3	54.5	47.0	50.1	45.8	53.0	70.1	66.9	54.0
mR	6.6	16.1	11.7	3.0	8.8	7.6	3.2	4.3	7.2	17.1	3.2	12.9

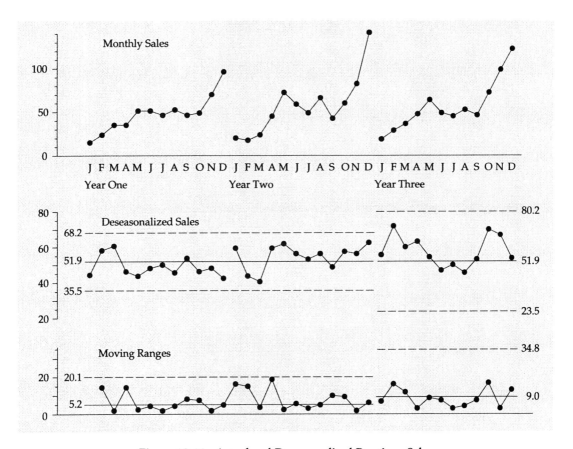

Figure 18.11: Actual and Deseasonalized Boutique Sales

So how can the manager of the boutique track her sales in the face of seasonality and noise? While it helps to remove the seasonality, she still has the problem of making sense of the current values in spite of the noise. When the data are noisy, a year-long moving average will allow you to smooth out both seasonal effects and noise so that you can see the underlying trend. The data of Figure 18.11 were shown with a twelve-period moving average in Figure 17.3. There the moving average made the gradual upward trend in sales visible. Given data that contain both a substantial seasonal component and considerable noise, the annual moving average will show the underlying trend better than the deseasonalized data.

18.6 The Appliance Store Data

The Appliance Store Sales Data will serve as an example of data where seasonal effects are weak and noise is substantial.

Table 18.11: Monthly Appliance Store Sales

Year	J	F	M	A	M	J	J	A	S	O	N	D	Average
One	86.9	78.3	97.2	77.3	113.5	99.5	75.0	81.8	113.4	122.3	74.4	80.4	91.67
Two	72.3	78.1	91.5	91.7	141.5	113.2	107.0	96.7	99.1	71.8	78.4	46.5	90.65
Three	82.0	117.1	98.0	85.5	105.6	69.8	63.7	81.9	78.8	96.1	70.1	58.9	83.96

Average and Range Chart for Seasonal Relatives

	Jan	Feb	Mar	Apr	May	Jun	Jul	Aug	Sept	Oct	Nov	Dec
Year One	0.948	0.854	1.060	0.843	1.238	1.085	0.818	0.892	1.237	1.334	0.812	0.877
Year Two	0.798	0.862	1.009	1.012	1.561	1.249	1.180	1.067	1.093	0.792	0.865	0.513
Year Three	0.977	1.395	1.167	1.018	1.249	0.831	0.759	0.975	0.939	1.145	0.835	0.702
Averages	0.9077	1.0370	1.0787	0.9577	1.3523	1.0550	0.9190	0.9780	1.0897	1.0903	0.8373	0.6793
Ranges	0.179	0.541	0.158	0.175	0.323	0.418	0.421	0.175	0.298	0.542	0.053	0.364

Figure 18.12: Average and Range Chart for Seasonal Relatives for Appliance Store Data

Table 18.12: Twelve-Period Moving Averages for the Appliance Store Sales

Year	J	F	M	A	M	J	J	A	S	O	N	D
One												91.7
Two	90.5	90.4	90.0	91.1	93.5	94.6	97.3	98.5	97.4	93.1	93.5	90.7
Three	91.5	94.7	95.3	94.7	91.7	88.1	84.5	83.3	81.6	83.6	82.9	84.0

The limits in Figure 18.12 show that a seasonal effect would have to be bigger than ± 31% in order to be detectable above the noise present in these data. These data contain weak seasonal effects and a lot of noise. In fact, only one month has a detectable seasonal effect. Therefore, the seasonal adjustment of the data in Table 18.11 would effectively change only 3 of the 36 values by any appreciable amount while shuffling the other 33 values around. Thus, deseasonalization will not clarify things in this case.

On the other hand, the 12-period moving average shows the overall trend for these sales data. Figure 18.13 contains both the individual values and the 12-period moving average for this store. The 12-period moving average shows that the appliance store sales have declined slightly over this three-year period.

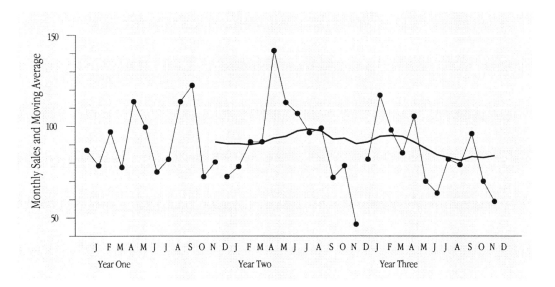

Figure 18.13: Monthly Sales and Moving Average for Appliance Store

Unless the seasonal components are substantially greater than the year-to-year variation in the seasonal relatives, you will gain little by deseasonalizing the data. The Average and Range Chart uses the calculations that are part of finding the seasonal effects to allow you to assess this aspect of your data.

18.7 The Claims Per Day Data

The claims processing division of a large health insurance company kept track of its productivity by dividing the number of claims processed each month by the total number of man-days worked that month. This ratio was known as "Claims Per Day" and was used, along with similar measures from other divisions, to evaluate and rank the division managers. The Claims Per Day values are shown in Figure 18.14. These values are aggregate values based upon the data from the eight regional offices.

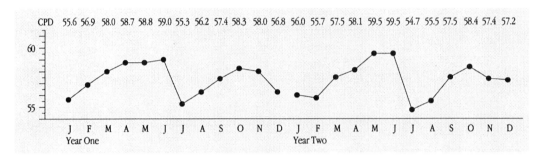

Figure 18.14: Claims Per Day Values for Years One and Two

The relative parallelism between the two years shown above suggests that strong seasonal effects are present in these data. The managers had an explanation for this seasonality—it was said to be a consequence of variable staffing in response to the seasonal variation in claims. While there was a core of full-time personnel who processed claims,

Figure 18.15: Average and Range Chart for Seasonal Relatives for the Claims Per Day Data

there was another group of personnel who were used on a part-time basis to help when the number of claims went up in the winter and when regular personnel were on vacation in the summer. Since the part-time personnel were not as efficient as the full-time personnel, the productivity measure suffered when they were used. The seasonal relatives for these two years are shown on the Average and Range Chart in Figure 18.15. As can be seen there, seven or eight months can be said to have detectable seasonal effects.

The average seasonal relatives are converted into seasonal factors in Table 18.13. The sum of the rounded values is 11.99, so December's value was rounded up to 1.00.

Table 18.13: Converting Average Seasonal Relatives into Seasonals

	J	F	M	A	M	J	J	A	S	O	N	D
Averages	0.9730	0.9820	1.0070	1.0185	1.0315	1.0335	0.9595	0.9740	1.002	1.0175	1.0065	0.9940
Rounded	0.97	0.98	1.01	1.02	1.03	1.03	0.96	0.97	1.00	1.02	1.01	0.99
Seasonals	0.97	0.98	1.01	1.02	1.03	1.03	0.96	0.97	1.00	1.02	1.01	1.00

Table 18.14: Claims Per Day Values and Deseasonalized Baseline Values

	J	F	M	A	M	J	J	A	S	O	N	D
Year One	55.6	56.9	58.0	58.7	58.8	59.0	55.3	56.2	57.4	58.3	58.0	56.8
Seasonals	0.97	0.98	1.01	1.02	1.03	1.03	0.96	0.97	1.00	1.02	1.01	1.00
Yr I Deseason	57.3	58.1	57.4	57.5	57.1	57.3	57.6	57.9	57.4	57.2	57.4	56.8
mR		0.8	0.7	0.1	0.4	0.2	0.3	0.3	0.5	0.2	0.2	0.6
Year Two	56.0	55.7	57.5	58.1	59.5	59.5	54.7	55.5	57.5	58.4	57.4	57.2
Seasonals	0.97	0.98	1.01	1.02	1.03	1.03	0.96	0.97	1.00	1.02	1.01	1.00
Yr II Deseason	57.7	56.8	56.9	57.0	57.8	57.8	57.0	57.2	57.5	57.3	56.8	57.2
mR	0.9	0.9	0.1	0.1	0.8	0.0	0.8	0.2	0.3	0.2	0.5	0.4

The deseasonalized baseline values shown in Table 18.14 have an average of 57.34 and a median moving range of 0.30. The *XmR* Chart for the deseasonalized baseline values is shown as part of Figure 18.16. Limits for deseasonalized future values are: *UNPL* = 58.97, *LNPL* = 55.71, *URL* = 2.01, and *CLR* = 0.52.

The Claims Per Day values for Year Three and the deseasonalized future values are shown in Table 18.15.

Table 18.15: Claims Per Day Values and Deseasonalized Future Values for Year Three

	J	F	M	A	M	J	J	A	S	O	N	D
Year Three	55.4	54.7	56.8	58.5	58.4	57.6	54.4	54.0	55.7	57.1	56.8	55.6
Seasonals	0.97	0.98	1.01	1.02	1.03	1.03	0.96	0.97	1.00	1.02	1.01	1.00
Yr III Deseason	57.1	55.8	56.2	57.4	56.7	55.9	56.7	55.7	55.7	56.0	56.2	55.6
mR	0.1	1.3	0.4	1.1	0.7	0.8	0.7	1.0	0.0	0.3	0.3	0.6

Figure 18.16: Claims Per Day Values and *XmR* Chart for Years One, Two, and Three

The top portion of Figure 18.16 shows the time series for Claims Per Day. These are the actual values without any seasonal adjustment. While the first three values for Year Three appear to be a little low, it is not clear from the actual values if there has been a change in productivity.

However, the X Chart for the deseasonalized future values shows evidence of a change by March of Year Three (two successive points in the outer one-third of the limits on an X Chart). While the productivity for April was back up to the previous average, it is the only month in Year Three that exceeded that average. The remainder of Year Three shows an overall decline in productivity, with the last five months hugging the lower limit. Something has changed for the worse, and the X Chart shows this change more clearly than the actual values.

The only explanation for the lower productivity in Year Three that they could find was the implementation of new corporate policies and procedures in late January. While we might expect a temporary dip associated with a learning curve following such a change, Figure 18.16 shows a sustained drop in productivity. In other words, the "improvements" put in place at the beginning of Year Three actually made things worse.

So what limits should we now use for Year Four? Since these data are report-card data it makes sense to revise the limits to reflect the current process behavior. To this end we shall use the deseasonalized values from Year Three to compute limits directly. The average for these values is 56.25, while the average moving range is 0.608. Using the regular formulas from Table 2 in the Appendix these values give Natural Process Limits of 57.87 and 54.63, and an Upper Range Limit of 1.99. These limits are shown in Figure 18.17.

Since the deseasonalized values for Year Three all fall within these limits, we might use these limits to forecast Year Four. Namely, if they do not change things for the better, and if they do not change things for the worse, the claim processing division should expect to average about 56 claims per day per operator during Year Four. To expect the process to do better than this is unrealistic. Improvement does not usually happen spontaneously.

Figure 18.17: *XmR* Chart for Deseasonalized Claims Per Day for Years One, Two and Three

Following the drop in productivity in Year Three, the CEO of this health insurance company decided that they needed to take action to remedy things—it was time to reengineer the whole organization. A thorough reorganization was undertaken, along with a thinning of the ranks of mid-level managers. Goals were set for each area of operations, and Year Four was declared to be the year of the turn-around. Everyone knew that it was just a matter of time until the benefits of the reshuffling became evident.

The claim processing division was given a "stretch goal" of 60 claims per day. Since the average in Year Three was about 56 claims per day, they were expecting the reorganization to yield an increase of about 4 claims per day.

Table 18.16 shows the Claims Per Day values for Year Four, along with the deseasonalized values. These values are shown in a composite running record and *XmR* Chart in Figure 18.18.

Table 18.16: Claims Per Day Values and Deseasonalized CPD Values

	J	F	M	A	M	J	J	A	S	O	N	D
Year 4	51.9	52.7	55.4	54.7	54.1	54.1	50.6	50.5	51.6	51.3	51.0	51.8
Seasonals	0.97	0.98	1.01	1.02	1.03	1.03	0.96	0.97	1.00	1.02	1.01	1.00
Deseas	53.5	53.8	54.9	53.6	52.5	52.5	52.7	52.1	51.6	50.3	50.5	51.8
mR	2.1	0.3	1.1	1.2	1.1	0.0	0.2	0.6	0.5	1.3	0.2	1.3

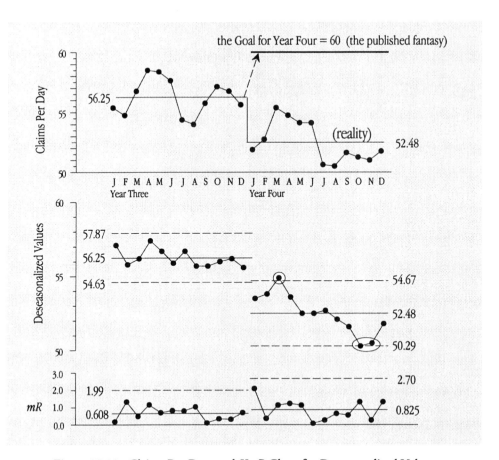

Figure 18.18: Claims Per Day, and *XmR* Chart for Deseasonalized Values

The published fantasy was that the productivity would go up about four units with the new system. The reality was that the productivity went down about four units—which is the usual result of wishful thinking. This drop in productivity at the beginning of Year Four can be seen in every portion of Figure 18.18. It is beyond question. The only real question is, "What happened?" Since the reorganization occurred in January of Year Four, it is the logical explanation for the overall drop in productivity. Moreover, the deseasonalized values also show signals of changes in productivity during Year Four.

Whenever goals or targets are proposed the question that should always be asked is, "By what method?" The setting of goals or targets is no substitute for studying the process to discover how to improve it by removing assignable causes of excessive variation.

Goals, targets, and reorganizations are frequently signs of desperation—admissions that managers do not have a clue as to what to do to change things for the better. They just roll the dice and hope things will improve. Process behavior charts provide an alternative to this everlasting game of chance. They give a way of learning about processes and systems so that we can improve them. They identify the opportunities for improvement, and they identify processes that are operating up to their potential. Knowing the difference is crucial. Not knowing the difference is a disaster.

Those who sponsor improvements often come to believe their own claims. The best anti-dote to this form of self-delusion is to listen to the Voice of the Process.

In the absence of effective ways of analyzing the data you may be subject to being misled by unsubstantiated claims of improvement. The best antidote to this form of misinformation is to listen to the Voice of the Process.

Without the Voice of the Process, it's just an opinion—and that opinion is likely to be based upon wishful thinking. And that is why, without process behavior charts, you are doomed to live and work in a fantasy world that becomes a nightmare whenever reality intrudes.

18.8 Working with Seasonal Data

When you suspect that your data contains seasonal patterns you may use the list below as a step-by-step guide on how to remove the seasonal effects.

1. Plot your data in a running record. If a repeating pattern is apparent, then go to Step 2. Otherwise go to Step 6.

2. Use a few complete cycles of the seasonal pattern to obtain seasonal relatives.

3. Place seasonal relatives on an Average and Range Chart where each subgroup represents a single "season." Points outside the limits on the Average Chart will indicate detectable seasonal effects, while points far outside these limits will denote strong seasonal effects. If data show only weak seasonality then go to Step 6.

4. Estimate the seasonal factors for every period. The seasonal factors for a five-day cycle must sum to 5; for a seven-day cycle they must sum to 7. Quarterly seasonals must sum to 4, while monthly seasonals must sum to 12.

5. Deseasonalize baseline and future values by dividing each value by the seasonal factor for that period. Place these deseasonalized baseline values on an *XmR* Chart. Use these values to compute limits for deseasonalized future values according to Table 18.6. Interpret the chart for deseasonalized future values in the usual manner.

6. Place the individual values on an *XmR* Chart. If this chart is useful then interpret it in the usual way. If the limits on the *X* Chart are so wide that they do not provide any useful information about your process (except the fact that noise is dominant), go to Step 7.

7. When noise dominates a time series it essentially becomes a report card on the past. In this case it can still be helpful to plot a running record of the individual values with a year-long moving average superimposed to show the underlying trends.

To help you with the judgment about the possibility of seasonal patterns in your data Figures 18.19 and 18.20 are provided. They are a recap of the figures in this and previous chapters. In general, whenever a recurring pattern exists there is a possibility of seasonality. If the shape of the pattern is changing from cycle to cycle the seasonality is likely to be moderate. If the shape of the pattern persists then the seasonality will be strong.

Figure 18.19: Some Time Series Which Display Moderate Seasonality

Figure 18.20: Some Time Series Which Display Strong Seasonal Patterns

18.9 Exercises

EXERCISE 18.1

Quarterly sales data are shown below. Compute the seasonal relatives (3 decimal places) and place them on an Average and Range Chart. Do these data display strong seasonality?

Monthly Sales

Year	I	II	III	IV	Average
One	141.8	148.3	137.1	142.6	142.45
Two	141.7	150.2	139.2	142.7	143.45
Three	141.3	151.9	139.5	143.1	143.95

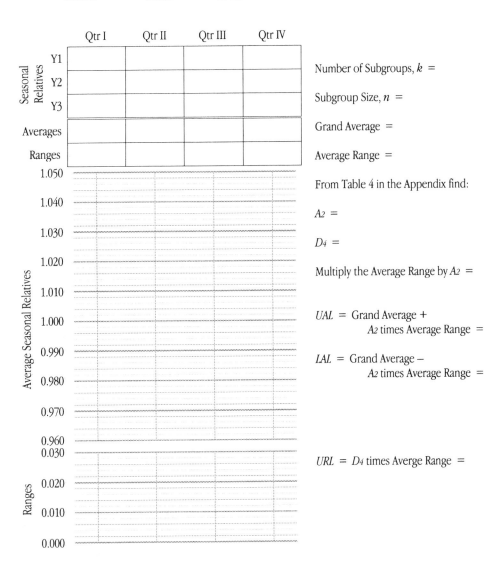

Number of Subgroups, k =

Subgroup Size, n =

Grand Average =

Average Range =

From Table 4 in the Appendix find:

A_2 =

D_4 =

Multiply the Average Range by A_2 =

UAL = Grand Average +
A_2 times Average Range =

LAL = Grand Average −
A_2 times Average Range =

URL = D_4 times Averge Range =

EXERCISE 18.2

Estimate the seasonal factors (3 decimal places) for the sales data in Exercise 18.1, compute the deseasonalized baseline values, and place these vales on an *XmR* Chart.

	I	II	III	IV	I	II	III	IV	I	II	III	IV
Sales	141.8	148.3	137.1	142.6	141.7	150.2	139.2	142.7	141.3	151.9	139.5	143.1
Seasonal Factors												
Deseasonalized Sales												
mR												

While the sales have increased from Year One to Year Three, is there any evidence of a detectable trend during these three baseline years?

What average quarterly sales would you predict for Year Four?

EXERCISE 18.3

1. Use the information from Exercise 18.2, along with Table 18.6, to obtain limits for the deseasonalized future values. Plot these limits below.
2. The sales for Years Four and Five are shown below. Deseasonalize these values and plot these deseasonalized future values on the *XmR* Chart.

Do the sales for Year Four agree with your prediction?

Are the sales for Year Five the same as the sales in the baseline period?

Chapter Nineteen

The Learning Way

Flowcharts and cause-and-effect diagrams help you visualize your process—to see it as a whole and to gain the perspective that is needed to improve your processes and systems. Bar charts allow you to make descriptive comparisons across categories. Running records allow you to see how a measure is changing over time—to spot trends and sudden changes that can be crucial to know about.

What do all of these techniques have in common? They are all graphical representations. The flowchart and cause-and-effect diagram are graphical representations of relationships. Bar charts and running records provide pictures of your data. In each case you obtain a picture that displays relationships or data in their context. When these graphical displays are combined with your own insight into the processes represented they will frequently show where and how you can make immediate improvements.

This is why context is the beginning of improvement. But what happens when context is not enough? What comes next? The next step is to characterize the behavior of your process so you can choose an appropriate improvement strategy. And to this end you will need a way of visualizing your process behavior. You will need a way of interpreting the graphs, and you will need a guide as to how to make improvements. This is where the process behavior chart comes in.

Process behavior charts tell you when your process has changed. They allow you to separate the noise of the routine variation from the signals of exceptional variation. In short, they are very powerful tools for understanding and using data.

Throughout this book I have tried to emphasize the importance of interacting with the tools in a process of discovery. The ultimate power of all these techniques is the power to stimulate your imagination—which brings us back to the Plan, Do, Study, Act Cycle. The PDSA Cycle provides a framework for organizing your use of these various tools. In this chapter you will see two extended examples of how people have used this cycle to build Continual Improvement into their processes.

19.1 Mail Order Improvement

In Chapter Two I told how a small mail order company used flowcharts as part of an improvement effort. Since they were working with an existing process they began at the "Study" step of the PDSA Cycle. They created a complete flowchart of their existing order process. Why would they take the time to do this when they were planning to purchase software that would automate the order entry system? Because without a good understanding of the current system they could easily end up with a new system that would not suit their needs.

Following the preparation of the current process flowcharts, the managers used those flowcharts to identify areas that could be improved. For example, they identified several places where different people did things differently and some places where no one knew what to do.

When they completed this study of the current process, the managers were ready to purchase a program that would meet their current needs, that could be set up according to the nature of their business, and that would allow them to do things that their current system could not do.

After they purchased and set up the new order-entry and accounting system, they had to plan how to introduce the new system to the staff. Here they began in a small way. Since the old system was a manual system, using nothing more sophisticated than a typewriter, employees had considerable anxiety about the computerization of the system. In addition, there were concerns about the possibility of layoffs.

To meet the concerns about layoffs the managers met with each employee and explained that they did not envision a reduction in personnel because they were currently understaffed.

To meet the concerns about the new system they devised a simple training program. When the hardware and software were installed they set up a dummy company and let everyone learn on this system where mistakes did not have real consequences. A side benefit of this was using the dummy system to learn how to fix mistakes. Each week every employee was given a set of practice orders to process using the new system. These were reviewed with their supervisor each week. Of course, with the process flowchart to use, the practice problems could be made to match the different types of orders that this company had to deal with. At first the exercises were simple. As proficiency grew, the complexity of the exercises was increased. Within two months this training program had everyone ready to switch over to the new system.

By practicing the use of the new system on a small scale, and with a dummy company, the actual change-over to the new system was extremely smooth. In fact, in the experience of the consultants from the software company, it was the most trouble-free changeover they had ever seen.

The new system was simpler than the old system. There were fewer steps, fewer decisions to make, and many of the decisions were automated—the system provided the operator with the appropriate information to facilitate the decision. In all, the order process was more standardized than it had ever been before. The direct labor cost of processing an order was cut by over one-third. The backlogs in invoicing and in the posting of accounts were eliminated. The new system provided much more effective inventory control, better accounting information, and more timely sales information than was formerly available.

The operators loved the new system. The customers got their orders faster, with fewer errors. The operators could respond to customer's questions more quickly, more completely, and with greater consistency. The standardization of procedures allowed flexibility of staffing that was not formerly available.

With the increased productivity, time was available to spend on crucial areas that had formerly been neglected. One such area was accounts receivable. Table 19.1 shows the accounts receivable as a percentage of the three-month sales for three years. The use of the new system began in February of Year Two.

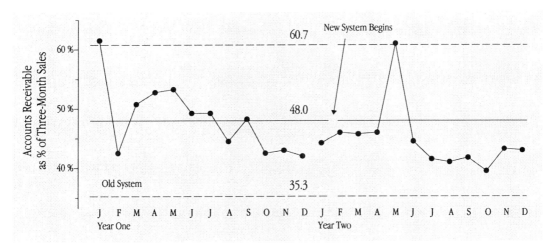

Figure 19.1: *X* Chart for Accounts Receivable for Years One and Two

Figure 19.1 shows the accounts receivable for the first two years. The limits shown were computed using the data from the old system. Under the old system accounts receivable were averaging about 48 percent of the three-month sales value. When they began to use the new system in February of Year Two they had three points below 48%, one above, and then seven more below the old central line of 48%. While this does not satisfy the run-of-eight rule, I think that you will agree that the average is no longer 48%. Ten out of eleven successive values below the central line provides compelling evidence of a weak but sustained shift. (The one large value in May of Year Two was due to a single large order that was current at the end of May.)

The limits shown on the right in Figure 19.2 were computed using the eleven months following changeover.

Table 19.1: Accounts Receivable as Percentage of Three-Month Sales

	J	F	M	A	M	J	J	A	S	O	N	D
Year One	61.5	42.6	50.8	52.8	53.3	49.3	49.2	44.4	48.2	42.5	43.1	42.1
Year Two	44.2	46.1	45.8	46.1	61.0	44.5	41.4	41.1	41.7	39.6	43.3	42.9
Year Three	36.2	40.2	38.9	42.8	44.8	42.5	38.4	36.7	28.8	27.0	40.4	34.7

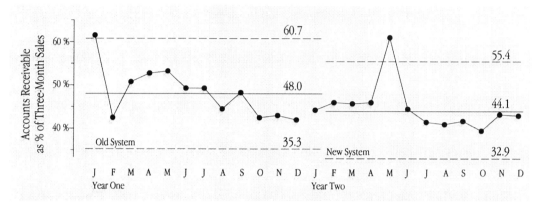

Figure 19.2: *X* Chart for Accounts Receivable Before and After the Change

After the change their accounts receivable averaged about 44 percent of the three-month sales value. As can be seen by comparing the central lines in Figure 19.2, this amounts to a four percent reduction in working capital. The new system had paid for itself in short order.

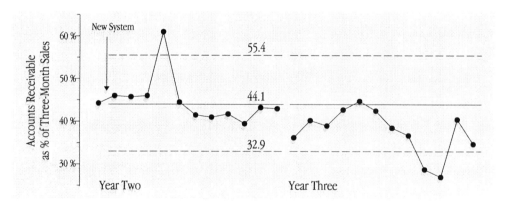

Figure 19.3: *X* Chart for Accounts Receivable Comparing Year Two and Year Three

Figure 19.3 shows the values for Year Three plotted against the limits from Year Two. Clearly, something happened to the accounts receivable in Year Three. As a result of the increased productivity and the enhanced reporting capabilities of the new system, the supervisors had been able to systematically study the overdue accounts. As they began to characterize the accounts that were going overdue, they were able to suggest changes to the managers, and they could document their recommendations. Based on these suggestions the company made changes in their credit policies. It was these changes that resulted in the drop in accounts receivable seen in Year Three. Figure 19.4 shows that at the end of Year Three their accounts receivable were averaging about 36 percent of the three-month sales. Think about what this number means—36 percent of the three-month sales is approximately one month's sales. Overdue accounts were minimal. Most of the accounts receivable were current.

Figure 19.4: Accounts Receivable for Years One, Two and Three

19.2 Plan, Do, Study, Act

Continual Improvement involves a *cycle* of activities, which have been characterized as the Plan, Do, Study, Act Cycle. This cycle provides a framework for learning about your process and then working to improve that process.

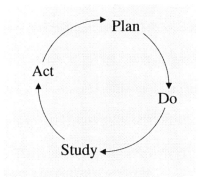

Figure 19.5: The PDSA Cycle

Plan: Determine the improvement to be made, the improvement method, and the method for evaluating the results. What do you want to accomplish? By what method will you achieve this objective? And how will you know when you have reached your objective? Until you have answered these questions you will not have completed the planning stage.

Do: Perform the activities defined in the plan. A pilot program is recommended. (Large starts lead to large consequences!)

Study: Compare the results with the desired results; learn from them. This step is sometimes referred to as "check" rather than "study."

Act: Take advantage of what you have learned. Make it part of your process, if appropriate, or decide what you will try next. Take action.

Implicit in the cycle is its repetition. After *Act*, it begins anew: *Plan* again, *Do* again, *Study* again, *Act* again; an unending cycle of learning, evaluating, and working on process improvement.

Another facet of the Plan, Do, Study, Act Cycle is the way that it facilitates, and even requires, standardized procedures. Standardized procedures are concerned with how you perform some action. They are the key to performing that action consistently. Since operational definitions are focused on making a decision, they may well be part of a standardized procedure, but I interpret standardized procedures more broadly than operational definitions.

The mail order company in the previous example studied their accounts receivable, acted on what they learned, planned changes and then put these changes into place. By doing this they increased their liquid capital and reduced the overdue accounts dramatically. Instead of merely reacting when things got bad, they studied their current system, learned what was happening, then planned and implemented changes to improve the system for the future.

While the story, and the work itself was virtually seamless, they still followed the Plan, Do, Study, Act Cycle. To make this explicit, the steps in the previous example are listed below in the order they occurred and labeled according to which of the PDSA steps was used. Since they were working on an existing system, they began at the Study step:

Study:	flowchart the current process
Act:	purchase software and hardware and set up new system
Plan:	prepare training program
Do:	train operators
Study:	review training exercises
Act:	revise new system
Plan:	extend and expand training
Do:	train operators
Study:	evaluate training
Act:	decide on activation date
Plan:	prepare for change-over
Do:	start using new system
Study:	monitor new system, look for prolems that need attention
Act:	continue using system, decide to work on overdue accounts
Plan:	identify characteristics of overdue accounts
Do:	change credit policies
Study:	look for impact of new policies
Act:	confirm new policies and enjoy the improvements

The Plan, Do, Study, Act Cycle is a methodology for learning. It is a framework for getting things done. The four steps not rigid rules to be slavishly followed. Instead they are guidelines for how to proceed in practice. They embody the feedback and follow-through that are essential for learning from your processes and improving them. Whether they are explicit or implicit, the steps will be present whenever improvements are made. They are the essence of Continual Improvement. And that is why the cycle will be part of the culture in those organizations that provide quality services and products.

In case after case, improvement begins with establishing operational definitions and standardizing procedures. In some cases these side effects of the work required by the PDSA Cycle are the major improvements themselves.

19.3 "Let's Reduce Losses on Beer and Sake Sales"

This is the story of a project undertaken by a QC Circle at a nightclub in Osaka, Japan. Since the original document is in Japanese I will show direct translations in italics.

The name of the QC Circle at the Esquire Club was *"The Minnow Sisters Wanting to Become Carp."* They met regularly at the club, for about 45 minutes at a time, with an average attendance of 70%. This project was the second project this circle had undertaken, and the supervisor prepared the written summary shown.

Page One of the three-page summary of this project is shown in Figure 19.7 on the next page. The first paragraph in the summary describes the selection of the theme for the project.

> *This theme was chosen after a brainstorming discussion among our circle. Some of the problems discussed in this session were the timing of filling an order, properly recording the number of drinks ordered, properly recording the number of guests in a party, and keeping employee lockers clean. The losses on beer and sake sales were finally selected as a topic because it improved the communication with the waitresses while realistically analyzing the effectiveness of the operation. In addition, it was a topic which was important to the continued operation of the club.*

Following the selection of the theme, a time-line for seven additional phases of the project was prepared (see Figure 19.6). This graph shows both the planned times and the actual times for each phase. The scale at the top represents the months. This project started in February and was finished in June.

Figure 19.6: Time Line for Project

Figure 19.7: "Let's Reduce Losses on Beer and Sake Sales," Page One

While the time line shows the general progression of the project, it does not show the detail of the various steps, nor does it show the concurrency of these steps in the way that the PERT diagram does.

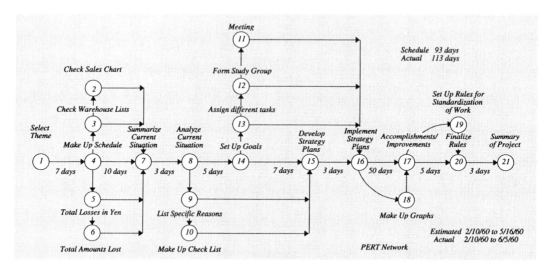

Figure 19.8: PERT Diagram for "Let's Reduce Losses on Beer and Sake Sales"

This PERT diagram was discussed in Chapter Two. It is essentially a flowchart of the work to be done on this project. They planned this project to last 93 days, and they actually completed it in 113 days. Notice the 50 day implementation period.

The next paragraph of text on Page One of the project summary is entitled *"Summary of the Current Situation."*

> *By analyzing the difference between the list of warehouse deliveries and the list of actual sales produced by the "guys" at the warehouse every month it was possible to create a Pareto chart for the losses.*
>
> *In total losses sake ranked first, beer second, followed by side orders, latecomers, and bottle losses as shown in Figure 1.*
>
> *Among these losses, sake accounted for 45% of the total loss in sales, and beer accounted for 33%, with a total of 78% for both sake and beer losses combined.*
>
> *The monthly amounts lost between October 24 and the end of February are shown in Figures 2 and 4. During this 4.3 month period, the total beer loss was 384 bottles, with an average of 89.3 per month, while the total sake loss was 73 liters, with an average of 17.1 liters per month. The average amount lost per month was 20,178 Yen for beer and 28,370 Yen for sake. This amounts to an average monthly loss on beer and sake sales of 49,088 Yen.*

Thus, they summarize the Pareto chart which appears on Page Two of the summary.

Figure 19.9: "Let's Reduce Losses on Beer and Sake Sales," Page Two

Since beer and sake losses were predominant, it was decided to concentrate on these two areas. The raw data for these losses were summarized in tables and running records.

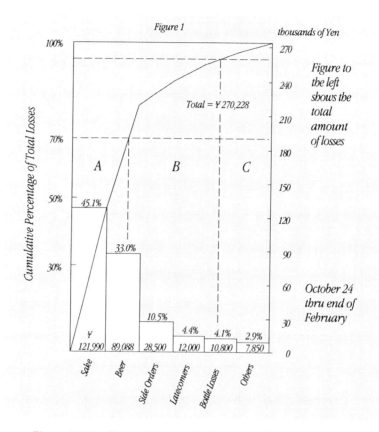

Figure 19.10: Pareto Diagram for Losses at the Esquire Club

Month		number of bottles used from warehouse	number of bottles sold	beer losses (bottles)		amount used from warehouse in liters	doubles.... singles sold	amount sold in liters	Sake Losses (Liters)
10	Beer	409	350	59	Sake	31.3	70 / 46	29.5	1.8
11	Beer	1047	972	75	Sake	125.3	316 / 78	111.2	14.1
12	Beer	1435	1297	138	Sake	190.1	538 / 83	180.9	9.2
1	Beer	883	835	48	Sake	181.1	462 / 62	153.8	27.3
2	Beer	844	780	64	Sake	151.0	379 / 71	129.6	21.4

Single = 170 ml Double = 310 ml

Figure 19.11: Physical Losses for Beer and Sake

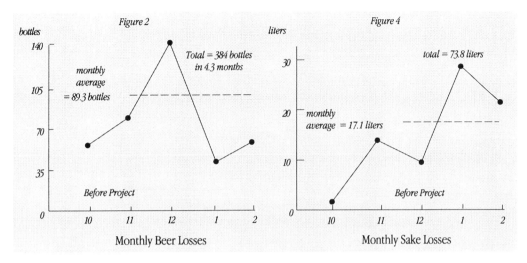

Figure 19.12: Running Records of Physical Losses for Beer and Sake

At this point the sequence of the project and the layout of the written summary diverge, mainly because of the spacing required to fit all of the information on the pages of the summary. It is apparent from the Pareto chart that they had also figured out the losses associated with the graphs and tables above. The running record for the losses for each month is tucked away on Page Three of the summary, while the table of values is on Page Two.

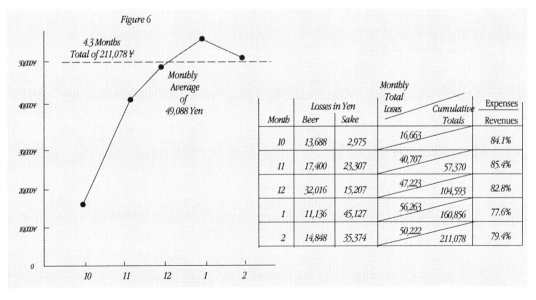

Figure 19.13: Total Losses on Beer and Sake

Figure 19.14: "Let's Reduce Losses on Beer and Sake Sales," Page Three

Following the summary and analysis of the current situation, the Minnow Sisters used a cause-and-effect diagram to organize their thoughts about the causes for the losses. Picking up the text from the middle of Page Two, the story continues:

(Establish Objectives)

We established our goal to be the reduction of loss by 50%: from the current monthly average loss of 89 bottles of beer and 17 liters of sake to [no more than] 44 bottles of beer and 8 liters of sake, respectively.

(Analysis of Causes)

We analyzed the reasons why there are so many losses in beer and sake according to three separate analysis groups—waitresses, work procedures, and others.

Waitresses, Work Procedures, and Others make up the three major branches of the fishbone (cause-and-effect) diagram.

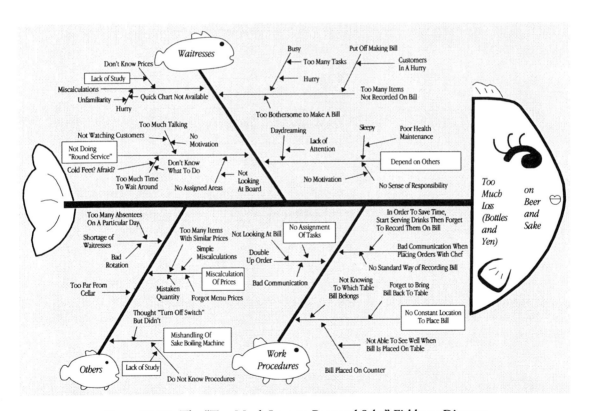

Figure 19.15: The "Too Much Loss on Beer and Sake" Fishbone Diagram

The Waitresses Branch had four sub-branches:

1. Miscalculations
   a. Don't know prices—lack of study
   b. Hurry—unfamiliarity / quick chart not available

2. Not doing round service
   a. Too much talking / not watching customers / no motivation
   b. Too much time to wait around—cold feet? Afraid /don't know what to do
   c. No assigned areas—not looking at board

3. Too many items not recorded on bill
   a. Put off making bill—customers in a hurry
   b. Busy—too many tasks / hurry
   c. Too bothersome to make a bill

4. Depend upon others
   a. Sleepy—poor health maintenance
   b. No sense of responsibility—no motivation
   c. Daydreaming—lack of attention

The Work Procedures Branch had three sub-branches:

1. Bad communication when placing orders with chef
   a. In order to save time, start serving drinks then forget to record them on bill
   b. No standard way of recording bill

2. No constant location to place bill
   a. Forget to bring back to table
   b. Bill is placed on counter—not able to see well when bill is placed on table
   c. Not knowing to which table bill belongs

3. Double up order
   a. Not looking at bill
   b. No assignment of tasks
   c. Bad communication

The Others Branch had four sub-branches:

1. Miscalculation of prices
   a. Too many items with similar prices
   b. Simple miscalculations
   c. Mistaken quantity
   d. Forgot menu prices

2. Shortage of waitresses
   a. Too many absences
   b. Bad rotation

3. Too far from cellar

4. Mishandling of sake boiling machine
   a. Thought "turn off switch" but didn't
   b. Do not know procedures—lack of study

Following the brainstorming session in which they created the fishbone diagram for the losses on beer and sake sales, the Minnow Sisters placed boxes around eight of the causes. These were the causes they felt were the major contributors to the losses. They listed these causes on the summary.

(Analysis of Causes)

> *Based on this Cause-and-Effect Diagram we came up with the following main reasons/causes:*
> > *No specific constant location to place the order/bill*
> > *Depend on others*
> > *Mishandling of the sake boiling kit*
> > *Miscalculations of the prices*
> > *Misassignments or no assignment of the work*
> > *Ill-prepared [lack of study shows up two places on the diagram]*
> > *Low frequency for making the rounds of the customers*

(The sake boiling kit is a water filled vessel which sits on a stove. The sake is placed in a bottle which is then placed in the hot water and heated. If the sake boiling kit is left turned on the sake will, of course, evaporate, to the tune of approximately $ 16 per liter.)

The *Corrective Actions* undertaken in order to fix the problems noted above were:

(1) *Make sure to leave bill at each table, do not carry bill away.*

(2) *During the busy periods mark mineral water, beer, and sake on the sheet that is attached to the back of the master bill before recording to the master—this should facilitate the recording and totaling of the bill.*

(3) *Develop procedure for allocating work in all areas of club. Once each hour person in charge of each area must check all bills.*

(4) *Person who brings out "oshibori"* [a steaming hand towel] *is responsible for recording any additional customers to a party.*

(5) *Whoever takes the order is responsible to record it on the bill. If she must ask somebody else to take care of the order, make sure to communicate whether the order is already recorded or not.*

(6) *Supervisor must provide training and study group for new employees.*

(7) *Change table allocation to "zone defense" to make it clear who is responsible for each table.*

Looking back at the PERT diagram in Figure 19.8, they have now arrived at step number 16. They have identified the most likely causes of the losses, and they have implemented some fixes for these problems. Now, as shown on the PERT diagram, they will collect data for the next 50 days to see the impact of these changes.

The data for the physical losses are shown in Figure 19.16. The running records for the physical losses compare the losses before and after these changes were put in place, and are shown in Figure 19.17.

Month		number of bottles used from warehouse	number of bottles sold	beer losses (bottles)		amount used from warehouse in liters	doubles / singles sold	amount sold in liters	sake losses (liters)
3	Beer	1026	1003	23	Sake	102.8	301 / 50	101.8	1.0
4	Beer	1230	1209	21	Sake	100.1	296 / 45	99.4	0.7
5	Beer	1176	1160	16	Sake	87.2	265 / 28	86.9	0.2

Figure 19.16: Physical Losses for Beer and Sake

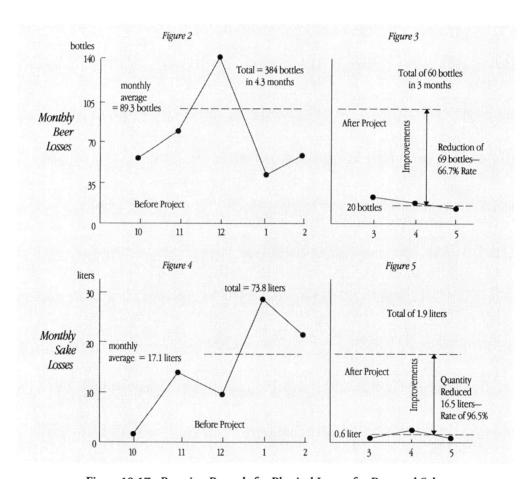

Figure 19.17: Running Records for Physical Losses for Beer and Sake

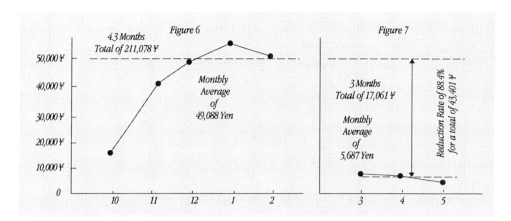

Figure 19.18: Running Records for Total Losses on Beer and Sake Sales

When these physical losses are converted into yen the running record of Figure 19.18 results. Beside this graph is a paragraph entitled *Improvements*:

> *In Yen, the beer and sake losses were reduced from a monthly average of 49,088 Yen to 5,687 Yen, for a reduction of 43,401 Yen, or 88%. This reduction easily exceeded our initial objective of a 50% reduction. In fact, the current losses are almost down to 10 percent of what they previously were.*

> *(Side Effects of the Project)*
> *Since the opening of the club on October 24, the operating expenses as a percentage of the revenues went down almost 15%—from 83% to 65% in May, 68% in June, and 67% in July. Half of this reduction can be attributed to the reduction of the losses on Beer and Sake sales.*

> *(Intangible Effects of the Project)*
> *In the course of several meetings dealing with the QC circle, there were several intangible improvements observed:*
> * *Improved communication with new waitresses*
> * *Significant reduction in mistaken orders due to the bill checking system by the waitress in charge of each area*
> * *Reduced complaints for delayed orders (Is my order ready yet?)*

So they have been successful. The targeted losses have been cut by about 90%, and the club is more profitable as a result. In addition, the customers are being better served. As is often the case, when procedures are standardized, when confusion is eliminated, when people are trained, and when steps are taken to avoid mistakes, we find that the quality goes up, the job gets easier to do, and everyone is better off.

Now how are they going to maintain these improvements in a business where turnover in personnel is the rule?

In the next to the last paragraph of the three-page summary, the Minnow Sisters list four things they are going to do to maintain these improvements. The names at the end of each item are those who are responsible for this item. Sakae Yuki is the supervisor and the leader of the Minnow Sisters QC circle. Ishiniwa and Ishikawa are the managers of the club.

> *(Final Checking Procedures)*
>
> (1)   *Continue assignment of particular waitress to a specific area in order to check that all orders are recorded on the bill.*
>
> > *(Yuki, Hirayama)*
>
> (2)   *Thorough training of new waitresses for work procedures, order taking, recording procedures, etc.*
>
> > *(Ikeda, Chief Waitress)*
>
> (3)   *Continue periodic meetings and study sessions for new and intermediate waitresses.*
>
> > *(Yuki, Chief Waitress)*
>
> (4)   *On the fifth day of every month continue to check the difference between the warehouse list and the sales list to determine the loss amounts.*
>
> > *(Ishiniwa, Ishikawa)*

Finally, they summarize where they are and where they plan to go in the future. Notice that there is no question about whether or not there will be another project. It is a foregone conclusion that there will be. It is part of the learning way known as Continual Improvement.

> *(Summary)*
>
> *During this project we received generous assistance from the warehouse QC team in the areas of graph development and the analyses of the warehouse charts and the sales charts. In the future we would like to plan a project which we can accomplish by ourselves. For example, promotion of new business meetings, improvement of bottle sales, and recommended side orders could be considered as an effective project to improve overall sales.*

Clearly this project could be organized according to the Plan, Do, Study, Act Cycle. There was a definite planning phase, followed by some changes in procedures. Next the effect of these changes were studied, and as a result certain specific actions were taken in the finalization phase of the project.

Another way to structure this project would be to use Hitoshi Kume's seven step breakdown of the PDSA Cycle, sometimes known as the QC Story:

1. Problem: Define the problem clearly.
    The Selection of a Theme paragraph, along with the time-line and the PERT diagram would fit under this heading.

2. Observation: Investigate the problem from a wide range of different viewpoints.
    The Pareto diagram, the collection of data on the losses, and the preparation of the running records on the beer and sake losses would fit under this heading.

3. Analysis: Find out what the main causes are.
    The construction and interpretation of the cause-and-effect diagram would fit under this heading.

4. Action: Take action to eliminate the main causes.
    The identification of the corrective actions listed in the summary would fit under this heading.

5. Check: Make sure the problem is prevented from occurring again.
    The collection of new data during the 50-day observation period, the preparation of the running records, the summary of the improvements, the observed desirable side-effects, and the intangible effects would all fit under this heading.

6. Standardization: Eliminate the cause of the problem permanently.
    This is clearly what they were doing with the paragraph entitled *Final Checking Procedures*.

7. Conclusion: Review the problem-solving procedure and plan future work.
    This is seen in their final paragraph entitled *Summary*.

However you may wish to outline the steps taken by the Minnow Sisters, it should be clear that this is an effective way of approaching the problem of improvements. At each stage they used the techniques and graphs that provided them with the insight they needed to understand where they were and to see where to go next. Then they documented their gains so that others could learn from them and the improvements could be maintained in the future.

So, if a bunch of 19 and 20 year-old kids can use these techniques so effectively, what possible excuse can the rest of us have for not using them?

19.4 What Should You Do Now?

There is an obstacle on the path from awareness to understanding. In order to move beyond awareness, you must begin to practice the use of these techniques. It is only after you use these tools that you begin to understand just how they work and why they work. Once this understanding has taken root, you can begin to actually explain the phenomena revealed by the tools. This feedback cycle continues and becomes the new way of thinking which is the basis for continual improvement. In short, you must first act—in order to understand—in order to explain—in order to be able to act effectively.

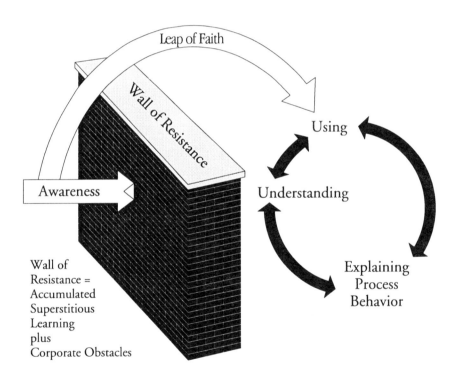

Figure 19.19: What You Have To Do

But there is one thing that you need before you take the flying leap. You need an operational definition of what you want to do. To create this operational definition you will need to answer the three fundamental questions.

1. What do you want to accomplish? What is your objective? What do you want to improve? Is there a problem that you need to solve? Until you can answer this question, you will not be able to get started.

2. How will you move toward your objective? What methodology will be used for improvement? Do you know where your process is currently operating? Is your current process operating up to its full potential?

3. How will you judge that you have met your objective? What direct or indirect measures are available that you? If you cannot measure progress toward your objective, you will be unable to document what you have done, and you will be unable to know if things have changed. How will you know when things have improved?

Of course, these three questions come from the three elements of the operational definition: the criterion, the test procedure, and the decision rule. Within this framework you can then begin the interactive use of the tools and techniques which is the heart of Continual Improvement.

Visualize your process with flowcharts and cause-and-effect diagrams. You may find that the very act of trying to draw a flowchart of your processes will reveal things that need to be worked on. When people finally start using flowcharts, they are generally amazed at what they can learn from this simple technique. Use cause-and-effect diagrams to visualize the contributing factors for a given problem.

Visualize your data using running records, bar charts, Pareto charts, or histograms as appropriate.

Visualize your process behavior using *XmR* Charts and Average and Range Charts as appropriate. These charts are the Voice of the Process—you can learn a lot by listening to your process.

Use the PDSA Cycle as your guide to action. It is the *learning way* that leads to discovery, implementation, and improvement.

What Do You Want to Accomplish?   **By What Method?**   **How Will You Know?**

Afterword

The Germ Theory of Management

by Myron Tribus[*]

Introduction

In a recent review of the Deming Theory of Management, William B. Gartner and M. James Naughton wrote:

> Medicine had been 'successfully' practiced without the knowledge of germs. In a pregerm theory paradigm, some patients got better, some got worse and some stayed the same; in each case, some rationale could be used to explain the outcome.

Doctors administer to the needs of their patients according to what they learn in school and in their training. They also learn by experience. They can only apply what they know and believe. They have no choice. They cannot apply what they do not know or what they disbelieve. What they do is always interpreted in terms of what they understand is "the way things work." As professionals they find it difficult to stray too far from the common knowledge and understanding. They are under pressure to follow "accepted practice." In this regard, doctors are no better and no worse than the rest of us. We are all prisoners of our upbringing, our culture and the state of knowledge of our teachers, mentors and fellow practitioners.

Today we smile when we read that after sewing up a wound with silken thread, the surgeons of 150 years ago recommended to leave a length of the thread outside the wound. This was done to draw off the pus that was sure to follow the insertion of unsterilized thread by unwashed hands using an unsterilized needle.

The doctors had a theory of how malaria was spread. They called it "mal-aria" to emphasize that it was the bad air, the unhealthy vapors in the night, that caused the disease. Their theory of medicine caused them to look in the wrong places for wrong answers to the solutions to their most pressing problems.

[*] Dr. Tribus is a consulting engineer who specializes in Quality Management. He was the director of the Center for Advanced Engineering Study at M.I.T. for 12 years. Prior to that he served as a Senior Vice-President for Research and Engineering at Xerox. His other positions include Assistant Secretary for Science and Technology in the U.S. Department of Commerce, and Dean of the Thayer School of Engineering at Dartmouth College. He has served on the boards of several companies and organizations.

Today our managers do the same. When they are up against tough international competition they look to changes in economic policy, in tax structure, in trade policy—everywhere except in their own understanding of what makes a company competitive. They question everything except their own theory of management.

Changing People's Beliefs is Not Easy

Try to imagine that it is now the year 1869. Pasteur has only recently demonstrated that fermentation is caused by organisms which are carried in the air. Only a few months ago Lister tried out the first antiseptic, carbolic acid, and found that it worked to prevent inflammation and pus after surgery.

120 years ago the spread of medical information was much slower than today. Imagine you are a young researcher in a medical school in the USA. The Civil War has just been finished and you are trying to develop your own career after army service. You are a serious young doctor who tries to learn the latest developments in your profession. Suppose that you have just learned about Pasteur's and Lister's work and that you have been invited to speak before a group of distinguished physicians, many of them having come to fame for their heroic service as surgeons during the American Civil War. What you now understand from your readings is that these famous physicians are actually killing their patients. Your responsibility is to explain to them, if you can, that because they do not wash their hands or sterilize their instruments, they sew death into every wound. Your assignment is to persuade them to forget most of what they have been taught, to abandon much of the wisdom they have accumulated over distinguished careers and to rebuild their understanding of the practice of medicine around the new theory of germs. Do you think you could do it? Do you think you could convince them? Do you believe they would be glad to hear you?

Suppose instead of being a speaker, you are a member of the audience. You are one of the good doctors who have earned respect and prestige in your village. You have a nice house on the hill, a pretty wife, a nice carriage, some fine horses and a few servants. You are part of the elite of your society. How will you feel if someone starts spreading the word that your treatments are a menace, that the theories you hold are bunk, and that your habit of moving from one patient to another, laying unwashed hands on each, guarantees the spread of disease to all who are so unfortunate as to become your patients? What do you think will happen to your practice if this kind of word gets bandied about? How would you be likely to greet the messenger?

This is not 1870—it is the end of the 20th Century. You are not doctors. You are all respected professionals. For most of you, managing is a part of your professional responsibility. You approach managing according to what you have been taught and what you have learned during your careers. I have worked among people like you and I know that no matter what happens, you always have a good explanation. I should be shocked and amazed if you were to explain your latest failure in this way: "You know, I really don't understand what I am doing and think that most of what I know is wrong."

You are no different than I was when I was an executive in industry a little over a dozen years ago. You don't get to a position of responsibility if you are continuously in doubt about the validity of what you believe. And you certainly don't get there if you broadcast your doubts about what you know and can do.

My task is similar to that of the young doctor trying to introduce the germ theory of medicine. There is a new theory of management, as different from what most of you now believe as the germ theory was from what the doctors believed. For reasons which will become clear shortly, I call this different approach the "germ theory of management."

Not everything the doctors did was wrong; just most things. Before the germ theory doctors interviewed patients, took medical and personal histories, prescribed changes in diet and lifestyle and were present at the arrival of babies. They developed a sense of social responsibility. They were sincere in their efforts to do the right things. Read, for example, the Oath of Hippocrates, which preceded the germ theory by many centuries. The earliest doctors did the best they could with what they knew at the time.

So do you.

What the doctors were taught was not good enough. Some things they did were downright dangerous and harmful. They learned. So can you.

But just as medical practice has been changed by the germ theory of disease, so managerial practice is about to be changed. The changes are already being adopted in different lands and in different organizations, more vital and more alive. In this fiercely competitive world, the unhealthy enterprises are going to die. The enterprises which continue to be managed the old way are going to disappear.

This is not some new fad which you shall be free to follow or not as you please. What I am talking about is your survival. Your jobs will depend upon whether you are willing to learn a new kind of behavior. I do not expect all of you to like it; the doctors didn't like it then, either. But that's the way it was; that's the way it is.

The Required Changes in Management are Profound

As I said in the start of this talk, in 1865 Pasteur was sent to the south of France to investigate what was killing the silkworms in the silk industry of France. There he isolated the bacilli of two distinct diseases and developed a method of prevent contagion. Lord Lister applied the same ideas in medicine in the same year.

In the 1920s Walter Shewhart at the Bell Laboratories was given an assignment to see what to do to increase the reliability of telephone amplifiers used to strengthen the signal in long distance communication. These amplifiers were required to be about a mile apart and were to be part of a transmission system in which the cables were underground. Unlike the doctors, the Bell System wanted to be sure the amplifiers were healthy so they could bury them! If they died, they would have to be dug up. The amplifiers contained vacuum tubes which were known to have an uncertain life. Shewhart's assignment was to find out what could be done to guarantee the life of the amplifiers, to keep them from getting sick, so to speak. In the process he discovered the virus of variability. Shewhart discovered what, in retrospect, ought to have been clear to everyone. When you assemble a vacuum tube, if every component that goes into the vacuum tube is the same as in every other vacuum tube and if each tube is put together precisely the same way and each is free of contamination, and if each is subjected to exactly the same load conditions, then each will live the same life. The problem is that not all vacuum tubes can be made the same. There are small variations in the chemical composition of the materials. There are small variations in the assembly process. There is always a small amount of dirt that falls by chance in different places. In short, there is always variability and this leads to uncertainty in how long the vacuum tube will last. If the process of assembly is sufficiently variable, it is almost certain that some of the vacuum tubes will have very short lives. The tubes are victims of the virus of variability. This was Shewhart's discovery.

Shewhart's investigations lead to the concepts of statistical quality control and in terms of our analogy, his work, like Pasteur's has laid the foundations for the "germ theory of management."

Few people understand what unpredictable variation does to the cost of doing business. Fewer still understand what can be done about it and what is management's role.

Just as Lister understood the broader significance of Pasteur's work in the field of medicine, so it was that Dr. W. Edwards Deming understood the significance of Shewhart's work to the general theory of management. He realized that the key to better management was the study of the *processes whereby things get done*. If you remove the sources of variability from any process, you make it more predictable. You can schedule activities closer together and eliminate waste and delay.

The key idea is the elimination of the virus of variability which results in the improvement of process capability. This idea was taught widely during World War II and was important to the successful development of America's mighty war machine. By 1956 a few people in the Bell System understood this idea well enough to write in the introduction to the Western Electric *Statistical Quality Control Handbook* the following comment:

> …it is possible to make process capability studies in connection with practically any type of Engineering, Operating, Inspection, or Management problem.

Unfortunately, most of our managers, in the period after WWII were so busy making quick money they forgot about the virus of variability and the theory disappeared from the American scene. None of our business schools picked it up. In fact, the few times I have tried to introduce these ideas to the prestigious business schools of America I have been listened to with polite amusement, if listened to at all.

Germs are invisible. That's what makes them so dangerous and so difficult to track down. You know about their presence only because of the symptoms. The same is true of the viruses of variability. They are invisible. You have to know where to look and how to look. Just as the doctor often has to use special instruments and may even have to culture a sample, so must the manager learn to take data and analyze it in a special way. Dr. Deming says it takes "profound knowledge" to understand.

An experienced doctor looks into your throat and says, "I believe you have an infection there—or have you just been eating some red candy?" The doctor feels for lumps in your glands and listens to the sounds of your lungs as you breathe. If the doctor does not understand the germ theory of disease, he cannot interpret the symptoms.

In the same way a manager skilled in dealing with the virus of variability can judge the health of an enterprise by looking at data, by observing behavior, by asking questions and judging the answers, and by listening to what goes on in meetings. If the manager understands how the virus of variability works, he or she will understand what is seen and heard. If not, they will be as helpless as the doctors of long ago, prescribing different vapors to counter "mal-aria."

Variability—the Virus of Systems

The first thing that Doctors had to learn was that germs, although invisible, could be transmitted by various means from one patient to another. They had to believe that these germs mattered. They had to learn about sterilization and antiseptics. They had to believe it was important to wash their hands. They had to learn about germ cultures and the causes of infection. They had to form new images of the world.

So will you. Let us consider an example.

Imagine a company which purchases castings from a foundry (or even has a foundry of its own) and passes these castings through a sequence of machining processes, carried out on different machines. The different machined parts are assembled into a product in which the parts move, deflect, and rotate, and are supposed to do so with some precision.

We suppose that the materials purchased by the foundry are not perfectly uniform. There is always some variability in the composition and the treatment of the materials. The processes in the foundry itself are not always the same. *We may say that the processes are infected with variability.* They yield castings which vary in composition, dimension, hardness, and porosity. The variations occur from point-to-point and part-to-part.

When these castings arrive at a machine tool to be scraped and cut by various tools, their variability infects the machine tools. The variation in hardness causes nonuniform tool wear. It also makes it difficult for the machinist to know at what speeds and feeds to set the controls. The tool wear is not predictable. Machine maintenance is not predictable, either. Thus the infection spreads to the tool room, where a larger inventory is carried than would be needed if the life of tools could be predicted accurately. Inventories are now subject to wider variations. The inability to predict the requirements for maintenance increases the number of people who need to be hired for maintenance and complicates the maintenance process.

With so many people to hire and train, the training system becomes overloaded and not everyone receives the same training. Thus the maintenance system is infected with variability. When a machine is "fixed" it may break down sooner than expected because the maintenance is not always done the same way. People with inadequate training do not follow standards of maintenance. The virus of variability spreads from the maintenance department to the personnel department where the records suggest there are large differences in the behavior of workers, when, in fact, the workers are subjected to uncontrolled variation. They are victims of a lottery, but they and the personnel department do not understand it. The virus of variability infects every department it touches.

Imagine a company making beer cans. The company purchases rolls of sheet aluminum from a supplier. As the sheet of aluminum passes through the can making machine it is cut into various shapes by dies and then drawn into beer cans and beer can tops. The aluminum varies in thickness from roll to roll. When a new roll is fed to the machine, it may jam and the controls will have to be reset. The output of the machines is now unpredictable. The variability virus has spread from the aluminum supplier to the machines. After a while some of the operators learn special tricks to apply when the aluminum rolls have to be changed. Because the management rates the operators individually and competitively, those who learn new tricks are not always willing to share them with their competitors. What the management then sees is a large variability in the performance of their operators. They think they are witnessing the capabilities of their operators. They think they are witnessing the results of the variability of people; they aim to fire the "bottom half." They do not know that the virus of variability is infecting their processes. They act on what they know. They have an explanation for everything and are confident in what they do. In the process they ruin the lives of some of their workers. They are a menace to the health of their companies, but because neither they nor their workers understand about the virus of variability, they are unaware. They know not what they do. And they do not like to be told.

When a product is assembled the variability in components causes variability in performance from one product to another. The variability of finished products may be so great that only a fraction of them can be used without being reworked. Some are so bad they have to be scrapped—or at best taken apart and reassembled using other parts, which may be similarly infected. What to do with the sick parts becomes an important policy issue for the company. These problems cause many management meetings, making the life of the managers hectic and unpredictable. The variability in the incoming materials has been allowed to infect all systems, including the managerial system. The symptom is managerial stress; the cause variability virus.

These infections of variability, which have spread from machine to machine, to the personnel, and even to the personnel records, are largely undetected by managers who do not understand the "germ theory." They have their own theories of how things work. The cures they apply may, in fact, make the infections more virulent.

The examples I have given are from the factory floor, but they occur in the office as well. In deference to my past experience as an executive in the Xerox Corporation, I shall not dwell on how variability in maintenance of copiers can cause variability in their performance and thereby infect the performance of an entire office.

Suppose you live in a small town served by a feeder airline. Suppose that the airline schedule is not reliable; that is, you cannot be sure when your airplane will take off. This variability of performance causes you to make your appointments at a distant city with considerable slack in your schedule. Sometimes, just to be safe, you travel the day before and must pay for a hotel room for one night. You dare not count on the morning flight to get you there and the evening flight to get you back. Consider the total effect on the other businesses in the community and you have a recipe for the decline of the local economy—the added expense may just be enough to drive your company out of business. Too many people think of these delays and missed schedules as "normal." They do not know what it means to be well. A few of them go to countries where the trains run on time, the mail gets delivered promptly, the phone system works without delays, the taxis are clean and the streets are free of debris. They marvel at the sense of good health.

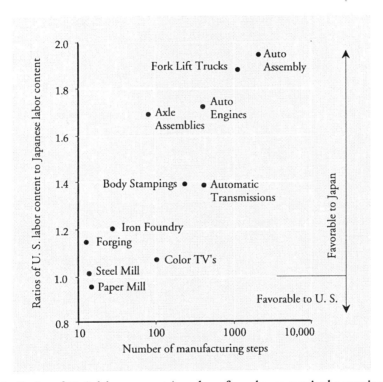

Figure 20.1: Ratios of U. S. labor content (number of manhours required per unit of product) to Japanese labor content for various operations. Ratios below 1.0 are favorable to the U.S. As the number of manufacturing steps increases the ratios become more unfavorable for the U. S. (Data from Boston Consulting Group)

How much could be saved if all processes had zero variability? Consider just this one example: In the early 1950s, to demonstrate just how quickly a house could be built, the Henry Beck company of Dallas, Texas, assembled a two bedroom, one floor house on a previously prepared concrete slab. As pictured in Life magazine, from the time they started to assemble the house until it was finished, painted, with one woman taking a hot bath in the bathroom and another cooking dinner on the kitchen stove was less than three hours. Think of that—three hours. The usual time is at least 30 days, often more. Why does it take more time? It is because the activities of all the people cannot be scheduled so closely. If the carpenter starts to drive a nail 1 second after the board has been cut, instead of 15 minutes, the time scale increases by 900. Three hours stretches into 2700 hours. No one expects to be able to schedule all the people who are required to build a house so that each one does his or her job with only seconds to spare. We do not expect to see the precision of the Rockettes or the ballet. In an industrial setting, we cannot expect that kind of precision. But we can make each process more precise, and as we do so, errors, goofs, flaws, and delays all begin to disappear. As we reduce the virus of variability, we find savings in time and money we never knew were there, savings which our methods of accounting hide so cleverly that we think that waste is "normal."

We are not accustomed to thinking about achieving such precision of control that we can assemble a house in a few hours. Instead we expect to wait half a day just for an appointment at the bank! The inability to schedule things accurately means that for a complex activity, the total time required to do something is as much as 1000 times as long as it needs to be. This is the cost of the virus of variability.

All of the variability cannot be removed. No one knows, however, just how much can be done. Until the students of Homer Sarasohn, W. Edwards Deming and Joe Juran applied these ideas in Japan and the results were seen on a large scale, it was not appreciated that costs could be cut by as much as 50% in many instances. We are not just talking about hardware. The results in the service industries are sometimes even more dramatic.

Processes can have an Immune System Deficiency, Too

Until doctors accepted the existence of germs and began to analyze illnesses in terms of infections, they could not consider the existence of an immune system. It is common knowledge, today, that the mere infection of a person with germs is not enough to cause an illness. Much depends upon how the immune system of the body reacts to the virus.

Dr. Genichi Taguchi in Japan has pioneered the concept of a robust design, one which does not amplify variability but rather tends to attenuate it and provide good performance even in the face of large variability.

Engineers and managers who are ignorant of elementary statistics simply cannot begin to think about how to design healthier products but spend dollars needlessly in attempting to control processes. When managers spend large amounts of money to get around the effects of variability, instead of learning how to reduce it, we call their approach a "technology fix." If you learn how to control variability and to make your processes immune to it, while your competitor spends millions of dollars on a completely automated process with complex controls designed to control variation, it is clear you will be able to undercut your competitor's prices. This line of reasoning explains why the NUMMI plant, operated by Toyota for General Motors, is the highest quality plant in the GM system although it has the least automation.

The Doctor or Manager as Detective

A common failure among doctors is misdiagnosis. Faced with a set of symptoms, the doctor is supposed to figure out what is wrong with the patient. A good doctor knows how to ask useful questions. The doctor has to be like a good detective. Indeed, it is not an accident that Sir Arthur Conan Doyle was a physician before he became a successful writer and that his model for Sherlock Holmes was the professor of clinical medicine who taught him that careful observation of a patient could reveal many things about lifestyle and habit.

Let me try you out as observers. Figure 2 shows data for [the flaws produced by] eight workers making the same product, all working at about the same rate, for 12 weeks. Good doctor, what do make of these data? What would you prescribe?

| | *Week* | | | | | | | | | | | | |
	1	*2*	*3*	*4*	*5*	*6*	*7*	*8*	*9*	*10*	*11*	*12*	**Sums**
Mary	0	0	0	0	0	0	0	0	0	0	0	0	**0**
Joe	0	0	0	0	0	0	0	0	0	0	0	0	**0**
Eva	1	0	0	2	0	0	3	0	0	1	0	0	**7**
Fred	0	0	0	1	0	0	2	0	0	0	0	0	**3**
Jim	0	0	0	0	0	0	0	0	0	0	0	0	**0**
Ed	0	0	0	0	0	2	0	0	0	0	0	0	**2**
Kate	0	0	0	0	0	0	0	0	0	0	0	0	**0**
Carl	0	0	0	1	0	0	0	0	0	0	0	0	**1**

Figure 20.2: Flaws by Worker by Week

How do you prescribe? If you were the supervisor of these workers, what would you do? How would you go about improving things?

I have presented this table to audiences across the USA, in Mexico, in Canada, in Australia, in the UK and I always get the same reaction. People always suggest a good talk with Eva. They propose putting Eva alongside Mary or asking Mary to help her. They propose to fire Eva. They propose to give Eva more training.

An astute statistician at a meeting of the Royal Statistical Society in London even went so far as to observe that there was a 30-day periodicity in Eva's output and that might have something to do with things.

After the audience suggests different cures based on the common wisdom, I explain to them that the numbers in the tables were actually generated by the random number generator in my computer. The flaws were generated and assigned to memory cells, to which I attached people's names. In other words, the faults were generated entirely by the system.

In only two or three instances, out of thousands of people, did anyone suggest that perhaps the problem was in the system itself—that the system had been infected with the virus of variability and it was not the fault of the workers. In the last four years, only three people have suggested that we analyze the data in the table to see if we could compute whether Eva's results should be expected in the light of the variability exhibited by the system.

The fact is the process itself is infected with the virus of variability. If you don't set about sterilizing the process, that is, reducing its variability, it will certainly infect the workers. Not only will it infect the workers, it will infect your judgment.

People change their views very slowly. I shall never forget the one manager who said afterwards, "Look, I know that the numbers were generated by a computer, but nevertheless, I would still talk to Eva!"

The output of these workers has been infected by the variability of the process over which they had no control. Suppose that the supervisor, with the objective of urging the workers to better performance decided to post Figure 2 on the bulletin board. Of course we do not expect the workers to understand the germ theory of management. They may think that the results are their fault and they will try to do better. Do you not see how the virus of variability of the system will infect their interpersonal relations and perhaps even the home lives of the workers? If the supervisor does not understand the theory, do you not see how the systems of supervision will become infected? Suppose there is an annual rating system for supervisors and the data in the above table are available to the upper management? Suppose the upper management does not understand the variability virus and therefore thinks the supervisor should have done something drastic about Eva. Suppose the supervisor, however, does know about variability and does understand it is the system that needs to be fixed. Given this disparity in understanding, how do you think the manager will rate the supervisor?

I am not describing a far fetched scenario. I am describing what goes on daily in factories and offices all around the world.

The variability in product performance also infects the purchasing process—the number of spare parts required is increased, making the purchasing and supply systems unhealthy.

We have seen, therefore, how this virus of variability can spread from the foundry to the personnel office to the top ranks of management.

The point I want to make is simple: Variability is a virus. It can infect every process it touches.

Juran has captured the essence of this spread of infection in what has become known as "Juran's Rule:"

> *Whenever there is a problem*
> *85% of the time it will be in the system, and*
> *15% of the time it will be the worker.*

The instinctive reaction of most managers I meet is to blame the person. Sometimes I find a manager who, when confronted with a problem will even say it is his own fault, he should have done something else. As a consultant I often find it difficult to persuade him that in fact it is the *system* which is at fault. Many managers will persist in thinking that they need to change something in their personalities when in fact it is the system which needs to be changed.

Who should be responsible to clean up these processes, to *sterilize* them, so to speak?

Just as germs are everywhere, so are the causes of variability. To sterilize a process will require someone to study what causes the variability and to remove the causes one by one. Managers are the only people authorized to tamper with the system. If you, personally, do not do this, it will not get done. Your entire operation will become sick. As a manager, you cannot delegate to someone else the responsibility for the health of the processes for which you are responsible. If you can delegate this responsibility, why do we need you?

Some Managerial Myths

In promoting this different approach to management Don Petersen of Ford Motor Company put it to his subordinates this way: "I hate to be the one to tell you this, but some of you were promoted a time or two for the wrong reasons."

I have collected a few managerial myths which I believe need to be eliminated. I am aware that many of you will feel deeply resentful. That's to be expected. You will either get over it or be pushed aside by those who do understand.

The Perversity Principle
If you try to improve the performance of a system of people, machines, and procedures,

by setting numerical goals for the improvement of individual parts of the system,

the system will defeat you

and you will pay a price where you least expected to do so.

This idea goes down hard for people who like to think that the organization chart defines how things get done. They like to issue crisp orders to subordinates. They think they can divide the system into parts, along the lines of an organization chart. They have a generic organization chart in their heads.

Figure 20.3: A Generic Organizational Chart

Their managerial strategy is "divide and conquer." They see the organization the way some friends of mine in Holland see it.

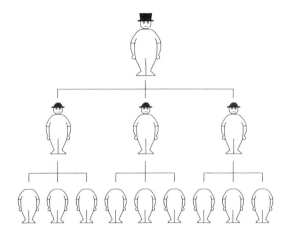

**Figure 20.4: The hidden assumption of many managers—
the people at the bottom have no heads.**

(Courtesy of MANS Organization, The Netherlands)

The conceptual framework of many managers is impoverished. They forget that the work flows *across* the organizational chart, more or less perpendicular to the lines of authority. They are unaware that the different steps in the process infect one another. They ignore that they are dealing with a system as a whole. They are determined to judge each person and each division on its own accomplishments.

They do not know how to recognize and define a system of processes. They do not understand what is meant by a process. They do not know how to recognize when processes which flow across an organization chart are unpredictable. They persist in thinking that organization charts describe how things get done when in fact things get done in spite of the organization chart.

In some organizations this method of management leads one department to regard the other as the enemy. They would rather defeat the other department than the competition.

The problem of thinking only in terms of the organization chart, apart from the failure to harness the intelligence of the majority of the workforce, is that the work flows *across* the organization. Suppose you set a target for the people in one department, telling them they are to process a certain number of orders per month. Then you give another target to your sales force. It certainly matters to the factory whether the orders arrive bunched up or spread out. It matters if they arrive in a predictable fashion. In other words, even if each person does the required amount of work on average, the variability in performance will cause extra expense and waste in other departments.

Consider for example the loading of a ship. The cargo arrives at the dock in trucks and is unloaded by hand. Then cargo is picked up by a stevedore and taken to a crane. Bundles of cargo are picked up and deposited on the deck where another stevedore loads it into a fork lift truck and moves it into the hold. A colleague of mine observed that this was the way it was done for the Nina, the Pinta, and the Santa Maria. If you watch this activity for awhile you will see that the variability of cargo sizes, the variability of movement of cargo and the variability of the performance of the individual performers does not speed up the process. It slows it down as each performer tries to look good at the expense of others.

The same difficulty arises whenever people have to work in sequence, whether it is in accounting, sales, maintenance and repair or in customer service. The work flows across the enterprise and attempting to treat it piecemeal, as independent operations, results in waste and expense.

Sometimes the variability is so inherent in the system there is no way to improve except to change the system itself. That is why container ships have been so successful. By pushing the inefficient packing problem onto someone else, they have eliminated the variability in the loading process. The turn around time for ships has been reduced to hours instead of days.

If you set targets for the people at the bottom of the system, or for the people in between, without regard for the *systems* aspect of the work, you are abdicating your responsibility. Remember what you tried to do to Eva. Don't do it to everyone.

The Manager's Job Has Changed

> *The people work **in** a system.*
> *The job of a manager*
> *is to work **on** the system,*
> *to improve it,*
> *with the help of the workers.*

There are several key words in this statement:

1. "work *in* a system" If you believe this you then have to acknowledge that workers do not control what goes on in their work. Managing in such a way that you tell people you are holding them accountable for results flies in the face of what you really know. When you do this, you are inconsistent with yourself. "But," you are certain to protest, "If I don't hold them responsible, they won't do anything." First of all, that's not true. But more importantly, you should hold them accountable to help you to improve the system.

2. "the job of a manager" What did you think your job was?

3. "work *on* the system" Do you know how to define the system upon which you are supposed to work? Do you know *how* to work *on* a system? Do you know what you have to learn to do it? Do you know where to go to learn?

4. "to improve it" Do you still hold to the admonition—"If it ain't broke, don't fix it?" Do you know you are supposed to be active about a third of the time trying to improve the system under your care? Do you do it? Do you believe you should do it?

5. "with their help" Do you accept that your people should help you? Do you accept that you should teach them to help you? Do you want them to help you? Are you afraid? Do you know what you have to do to make it possible for them to help you?

The State of Health of An Enterprise

This audience, of course, is different. It is filled with enlightened people. Surely you would not behave as the doctors a century ago behaved when they were told they should see that their operating rooms were sterile. They fought it tooth and nail.

"What, stop to wash my hands? Don't be silly. I have important things to do."

It was a lot of work to change and it required them to admit they had a lot to learn. They were human. They resented the need to change and hoped in their heart of hearts that it would all blow over.

In the first place, changing the practices and procedures in the operating room was not something they could do alone. They needed nurses and orderlies to help them. They had to begin by first understanding the germ theory of disease themselves. It is one thing to learn a new theory when you are a young student in medical school; it is another when you are busy supporting your family through your practice of medicine. After they learned the theory themselves they had to teach the nurses and orderlies how to sterilize instruments and medical facilities. They could not just leave these things to chance. They had to institute practices and procedures and train people to follow them. They had to influence the training and education of nurses so that these nurses would do the right things without having to be told. Such changes could not come about over night. Many patients would have to die along the way as the changes slowly made their way through medical practice.

The history of medicine is full of examples of doctors who fought the changes and ridiculed the change agents. They buried their mistakes, and few people outside of medicine knew what was happening.

Today I meet managers who do not want to learn. They are busy with mergers and acquisitions and with plant closings. They are busy beseeching the government to do something to somebody else, all the while leaving them alone. With their false images of how an enterprise ought to be managed, they make demands on their workers and thereby provide job security only for labor leaders.

Even if you personally are convinced that a different theory of management ought to be adopted, you will quickly discover you cannot apply it alone. You are answerable to your boss and if the boss does not go along with the new ideas your job may be put at risk. You will have some hard choices to make. If you are low enough in the enterprise you will be entirely frustrated.

The question I am most frequently asked is "Will you please come and explain about quality to our top management?" I have a stock answer to such requests: "I'm sorry but I do not do that sort of thing. I have a colleague, however, who will accept such assignments. His name is Don Quixote."

We started this example with the factory floor, but the variability virus will infect any system it touches. This includes the managerial system itself. Doctors can get sick, too, you know. When you work in an enterprise that is sick, it gets to you. You don't enjoy the work. You have to work hard just to keep things going. If you stay in the job too long, you can burn out.

It is important that a manager learn how to diagnose the situation in an enterprise by observing what happens in meetings.

Since managers spend so much time in meetings, my colleague Professor Tsuda, of Rikkyo University in Tokyo, has prepared the following chart to help a manager make a diagnosis from the symptoms which will be exhibited in typical meetings.

Professor Tsuda's Classification Scheme for Organizations

	Style of Meeting	Decision Making	Diagnosis	Status
1.	Discussions without data	Decisions are based on politics, emotion, turf, etc.	People do not want to see problems, so they deny their existence	Drugged or Comatose
2.	Data are discussed, but only if they are favorable	Decisions are based on raw data without analysis— options accepted on boss' hunch	People see problems but are habituated to their presence	Asleep
3.	Good and bad data are discussed and analyzed	Decisions are based on data, analysis, and options proposed by the presenters	People see problems but do not know what to do because problems are systemic	Alive
4.	Data are presented, analyzed statistically, and options are also analyzed, including the option of changing policies	Decisions are based on analyses and data— options and policies are questioned	People want to see their problems and are quick to seek out data—they want to solve problems	Alert Sensitive Alive

(courtesy of Professor Yoshikazu Tsuda, Rikkyo University, Tokyo)

Perhaps with the aid of the people in finance you have tried to divide your company into separate "profit centers," with ratings for the performance of each. Everyone in your enterprise has a well defined job and is held accountable for it. Well, whether you like it or not, the enterprise is one system. You can divide it up anyway you want to in your head; in reality it is what it is—a highly interactive complex system in which each unhealthy part infects the others. If you ignore this elementary fact, the system will never be healthy. It will not be able to compete against healthy systems. In due course, unless protected artificially against competition, it will die. Your job will go with it.

The Transition of a Culture

In my opinion, what this country now needs more than anything else is a better understanding of what it means to be a leader. Don Alstadt has described the situation in the USA by the phrase "Overmanaged and underled." We need to lead our enterprises into a new way to manage. We need to lead in the transition of our managerial cultures from one norm to another. This transition started in Japan in the late 1940s as a result of Homer Sarasohn's intervention after WWII. It accelerated when Deming and Juran went there in the 1950's and it has continued to accelerate ever since. In the early 1980s a few companies learned about the Deming Prize and the impact of quality management on Japanese industry. Now we have quite a few examples in many countries of the world of what it means to change the corporate culture.

What I can tell you about, from the experience of others, is the path you are most likely to follow in changing the company culture. There are seven stages, once you start to change. My own observations bear out the validity of the following table which was originally prepared by Professor Tsuda.

Stage 0

The management expresses concern only over market share, profits and return on investment.

Stage 1

The management is concerned about quality of the product because of its impact on warranty cost and customer complaints. Loss of market share becomes apparent. The action taken is to add more inspectors so that the "bad stuff doesn't get out."

Stage 2

Management recognizes that control of the production process will lead to less waste and a lower cost to obtain acceptable products. Manufacturing is supported in increasing QC activities.

Stage 3

The results of QC are limited by reactions of personnel so management begins to emphasize quality management. Manufacturing introduces methods of continual improvement (also known as SPC).

Stage 4

Management asks that SPC and quality management methods be applied to all departments which border on the production department (purchasing, transportation, warehousing, etc.)

Stage 5

Management attempts to persuade R&D, engineering and finance to consider quality management principles but these departments think they are not part of the problem. Gradually professionals learn that quality is their mission (a difficult stage).

Stage 6

Management begins to recognize that quality management principles will be useful if applied to all departments of the enterprise but doesn't know how to make it happen. It organizes actions all over the company to see what to do.

Stage 7

Management proclaims (and acts consistently with the proclamation) that "Company wide quality control is the company policy."

Specifically, this means:

Quality is first priority

Customer oriented decision criteria

Personnel policies respect humanity

All departments coordinated

All departments cooperative

All employees involved in improvement

Solid relations with suppliers

Good communications based on

Factual data

Statistical Process Control

A Checklist of Things Managers Need to Learn

Every manager should be competent in the basic techniques:

1. Process Flow Charting
2. Fishbone Diagrams
3. Run Charts
4. Histograms
5. Pareto Diagrams
6. Scatter Diagrams
7. Process Behavior Charts
8. Elementary Design of Experiment

Every manager should learn how to:

1. Recognize, define, describe, diagnose, and improve the systems for which he or she is responsible.

2. Diagnose the variability of a system and decide which variations are special, and require special action and which are common and will require a change in the system design and operation. The manager must be able to tell the difference between signals and noise.

3. Lead teams of people, having different educational levels, in problem identification, data gathering, data analysis, and generation of proposals for solution, implementation, and test.

4. Diagnose the behavior of humans and distinguish those difficulties which are due to the variations in human abilities (15%) and those which are caused by the system (85%) [Juran's Rule].

> *A leader's main obligation*
> > *is to secure the faith and respect of those under him.*
> *A leader must himself be the finest example*
> > *of what he would like to see in his followers.*

Homer Sarasohn in Japan, 1948

Appendix

Answers to Exercises

Exercise 2.1:

The box marked Limbo represents a problem in that there is no mechanism for clearing an order out of Limbo. This is the land of the forgotten orders. Of course this has the potential for poorer customer service and lost sales.

Exercise 2.2:

While your flowchart will look different, does it have the three decision diamonds and the one feedback loop?

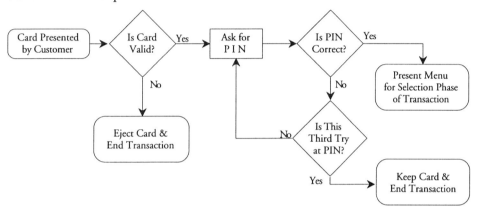

Exercise 2.3:

While your flowchart will look different, does it have the four decision diamonds and the two feedback loops?

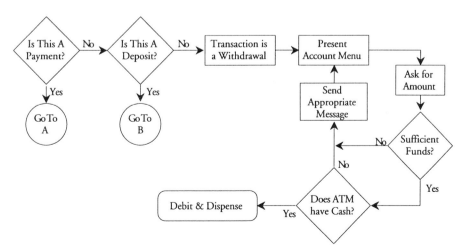

Exercise 2.4:

Your Cause-and-Effect diagram will look different, but does it convey roughly the same story?

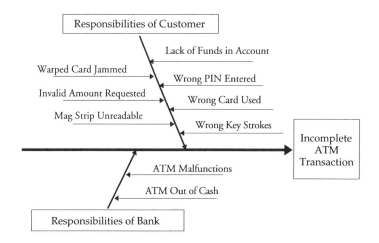

Page 71 Practice:

The next two values are 14.2 and 11.7.

You would place a 2 after the 14, and a 7 after the 11.

Exercise 4.1:

The average number of transactions per day is approximately 7550.

70	51
71	67
72	92 90
73	65 50 47
74	35 64 96 67
75	52 13 77 14 68 44 52 86
76	30 43 20 25 08
77	57 20 45
78	64
79	00
80	25
81	31

Exercise 4.2: This running record shows a potential weekly cycle.

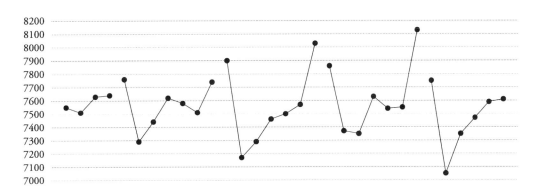

Exercise 4.3:

R6	916	Wrong PIN	39.8%	39.8%
R1	673	Wrong Card Used	29.2%	69.0%
R2	237	Invalid Amount Requested	10.3%	79.4%
R3	118	Lack of funds in Account	5.1%	84.5%
R8	100	Wrong Key Strokes	4.3%	88.8%
R4	68	Warped Card Jammed	2.9%	91.8%
R7	68	Mag Strip Unreadable	2.9%	94.7%
R9	68	ATM Out of Cash	2.9%	97.7%
R5	53	ATM Malfunctions	2.3%	100.0%

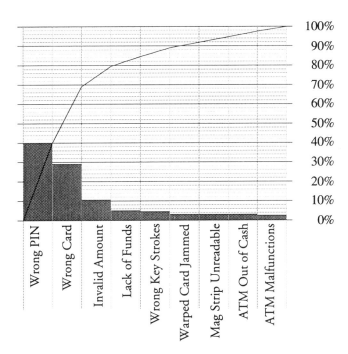

Exercise 4.4:

ATM Out of Cash and ATM Malfunctions are responsibilities of the bank.
Based on the Pareto Chart in Exercise 4.3, these two categories do not constitute a major opportunity for improvement.

Exercise 4.5:

This running record does not show the same sort of weekly cycle as Exercise 4.2.

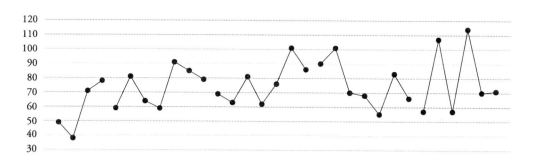

Page 112 Practice:

The average of the data set {10, 25, 12, 32, 26} is 21.
The median is 25.
The range is 22.

Exercises 7.1 and 7.2:

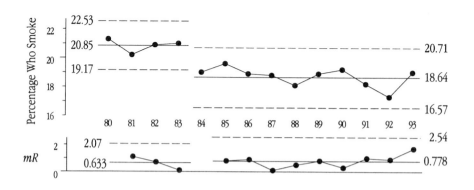

Exercise 7.3:

One presenter, T.J., stands out from the crowd as being detectably better.
The moving ranges are used to compute the limits, but with an arbitrary ordering
like this the Moving Range Chart does not have any direct interpretability.

Exercise 8.1:

Exercise 8.2:

This accident process is predictable.
The prediction would be about 35 accidents per million man-hours.
The monthly values could range from 26 to 44.
To signal a reduction a single month's value would have to fall below 25.

Exercise 8.3:

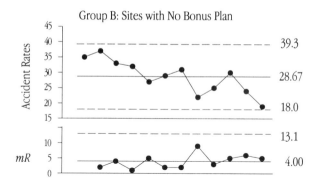

Exercise 8.4:

This accident process is predictable.

The prediction would be about 29 accidents per million man-hours.

The monthly values could range from 18 to 39.

To signal a reduction a monthly value would have to drop below 18.

Exercise 10.1 and 10.2:

The median moving range is 2.8.

The *UNPL* is 18.82. The *LNPL* is 1.24. The *URL* is 10.8.

Exercise 10.3:

The average is 18.64. The median moving range is 0.8.

The *UNPL* is 21.15. The *LNPL* is 16.13. The *URL* is 3.1.

Exercise 10.4:

The *UNPL* is 4.51. The *LNPL* is 2.49. The *URL* is 1.24.

Four individuals stand out from the crowd, rather than just one.

Two are detectably better than the rest, and two are detectably worse.

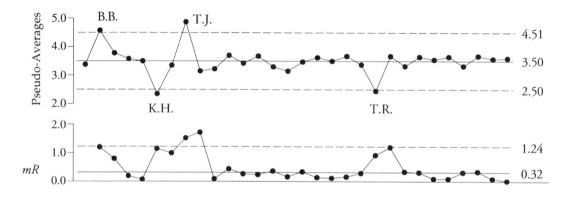

Exercise 10.5:

The median value is 238. The median moving range is 125.

Exercise 10.6:

The median moving range is 2.7. The average is 2.0.
The *UNPL* is 10.48. The *LNPL* is − 6.48. The *URL* is 10.4.

Exercise 10.8:

There are six points outside the limits, thus we have a detectable weekly cycle.

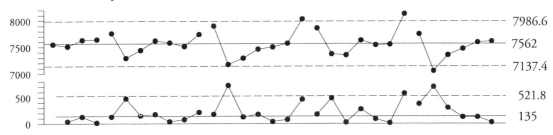

Exercise 11.1:

Even though the average moving range has been inflated by the four large ranges, there are two runs near the upper limit on the *X* Chart and three moving ranges outside the limits.

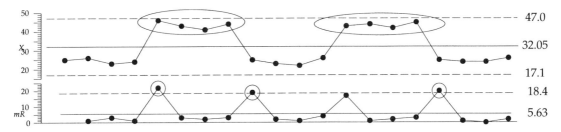

Exercise 11.2:

Using the median moving range we find 17 individual values and four moving ranges outside the limits.
No evidence of chunky data. There are eight possible values below the upper range limit.

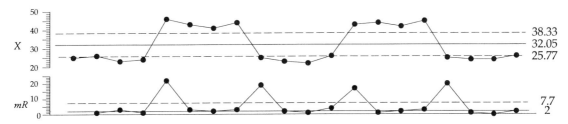

Exercise 11.3:

    a. The global standard deviation statistic does not differentiate between routine variation and exceptional variation because it lumps all the variation together into a single numerical summary.

    b. Moving ranges are, by definition, localized measures of dispersion.

    c. By showing the variation from point-to-point the moving ranges allow you to distinguish between routine and exceptional variation. In Exercises 11.1 and 11.2 the exceptional variation is seen as four spikes on the Moving Range Chart.

    d. The median moving range performs better because it is less contaminated by the exceptional variation in these data.

Exercise 11.4:

There are three successive values in the upper 25% of the limits (a run near the limit). This is a moderate signal.

Exercise 12.1:

The half averages are 410.5 and 430.1. The average moving range is 42.8. The upper range limit is 140. The three-sigma distance for the X Chart is ± 114. The forecast for time period 21 would be about 440. The range of possible values for time period 21 would be about 330 to 550.

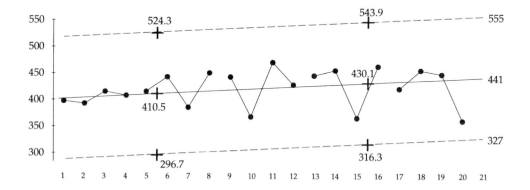

Exercise 12.2:

The half averages are 20.3 and 18.4.

The value for 1993 does not signal an end to the "downward trend."

| X | 21.3 | 20.2 | 20.9 | 21.0 | 18.8 | 19.6 | 18.7 | 18.6 | 18.1 | 18.9 | 19.2 | 18.2 | 17.3 | 19.0 |
| mR | | 1.1 | 0.7 | 0.1 | 2.2 | 0.8 | 0.9 | 0.1 | 0.5 | 0.8 | 0.3 | 1.0 | 0.9 | 1.7 |

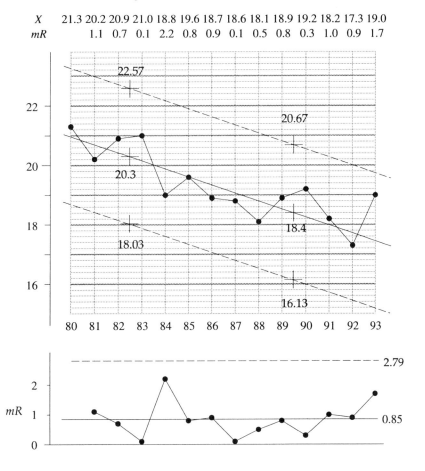

Exercise 12.3:

The computed limits are –3 to 1789. There is no detectable difference between these 24 providers for this Episode Treatment Group. Tracking the individual providers over time might allow you to detect some differences, but this cross sectional comparison shows none.

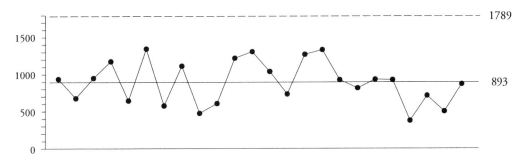

Exercise 12.4:

These are the average scores for the 46 golfers who played in the 1997 Masters Tournament, and W5's first name is Tiger.

Exercise 13.1:

The average proportion of cases with excessive costs was 0.13875, and the average moving range was 0.0722. There is no detectable difference between these 24 providers in terms of the proportion of cases with excessive costs.

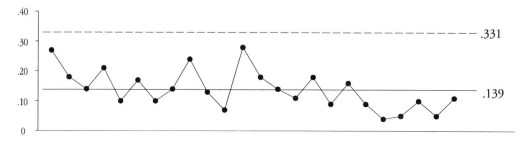

Exercise 14.1:

Provider	n_i	X_i	p_i	$3\sqrt{\overline{p}(1-\overline{p})/n_i}$	LLp	ULp
104	30	8	.27	0.189	-0.051	0.328
140	40	7	.18	0.164	-0.025	0.303
147	37	5	.14	0.170	-0.032	0.309
376	34	7	.21	0.178	-0.039	0.317
378	20	2	.10	0.232	-0.093	0.371
411	30	5	.17	0.189	-0.051	0.328
564	40	4	.10	0.164	-0.025	0.303
643	21	3	.14	0.226	-0.088	0.365
664	21	5	.24	0.226	-0.088	0.365
668	24	3	.13	0.212	-0.073	0.350
698	30	2	.07	0.189	-0.051	0.328
703	29	8	.28	0.193	-0.054	0.331
704	22	4	.18	0.221	-0.082	0.360
706	29	4	.14	0.193	-0.054	0.331
708	37	4	.11	0.170	-0.032	0.309
714	22	4	.18	0.221	-0.082	0.360
719	23	2	.09	0.216	-0.078	0.355
725	32	5	.16	0.183	-0.045	0.322
740	34	3	.09	0.178	-0.039	0.317
741	24	1	.04	0.212	-0.073	0.350
747	20	1	.05	0.232	-0.093	0.371
776	29	3	.10	0.193	-0.054	0.331
977	20	1	.05	0.232	-0.093	0.371
1021	37	4	.11	0.170	-0.032	0.309

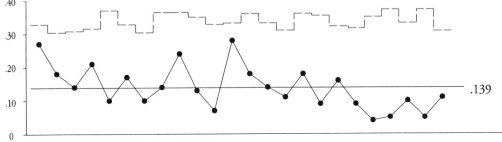

This chart tells the same story as the chart in Exercise 13.1.

Exercise 16.1:

The average for Hour 15 is 755.0. The range for Hour 15 is 3.
The average for Hour 16 is 753.4. The range for Hour 16 is 6.
The grand average is 754.8, and the average range is 4.5.

Second Shift Average and Range Chart

Subgroup	-9-	-10-	-11-	-12-	-13-	-14-	-15-	-8-
Weights	755	757	757	759	756	755	757	750
	754	758	755	758	754	750	754	756
	753	755	756	755	756	755	756	752
	754	753	753	756	755	757	754	755
	755	754	752	753	755	755	754	754
Averages	754.2	755.4	754.6	756.2	755.2	754.4	755.0	753.4
Ranges	2	5	5	6	2	7	3	6

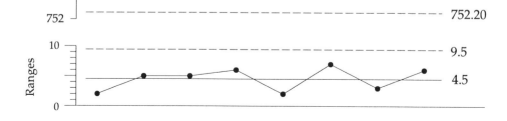

Exercise 16.2:

Average and Range Chart for Seasonal Relatives

	Jan	Feb	Mar	Apr	May	Jun	Jul	Aug	Sept	Oct	Nov	Dec
Year One	0.316	0.490	0.749	0.736	1.075	1.067	0.959	1.094	0.985	1.014	1.483	2.032
Year Two	0.355	0.311	0.422	0.793	1.276	1.044	0.857	1.179	0.747	1.064	1.456	2.495
Averages	0.3355	0.4005	0.5855	0.7645	1.1755	1.0555	0.908	1.1365	0.866	1.039	1.4695	2.2635
Ranges	0.039	0.179	0.327	0.057	0.201	0.023	0.102	0.085	0.238	0.050	0.027	0.463

Exercise 16.3:

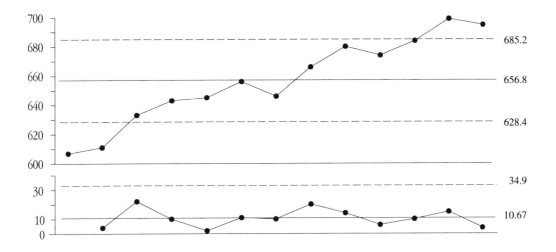

Exercise 16.4:

The half-averages are 632.5 and 683.

The sales are trending upward by an average amount of;

$$\frac{683 - 632.5}{7 \text{ weeks}} = 7.2 \text{ units per week}$$

The estimated sales for week 14 would be about 709.
Sales below 680 would signal lower growth.
Sales above 737 would signal faster growth.

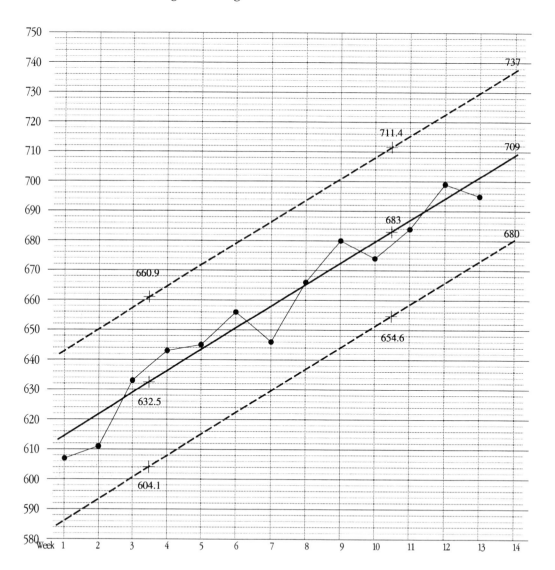

Exercise 16.5 (b):

$$
\begin{aligned}
UAL &= 803 + 0.495\,(850) &= 1224 \\
LAL &= 803 - 0.495\,(850) &= 382 \\
URL &= 2.055\,(850) &= 1747
\end{aligned}
$$

Exercise 17.1:

Exercise 17.2:

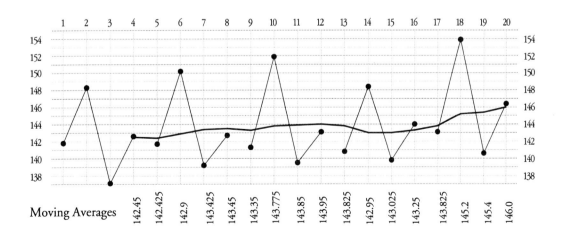

Answers to Exercises

Exercise 18.1:

	Qtr I	Qtr II	Qtr III	Qtr IV
Y1	.995	1.041	.962	1.001
Y2	.988	1.047	.970	.995
Y3	.982	1.055	.969	.994
	.9883	1.0477	.9670	.9967
Ranges	.013	.014	.008	.007

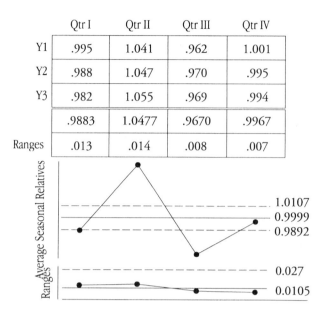

Exercise 18.2:

	I	II	III	IV	I	II	III	IV	I	II	III	IV
Sales	141.8	148.3	137.1	142.6	141.7	150.2	139.2	142.7	141.3	151.9	139.5	143.1
Seasonal Factors	.988	1.048	.967	.997	.988	1.048	.967	.997	.988	1.048	.967	.997
Deseasonalized Sales	143.5	141.5	141.8	143.0	143.4	143.3	144.0	143.1	143.0	144.9	144.3	143.5
mR		2.0	0.3	1.2	0.4	0.1	0.7	0.9	0.1	1.9	0.6	0.8

Exercise 18.3:

	Y4 QI	Y4 QII	Y4 QIII	Y4 QIV	Y5 QI	Y5 QII	Y5 QIII	Y5 QIV
Sales	140.8	148.4	139.8	144.0	143.1	153.9	140.6	146.4
Seasonal Factors	.988	1.048	.967	.997	.988	1.048	.967	.997
Deseasonalized Sales	142.5	141.6	144.6	144.4	144.8	146.9	145.4	146.8
mR		0.9	3.0	0.2	0.4	2.1	1.5	1.4

Bibliography

Cheaney, Lee, and Maury Cotter, *Real People, Real Work,* SPC Press, Inc., Knoxville, Tennessee, 1991.

Deming, W. Edwards, *Out of the Crisis,* MIT Press, Cambridge, Massachusetts, 2000.

Deming, W. Edwards, *The New Economics, Second Edition,* MIT Press, Cambridge, Massachusetts, 2000.

Joiner, Brian L., *Fourth Generation Management; The New Business Consciousness,* The McGraw-Hill Companies, New York, 1994.

Langley, Gerald J., Kevin M. Nolan, Thomas W. Nolan, Clifford L. Norman, and Lloyd P. Provost, *The Improvement Guide,* Jossey-Bass, Inc., San Francisco, 1996.

Neave, Henry R., *The Deming Dimension,* SPC Press, Inc., Knoxville, Tennessee, 1990.

Scherkenbach, William W., *Deming's Road to Continual Improvement,* SPC Press, Inc., Knoxville, Tennessee, 1991.

Scholtes, Peter, *The Team Handbook, Second Edition,* Oriel Inc., Madison, Wisconsin, 2001.

Scholtes, Peter, *The Leader's Handbook,* The McGraw-Hill Companies, New York, 1998.

Shewhart, Walter, (1931) *Economic Control of Quality of Manufactured Product*, republished by American Society for Quality, Milwaukee, Wisconsin, 1980.

Shewhart, Walter, (1939) *Statistical Method from the Viewpoint of Quality Control,* republished by Dover Publications, New York, 1986.

Tribus, Myron, *Quality First,* National Society of Professional Engineers, Washington, DC, 1987.

Tufte, Edward R., *The Visual Display of Quantitative Information,* Graphics Press, Cheshire, Connecticut, 1983.

Wheeler, Donald J., *SPC at the Esquire Club,* SPC Press, Inc., Knoxville, Tennessee, 1992.

Wheeler, Donald J., and David S. Chambers, *Understanding Statistical Process Control, Second Edition*, SPC Press, Inc., Knoxville, Tennessee, 1992.

Wheeler, Donald J., *Understanding Variation, the Key to Managing Chaos,* SPC Press, Inc., Knoxville, Tennessee, 1993.

Table 1: Bias Correction Factors

The values below are those factors which convert average ranges and median ranges into appropriate measures of dispersion, namely, either *Sigma(X)*, *Sigma(X̄)* or *Sigma(R)*. *

n	d_2	d_3	d_4	n	d_2	d_3	d_4
2	1.128	0.8525	0.954	21	3.778	0.7242	3.730
3	1.693	0.8884	1.588	22	3.819	0.7199	3.771
4	2.059	0.8798	1.978	23	3.858	0.7159	3.811
5	2.326	0.8641	2.257	24	3.895	0.7121	3.847
6	2.534	0.8480	2.472	25	3.931	0.7084	3.883
7	2.704	0.8332	2.645	30	4.086	0.6927	4.037
8	2.847	0.8198	2.791	35	4.213	0.6799	4.166
9	2.970	0.8078	2.915	40	4.322	0.6692	4.274
10	3.078	0.7971	3.024	45	4.415	0.6601	4.372
11	3.173	0.7873	3.121	50	4.498	0.6521	4.450
12	3.258	0.7785	3.207	55	4.572	0.6452	4.521
13	3.336	0.7704	3.285	60	4.639	0.6389	4.591
14	3.407	0.7630	3.356	65	4.699	0.6333	4.649
15	3.472	0.7562	3.422	70	4.755	0.6283	4.707
16	3.532	0.7499	3.482	75	4.806	0.6236	4.757
17	3.588	0.7441	3.538	80	4.854	0.6194	4.806
18	3.640	0.7386	3.591	85	4.898	0.6154	4.849
19	3.689	0.7335	3.640	90	4.939	0.6118	4.892
20	3.735	0.7287	3.686	100	5.015	0.6052	4.968

Given k subgroups of size n:

$$\text{Sigma(X) is found using either} \quad \frac{\bar{R}}{d_2} \quad \text{or} \quad \frac{\tilde{R}}{d_4}$$

$$\text{Sigma(X̄) is found using either} \quad \frac{\bar{R}}{d_2\sqrt{n}} \quad \text{or} \quad \frac{\tilde{R}}{d_4\sqrt{n}}$$

$$\text{while Sigma(R) is found using either} \quad \frac{d_3\bar{R}}{d_2} \quad \text{or} \quad \frac{d_3\tilde{R}}{d_4}$$

For the average moving range, or the median moving range, the effective subgroup size is $n = 2$.

---

* The *Sigma(X)* notation used in this book is a generic representation of an adjusted dispersion statistic. Some of these formulas are shown above. While these statistics might be used to estimate the dispersion parameter of some probability distribution, they are not a representation of any such parameter. They are simply a convenient way of representing any one of a collection of within-subgroup measures of dispersion.

Table 2: Charts for Individual Values and Moving Ranges

When a *time series* has a logical subgroup size of $n = 1$ we can plot the individual values and use a two-point moving range to measure the dispersion. The average moving range or the median moving range may then be used to compute the Natural Process Limits for the individual values and the Upper Range Limit for the moving ranges according to the formulas:

$$UNPL = \bar{X} + E_2\,\bar{R} \qquad \text{or} \qquad \bar{X} + E_5\,\tilde{R}$$

$$CL = \bar{X}$$

$$LNPL = \bar{X} - E_2\,\bar{R} \qquad \text{or} \qquad \bar{X} - E_5\,\tilde{R}$$

$$URL = D_4\,\bar{R} \qquad \text{or} \qquad D_6\,\tilde{R}$$

$$CL = \bar{R} \qquad \text{or} \qquad \tilde{R}$$

For two-period moving ranges these scaling factors are:

$$E_2 = \frac{3}{d_2} = 2.660 \qquad\qquad E_5 = \frac{3}{d_4} = 3.145$$

$$D_4 = \left[\, 1 + \frac{3\,d_3}{d_2} \,\right] = 3.268 \qquad\qquad D_6 = \frac{d_2 + 3\,d_3}{d_4} = 3.865$$

Moving ranges which fall above the upper range limit may be taken as indications of a potential break in the time series—some sudden shift which is so large that it is unlikely to have occurred by chance.

There is no advantage to using any other measure of dispersion besides a two-point moving range. Moving ranges based on any $n > 2$ will be harder to compute and less efficient than the two-point moving ranges. Mean square successive differences will be harder to compute and more prone to being inflated by extreme values while being no more efficient than the two-point moving range. Global measures of dispersion beg the question of predictability by making a strong assumption that the data are completely homogeneous (i.e. already predictable). That is why global measures of dispersion can never be properly used to compute limits for process behavior charts.

If the data do not come from a time series, i.e., if the individual values do not possess a definite and known time order, then the use of a moving range to measure the dispersion of the data is essentially arbitrary because the order of the data is arbitrary.

Moreover, if the individual values are *known* to come from different cause systems, as would be the case in a sequence of experimental runs, then the moving ranges may not be used to construct limits even when the data constitute a time series.

When computing limits for deseasonalized future values based upon deseasonalized baseline values use the formulas on the next page rather than those in this table.

Table 3: Factors for Computing Limits
for Deseasonalized Future Values
Based on the Deseasonalized Baseline Values

m	E_7	D_7	$\sqrt{\dfrac{m+1}{m-1}}$	E_8	D_8
2	4.607	5.660	1.732	5.447	6.694
3	3.762	4.622	1.414	4.448	5.466
4	3.434	4.219	1.291	4.060	4.990
5	3.258	4.002	1.225	3.852	4.734
6	3.147	3.867	1.183	3.721	4.573
7	3.072	3.774	1.155	3.632	4.463
8	3.016	3.706	1.134	3.566	4.382
9	2.974	3.654	1.118	3.516	4.321
10	2.941	3.613	1.106	3.477	4.273

Given an **Average** and an **Average Moving Range**
computed from the m years of *deseasonalized baseline values*,
compute limits for the *deseasonalized future values* according to:

$$UNPL = \bar{X} + 2.660 \sqrt{\frac{m+1}{m-1}}\ \bar{R} \qquad = \quad \bar{X} + E_7\ \bar{R}$$

$$CL = \bar{X}$$

$$LNPL = \bar{X} - 2.660 \sqrt{\frac{m+1}{m-1}}\ \bar{R} \qquad = \quad \bar{X} - E_7\ \bar{R}$$

$$URL = 3.268 \sqrt{\frac{m+1}{m-1}}\ \bar{R} \qquad = \quad D_7\ \bar{R}$$

$$CL_R = \sqrt{\frac{m+1}{m-1}}\ \bar{R}$$

Given an **Average** and a **Median Moving Range**
computed from the m years of *deseasonalized baseline values*,
compute limits for the *deseasonalized future values* according to:

$$UNPL = \bar{X} + 3.145 \sqrt{\frac{m+1}{m-1}}\ \tilde{R} \qquad = \quad \bar{X} + E_8\ \tilde{R}$$

$$CL = \bar{X}$$

$$LNPL = \bar{X} - 3.145 \sqrt{\frac{m+1}{m-1}}\ \tilde{R} \qquad = \quad \bar{X} + E_8\ \tilde{R}$$

$$URL = 3.865 \sqrt{\frac{m+1}{m-1}}\ \tilde{R} \qquad = \quad D_8\ \tilde{R}$$

$$CL_R = \sqrt{\frac{m+1}{m-1}}\ \tilde{R}$$

Table 4: Average and Range Charts:
Factors for Using the Average Range, $\bar{R}$

n	A_2	D_3	D_4	E_2	
					Given k subgroups
2	1.880	--	3.268	2.660	each with n observations
3	1.023	--	2.574	1.772	with Grand Average, $\bar{\bar{X}}$
4	0.729	--	2.282	1.457	
5	0.577	--	2.114	1.290	and Average Range, $\bar{R}$
6	0.483	--	2.004	1.184	use the tabled constants
7	0.419	0.076	1.924	1.109	
8	0.373	0.136	1.864	1.054	with the formulas below to obtain
9	0.337	0.184	1.816	1.010	
10	0.308	0.223	1.777	0.975	• limits for Subgroup Averages,
11	0.285	0.256	1.744	0.945	• limits for Subgroup Ranges, or
12	0.266	0.283	1.717	0.921	
13	0.249	0.307	1.693	0.899	• Natural Process Limits for X.
14	0.235	0.328	1.672	0.881	
15	0.223	0.347	1.653	0.864	

Limits for Subgroup Averages are obtained from:

$$UAL_{\bar{X}} = \bar{\bar{X}} + A_2 \bar{R} \quad = \textit{Grand Average} + A_2 \textit{ times the Average Range}$$

$$CL_{\bar{X}} = \bar{\bar{X}} \quad = \textit{the Grand Average}$$

$$LAL_{\bar{X}} = \bar{\bar{X}} - A_2 \bar{R} \quad = \textit{Grand Average} - A_2 \textit{ times the Average Range}$$

Limits for Subgroup Ranges are obtained from:

$$URL_R = D_4 \bar{R} \quad = D_4 \textit{ times the Average Range}$$

$$CL_R = \bar{R} \quad = \textit{the Average Range}$$

$$LRL_R = D_3 \bar{R} \quad = D_3 \textit{ times the Average Range}$$

while Natural Process Limits for individual values may be obtained from:

$$UNPL_X = \bar{\bar{X}} + E_2 \bar{R} \quad = \textit{Grand Average} + E_2 \textit{ times the Average Range}$$

$$CL_X = \bar{\bar{X}} \quad = \textit{the Grand Average}$$

$$LNPL_X = \bar{\bar{X}} - E_2 \bar{R} \quad = \textit{Grand Average} - E_2 \textit{ times the Average Range}$$

The formulas for these constants are:

$$A_2 = \frac{3}{d_2 \sqrt{n}} \qquad D_3 = \left[1 - \frac{3 d_3}{d_2} \right] \qquad D_4 = \left[1 + \frac{3 d_3}{d_2} \right] \qquad E_2 = \frac{3}{d_2}$$

Table 5: Average and Range Charts:
Factors for Using the Median Range, $\tilde{R}$

n	A_4	D_5	D_6	E_5
2	2.224	--	3.865	3.145
3	1.091	--	2.745	1.889
4	0.758	--	2.375	1.517
5	0.594	--	2.179	1.329
6	0.495	--	2.055	1.214
7	0.429	0.078	1.967	1.134
8	0.380	0.139	1.901	1.075
9	0.343	0.187	1.850	1.029
10	0.314	0.227	1.809	0.992
11	0.290	0.260	1.773	0.961
12	0.270	0.288	1.744	0.935
13	0.253	0.312	1.719	0.913
14	0.239	0.333	1.697	0.894
15	0.226	0.352	1.678	0.877

Given k subgroups

each with n observations

with Grand Average, $\overline{\overline{X}}$

and Median Range, $\tilde{R}$

use the tabled constants

with the formulas below to obtain

• limits for Subgroup Averages,

• limits for Subgroup Ranges, or

• Natural Process Limits for X.

Limits for Subgroup Averages are obtained from:

$$UAL_{\overline{X}} = \overline{\overline{X}} + A_4 \tilde{R} = \text{Grand Average} + A_4 \text{ times the Median Range}$$

$$CL_{\overline{X}} = \overline{\overline{X}} = \text{the Grand Average}$$

$$LAL_{\overline{X}} = \overline{\overline{X}} - A_4 \tilde{R} = \text{Grand Average} - A_4 \text{ times the Median Range}$$

Limits for Subgroup Ranges are obtained from:

$$URL_R = D_6 \tilde{R} = D_6 \text{ times the Median Range}$$

$$CL_R = \tilde{R} = \text{the Median Range}$$

$$LRL_R = D_5 \tilde{R} = D_5 \text{ times the Median Range}$$

while Natural Process Limits for individual values may be obtained from:

$$UNPL_X = \overline{\overline{X}} + E_5 \tilde{R} = \text{Grand Average} + E_5 \text{ times the Median Range}$$

$$CL_X = \overline{\overline{X}} = \text{the Grand Average}$$

$$LNPL_X = \overline{\overline{X}} - E_5 \tilde{R} = \text{Grand Average} - E_5 \text{ times the Median Range}$$

The formulas for these constants are:

$$A_4 = \frac{3}{d_4 \sqrt{n}} \qquad D_5 = \frac{d_2 - 3 d_3}{d_4} \qquad D_6 = \frac{d_2 + 3 d_3}{d_4} \qquad E_5 = \frac{3}{d_4}$$

Glossary of Symbols

a_i area of opportunity for the Poisson count from the ith sample, p. 220

A_2 a scaling factor: Table 4, p. 386

A_4 a scaling factor: Table 5, p. 387

$\bar{c}$ average count per sample for Poisson count data, p. 219

CL the central line of a process behavior chart, pp. 163-164, 215, 384-387

D_3, D_4 scaling factors: Table 4, p. 386

D_5, D_6 scaling factors: Table 5, p. 387

d_2 a bias correction factor for converting ranges into $Sigma(X)$, p. 383

d_3 a bias correction factor used in converting ranges into $Sigma(R)$, p. 383

d_4 a bias correction factor for converting median ranges into $Sigma(X)$, p. 383

k the number of subgroups in a set of data, pp. 280, 386-387

LAL Lower Average Limit on chart for subgroup averages, pp. 386-387

LL Lower Limit for a process behavior chart, pp. 214

$LNPL$ Lower Natural Process Limit, pp. 101, 163-164, 384-387

mR the moving range, pp. 100-101

$\overline{mR}$ the average moving range, pp. 100, 163 (denoted as $\bar{R}$ on pp. 384-385)

$\widetilde{mR}$ the median moving range, pp. 146, 164 (denoted as $\tilde{R}$ on pp. 384-385)

n the number of items in a subgroup, p. 267

$\mathbf{n}$ or $\mathbf{n}_i$ the area of opportunity for a binomial count, pp. 201, 213-216

$\bar{\mathbf{n}}$ average size of areas of opportunity, p. 225

$\mathbf{n}\,\bar{p}$ central line for np-chart, p. 214

$\mathbf{p}$ a parameter for the binomial probability model, p. 213

$\bar{p}$ average proportion nonconforming statistic for binomial data, p. 214

p or p_i	a sample proportion, pp. 216
R	the range of a set of data, p. 83
$\bar{R}$	the average range, p. 266
$\tilde{R}$	the median range, p. 387
s	the sample standard deviation for a set of data, p. 85, 161
s_n	the root mean square deviation of a set of data, p. 84
$Sigma(X)$	a measure of dispersion for individual values, pp. 165, 383
$Sigma(\bar{X})$	a measure of dispersion for subgroup averages, p. 383
$Sigma(R)$	a measure of dispersion for subgroup ranges, p. 383
u_i	the Poisson rate for the ith sample, p. 220
$\bar{u}$	the average rate of nonconformities per unit area of opportunity, p. 221
UAL	Upper Average Limit on chart for subgroup averages, pp. 386-387
UL	Upper Limit for a process behavior chart, pp. 214
$UNPL$	Upper Natural Process Limit, pp. 101, 163-164, 384-387
URL	Upper Range Limit, pp. 163-164, 384-387
w_i	the scaling factor for chunky ratios, p. 225
$\bar{X}$	the average of a set of data, pp. 81, 163-164
$\bar{\bar{X}}$	the grand average, the average of the subgroup averages, p. 266
X or X_i	a single measurement, pp. 81, 141, 216
X Chart	a chart for individual values, p. 101
$\tilde{X}$	a median for a set of data, p. 82
XmR	symbol for an Individual Value and Moving Range Chart, p. 99
Y_i	an alternative for the symbol X, p. 141

Index

Index